OVER A

OVER AND UNDER

by
John Misterly, Jr.

A Geneva Book

Carlton Press, Inc.   New York, N.Y.

To the memory of my mother, Jenny R. Misterly, my father, John Misterly, Sr., and to my wife, Jean Marie Misterly, who kept me going with her encouraging words during those years of hard work. Also, my heartfelt thanks to my daughter, Susan Misterly Adams and Mrs. Adair Hubbard, who worked so hard on the editing of this story to make it presentable to the publishers.

OVER AND UNDER

1.

It was a bright sunny day in December. The azure southern California sky was cloudless and clear as the blue Air Force staff car pulled up to the private entrance of the wing operations building at George Air Force Base in the California desert. Four occupants stepped from the sedan, three Air Force officers and a lady. The lady walked close to the colonel followed by the others. "Let's step into my office for a few minutes," said Colonel John Lea.

"That was one damn fine parade they put on in your honor, Colonel," said Captain Danny Davis as he closed the door behind him.

"Well, I guess they figured I couldn't change my mind and stay if they put on a retirement parade for me," said Lea as he slid behind his mahogany desk and slouched in the leather swivel chair. He was a man of fifty-two years, handsome in a rugged way. He was a shade under six feet tall with a dark tan that blended with his hair, except for slight graying at the temples. His uniform was neatly tailored and very attractive with silver wings crowded above the many rows of multi-colored ribbons. Below the ribbons and over his heart he wore, with pride, the round gold and silver badge of the Office of the Secretary of Defense which had been presented by the secretary himself. He had earned the award while being assigned to that august body some years prior. Under his ribbons and above the SOD badge was a new medal presented during his parade. He knew when an officer was presented the Legion of Merit it was the last nudge into retirement. The citation had read, "For exceptional meritorious conduct in the performance of outstanding services."

He wondered if he were doing the right thing. The Air Force had been his life and now he would have to change. No looking back, he told himself. After all, he owed his wife some consideration. She had never complained about his time away from her.

She didn't like being alone but put up with it because she knew it was his sworn duty. He couldn't help thinking of the news he had received some months earlier from an old buddy assigned at Headquarters USAF advising of his pending promotion to brigadier general if he stayed on. He had made his decision and it was final; he would soon be a civilian. The many ribbons on his left breast represented decorations, battle campaigns, awards of three wars, and other emergencies during thirty-five years of service to his country.

"Danny, would you please pour us all a drink? You know where it's kept," said Lea as he straightened up in his chair.

"Make the drinks short ones or you fellows will never make it to the retirement party," added Mrs. Lea. She was an attractive lady the same age as her husband. She had light brown hair, was deeply tanned, and always well dressed.

The tall lieutenant colonel standing next to her spoke as he took his drink, "I have mixed emotions about you leaving me with this operation; it may be more than I can handle. I want the job, but I think I'd rather have you stay on, Johnny."

"Hell's fire, Ralph, you're ready! I'm not worried. While I was away on TDY you didn't have much trouble filling in for me. You made sound decisions. I have faith in you."

"Only because I knew you wouldn't be gone long."

"Bullshit! You're ready or I wouldn't have recommended you! Besides, you've got good people around you—don't forget that."

"I hope you know how much it's meant to me to be your assistant. You've taught me plenty!"

"Hell, I didn't select you because your father's a congressman."

"I appreciate that, everyone gives me a bad time about my dad. You know I'll do my very best and if I run into trouble and can't get out, I'll call you to bail me out."

"By the way, Colonel, are you still thinking of moving up north?" asked Danny.

"Probably next year sometime. We have to sell the house and take care of some other business. We're looking forward to moving to the redwood country. We have eight acres and a house on the north coast."

"It sounds like you may hang around here for a while to make sure we don't screw up your operation," said Danny smiling.

"I don't mind hanging around just in case you have some unanswered questions and to hang out the crying towel. While you people are sweating out the next flap, you'll probably find me on the golf course."

"We're supposed to be at the club now," said Ralph.

"You two go ahead; we'll be along directly. I feel as if I'm going to the last supper."

"Good enough, sir. Don't be too long. You know some of the people will leave early and I'd hate to see you miss any of them because you were having a private party in here. Let's go, Danny," said Ralph as he picked up his hat and headed for the door.

When Johnny and Jean were alone, Jean said, "Darling, I know how tough this is for you and how you hate to retire, but I've shared you for many years with the Air Force and now it's my turn! I'm very proud of you and I understand why your people have always thought so much of you. The big parade, with that magnificent fly-by in such beautiful formation, and the medal they presented you. All of this has been so wonderful and we'll never forget it, but it's time for a change and we'll finally be able to do all the things we've always wanted to do."

"Please, honey, you know it's kind of hard to think about leaving, but I'm ready. The pressure's been on for a long time and it'll be good to relax. Still the change will be difficult and I'm glad you're here to help me. I guess we'd better get over to the club before they fire me!"

She smiled, reached up kissed her husband, then took his hand and walked with him to the officers' club. They approached the door, opened it and entered. As they came into view of the waiting throng a big roar of approval was heard throughout the club. He looked at the large gathering and took a deep breath. It was going to be a party to remember. The sizable crowd was made up of officers, enlisted people, civilians, and a few dignitaries. They were all gathered for his send-off. There were two tables in the center of the room. One had fancy foods of all description and the other was loaded with gifts. The magnitude of the reception left him speechless.

Major Manny McKias was the first to greet them. Manny was the wings unofficial master of ceremonies, self appointed of course. He was a very funny fellow with tremendous originality.

"You don't expect me to get up there without first giving me a drink?" asked Colonel Lea.

"Sorry about that, sir. What's it going to be?"

"Make it scotch and soda since I know you can't get me a mint

9

julep, and thanks."

"This way, Colonel," Manny held his arm out as if directing traffic, "I guess it's time for the roast or should I say, deliverance."

"I would say this is more like a firing squad."

"Call it what you like, sir. It's your day and we want to send you off in style, even if we have to pour you out at home," said Manny as he escorted the colonel to the stage.

"Christ, Manny, let me catch my breath and composure. It's not every day you get drummed out of the service!"

"I wish I had that drum. From where I stand it looks as if you've got the world by the ass. You've earned the rest so you might as well enjoy the show. Hell's fire, let's have a party, it's too quiet in here! I think it may get a little drunk out tonight." Manny slurred his words in a mock gesture of being intoxicated. "Everyone gather around. It's time for the 'big honcho' to open gifts," Manny announced. He kept a steady line of jokes and anecdotes going and promised after the gifts were opened to give the McKias version of the colonel's military career. It'd get a lot of laughs.

There was a great variety of gifts, some serious, some humorous, and even some that would come in handy. The last one handed to the colonel brought tears to his eyes. It was a large and beautifully colored lithograph of his B-29 group of World War II in action over a Japanese target. It instantly brought back many old memories. Some good, some not so good. Then came the biggest greeting card Colonel Lea had ever seen. It had Air Force continuation forms attached to accommodate the hundreds of signatures and notes from Lea's many friends and comrades. He was overwhelmed. It would take a few seconds for this man so used to pressure to compose himself. Then the request for a speech was heard throughout the room. Colonel Lea was still a bit choked up; however, he regained his composure and walked to the microphone.

Lea took a long breath followed by a pull on the glass of booze. "As most of you know I try to make all my speeches short and this'll be no execption. I'll do my best not to put you all to sleep. I'd like to tell you all how much I appreciate your coming here today to see me and my wife, Jean, off. I'm deeply touched by this reception and the fact that I'm able to end my career here among friends. I'll never forget any of you and how wonderful it's been to work with you. I remember some of you from as far back as my first assignment here prior to the Korean War. This base was full of sand and tumble weeds. After thrty-five years, I can honestly say I've never been with more cooperative and eager people all pulling together to get the job done without waste of talk and energy. You're all a credit to the Air Force and I'm proud to have been associated with you. Jean and I thank you one and all."

A great cheer went up and all the club rocked with so much whistling and applause it was hard on the ears. The colonel raised his arm and waved as he stepped from the stage. It was time for Manny to take over. He was very cleverly highlighting some of the main events of Colonel Lea's many years of service. Where Manny got some of his information was a mystery. Most of it was close to the truth but a hell of a lot funnier than when it actually happened and he made everyone laugh. The roast went on for some time. He finally ran out of lies and said he needed some refreshment. That ended the formal part of the program and it was time to just relax and shoot the breeze.

Jean and Colonel Lea sat at a table near the bar. The people who were leaving came by, wished them well and said good-bye, but most of them stayed. They came for a party and a party they would have. The noise grew as more drinks were poured. It reminded him of days gone by when the bar was full of flyers after a hard day in the air, but those days were gone forever. The din grew until it was difficult for them to hear themselves, much less the well wishers who came by the table.

"Honey, I think I'll go home. I'm tired and I know you'll be here for awhile. Have a good time and be careful on your way home," said Jean.

He agreed, and walked her out to their car. He kissed her, and said, "Don't worry, I won't be driving. I've got a driver all set to take me home in a staff car. I'd hate to get thrown in the hoosegow on my last day in the military!"

He watched her drive toward the gate and when she was out of sight he returned to the officers' club to continue with the fun. He joined a group of his flying officers who wanted to buy him a drink. He accepted. These were the fun guys. It seemed for the most part they were happy-go-lucky. Nothing had changed. The flyers always seemed to have a different view of life. One of the newer pilots said, "I wonder if any of us sitting here will be around thirty-five years from now."

Colonel Lea expressed his opinion, "Probably some of you will make it. A lot depends on circumstances. Some of you will see the

11

greener pastures of the air lines. I had those decisions during my time, but I could never give up what I had with the Air Force. I never intended to stay this long. As many of you may know I was asked to stay longer because my name was on the Brigadier General list for promotion, but I told them I'd been around long enough. It was time for me to step aside and let the younger people move up. It seems only yesterday, I was a boy of seventeen and eager to get in the service and go to war. The war had just started with the attack on Pearl Harbor and I felt the desire to get in and do my part for victory. I had no idea what war was all about; it seemed to me that I would be going sooner or later, so why not now? I was so young and naive. Now, I'm an old war horse ready for pasture."

"Like hell," came a response from someone who had just entered the room.

Lea turned to see who had made the remark. "For crying out loud, if it isn't Dave Lewis!" They had been friends since their cadet days during the big war. They hadn't seen each other for a number of months, but their paths had crossed many times in the years since their first meeting, and they thought of each other as brothers. "How the hell are you, Dave? Long time no see!"

"Great. Now, am I in time for the party?"

"Hey everyone, this is Colonel Dave Lewis, my ole asshole buddy from the head shed. He's a big shot in the Pentagon."

"Not such a big shot. Anyway I escaped from the Puzzle Palace for a few days."

Introductions were made and the party continued. Lea was not really surprised at Dave's appearance. Unannounced meetings were characteristic of the two.

"Jean just left. She'll be disappointed she missed you."

"Christ, Johnny, I'm not leaving right away. You're going to have to put me up for a couple of days!"

"Great! We have a lot to talk about!"

"I'd have been here for your parade except I had a squawk on my bird and I landed at Williams. Willy's is still cranking out cadets. The sky was full of T-38s when I was coming in for a landing. They were like hornets around a nest."

"I liked Willy. We were there going through pilots flying school after the war. That was a long time ago, but what's thirty-two years among friends, it goes by so damned fast."

"How does a guy get a drink around here?"

"Real easy, Colonel. What's your pleasure?"

"How about a scotch, neat?"

"Dave and I have had some hairy times together. It all started during World War II and continued for each war or emergency since."

"You had a lot more hairy times than I did, but that's the way you were. Always looking for and finding trouble."

"Don't exaggerate. After all, we won that war. Not so with the last two we were in."

A crowd had gathered. Most of the young flyers had heard the commotion and were curious. One of the young fellows asked a few questions about World War II and we tried to answer.

A young pilot spoke up, "Colonel Lea, some of us sure would like to hear about your experiences during the big war."

"Yeah, Colonel, let's hear about the old brown shoe days," another young pilot said with a big grin on his face.

"I don't want to bore you all."

"We're serious, sir. We'd like to get an idea of what it was like back then." They all looked eager to hear some old war stories.

"Okay, but where do you want me to start?"

"In the beginning," came the unanimous response.

* * *

"Well, to begin with, I was just a kid finishing high school when the war started and most of us thought we should get in the service before we got drafted. I was all for it. I hung around with eight guys. We played ball together and had gotten pretty close. We thought it would be great fun to join up and stay together. My choice was one of the flying services, preferably the Army Air Force. We all went to visit the recruiters in downtown Los Angeles. After visiting all the different service recruiters, we decided our only chance was with the Army. None of the services would guarantee that we'd stay together. I talked to the sergeant recruiter and he told me we could get an eye exam to determine if we could request aviation cadets. All eight of us took the eye test but only five of us passed. It looked as if my chance to fly had already been shot down. We'd made a pact to stick together and I couldn't go back on my word, though in the months to come I would regret my decision. After much haggling we decided the pact had been made and we'd join the Army and take our chances.

13

At least we were assured we'd all go together. I wasn't very happy about the prospects but the recruiter had promised, so we signed on the dotted line. We were tested to see what our new assignments would be. After a few days at Fort McArthur the word came out. I was to leave shortly for Camp Wolters, Texas for Infantry training. However, none of my buddies were going with me. I was fit to be tied. That lying bastard of a recruiter knew we wouldn't go to the same place. I tried in vain to get them to let me take the test for flying school. Their answer was that I'd already been classified and nothing could be done now. I was to be ready for shipment in two days. I was going to the walking army only because I had been in the school ROTC Band. That made me a semi-skilled infantryman! I'd been had and no amount of moaning would change it. I didn't see my buddies again after I stepped on the troop train on my way to Texas.

I arrived at Camp Wolters near Mineral Wells. The flat wheel troop train had wasted no time getting there. Nothing I saw was to my liking. I was homesick and wanted to go back. I had thirteen weeks of training to look forward to and I knew it'd be a bitch. When I'd finally finished my training and was ready to be shipped to a POE for overseas shipment, my company commander called me to his office and informed me I was promoted to corporal and was to stay as part of the training cadre. That was fine by me. Anything was better than a fox hole on some Pacific island.

It took but a few weeks to get promoted to buck sergeant. What a break. A lot of non-coms had been shipped out and some vacancies were available and, since the captain thought I was doing a good job, he rewarded me. A few more weeks passed and the shipments increased. They were taking all the NCOs with the most experience. That made more openings available and again I was called into the captain's office and told of my next promotion, which was effective immediately. I was a staff sergeant and only in the Army for five months. Hell, at this rate I would be camp commander in a year. Only kidding! I still longed for the wild blue yonder and would give back all my promotions in exchange for cadets. I had just sewn on my new chevrons and had decided that I'd been had as far as the Air Forces were concerned when a bulletin came out from post headquarters stating that any enlisted man physically and mentally qualified could be assigned to the Air Force for cadet training. I couldn't believe what I was reading. Could it be true? I lost no time getting over to headquarters to get all the poop. I was given a color blind test followed by an eight hour written exam. After the test had been graded I was informed I would soon be making a trip to Tarrant Field near Fort Worth for my flying physical. I was delighted with my future prospects.

The war in Europe had decimated the Air Forces and they were in need of qualified men and right now. I was on pins and needles. I made the trip to Tarrant Field and took the physical and passed. I was immediately placed on an order transferring me to the Army Air Forces, unassigned awaiting orders.

Captain McCutchens, my company commander, heard of the orders and ordered me to report to him. He was so damn mad I thought he was going to have me shot. I tried in vain to convince him that I was not disloyal. I just wanted to be an officer like him. He didn't buy it, he was so pissed off! He claimed I'd gone over his head. I tried to explain that the edict had come from the Commanding General and I thought he knew about it. The First Sergeant, a guy named Smith, was a no good bastard hated by every NCO in the company. He hated all of us in return. He'd convinced the company CO that I'd taken liberties and should have consulted the CO first. I explained that I'd had no intention of circumventing his authority. Instead, I was merely following a directive. The directive made no mention of reporting my desires except to the camp headquarters. After all, I thought the CO had been informed. He got a little incensed when I called First Sergeant Smith a lying bastard.

"Now, see here, Sergeant Lea, you can't talk like that about the first Soldier."

"Well sir, I'm sorry this got blown out of proportion but that son-of-a-bitch knew I was taking the tests. I checked out of the orderly room for the testing center as well as the trip to Fort Worth. He's trying to stir up trouble, as usual. There isn't a man in this company that doesn't hate him, including the NCOs. I'll give you a month's pay if I'm wrong."

"Now, see here, Lea. I told you I don't want talk like that in my office!"

"Sorry, sir, but what I told you about this company is true. I didn't want to disappoint you but to get away from Smith is worth anything."

First Sergeant Smith was getting red as a beet and couldn't hold it back. He started yelling at me, then moved toward me. I turned to meet the challenge when the captain yelled at Smith, "At ease, Sergeant Smith, and stay where you are!"

That made me momentarily unhappy. I wanted him to swing at me. I was ready to deck the SOB and then everyone in the company would've thought of me as a hero.

A new bulletin had been published at camp headquarters that morning with more good news. I had a copy in my pocket when I reported. Sir, I am requesting a furlough in accordance with the latest camp bulletin which states that any member held for assignment to the Air Forces could be granted a furlough for a period of fifteen days providing he is back here within thirty days of assignment to the Air Force. I therefore make my request.

"I have never seen the bulletins you make reference to."

"It is a shame, sir. Sergeant Smith only shows you things he wants you to see."

"Damn it Smith! Is that true?"

"Well, sir, I don't bother you with insignificant material."

"You call camp bulletins that pertain to this command insignificant? Henceforth, you will not make those decisions. I'll let you know if I no longer want to see paper work of any kind, is that clear? Get those bulletins now." Smith left the office and returned in seconds with the clipboard containing the camp bulletins. He handed them to the captain as he glared at me. I smiled and waited for the captain to read the part pertaining to me. He looked at the bulletins and said, 'It's all here but I still think you should have brought this to my attention, Sergeant Lea."

"I'm sorry sir for causing you any problems. As I said, I want to get a commission and fly. I do appreciate all you've done for me. I've worked hard here and never goofed off."

"I know that, but I'm still going to have to give you company punishment. I'll submit your furlough request to Battalion but until then you are restricted to the Battalion area, understood?"

"Yes sir." I saluted smartly, did an about face and left his office. I waited for that shithead Smith to come out and I told him, "I'll be back in an hour to sign the furlough papers and they'd better be ready. And one other thing, if you are man enough I'll meet you at a place of your choosing within the Battalion area, if you have the guts." He was so mad he almost accepted my challenge, but he was a coward and backed down. He was the biggest bastard I'd ever come in contact with before or since and that covers a lot of territory.

I turned and started out when I heard the captain call Smith into his office. I hesitated to eavesdrop. "You made me look foolish because I wasn't informed. That had better never happen again or you'll be on the next shipment out of here for overseas and that'll be the end of it!"

"I'm sorry, sir, it won't happen again."

"It'd better not. Now get the hell in there and get Lea's leave prepared and bring it to Battalion yourself. Understand?"

"Yes, sir."

I was glad I'd listened. It did my heart good to be able to report to all the guys that Smith got his tit in the wringer. I was sure Captain McCutchens was worried he'd have a mass exodus, but as it turned out only one other man in our company qualified and he never made it past the Aviation Cadet Center at San Antonio.

The drama did not end there. In spite of what the captain had said, Smith put me on a shipping order for Pittsburg, California for shipment to the Pacific as a replacement in the Infantry. One of the company clerks informed me. I stormed down to the orderly room and found both Smith and the captain gone. I then went the Western Union office which was next to the PX and prepared a telegram. I sent it to the Commanding General, Central Flying Training Command. My message was simple. I informed him that I was unassigned Air Force awaiting orders for aviation cadets at Camp Wolters, and had been placed on a shipping order to ship out as an Infantryman. Within hours the shit hit the fan. I was in more trouble with my CO but he was in trouble with the Post Commander as well as all the intermediate commanders.

I finally got my leave orders and First Sergeant Smith lost two stripes and replaced me on the shipping list to the POE.

When I left for Los Angeles I was sure Captain McCutchens was happy to see me go. After a long and tiring trip by Greyhound I was in heaven for ten days. After my leave I returned to Camp Wolters and within a few days was off to my new assignment at Sheppard Army Air Field in northern Texas.

2.

Camp Wolters looked the same after ten days. Somehow I'd expected some miraculous change. I was to pick up my orders and then depart for Sheppard Field. It was a happy day as I said good-bye to the dog's life of an infantryman. It really hadn't been that bad for me, but better to have it behind me. Soon life would improve and no longer would I have to brave the elements as a dogface.

I arrived at Sheppard AAF the same afternoon. I was finally in the Army Air Force. This base was much different. The buildings were larger and grass grew everywhere. In the Infantry dirt would do. This was going to be the good life, I could tell.

It had been planned to bring together all the Ground Forces types who had been assigned to the Air Force for cadet training. We were to receive Air Force basic training. It turned out to be an error in judgment. All the walking Army types were experienced soldiers, most were NCOs. We were assigned flights and each flight had a Tac Officer, an NCO and a couple DI's. I was really unlucky. My NCO was a guy named Blankenship. He was a corporal and almost every man assigned his flight out-ranked him. We soon found that he was a bitter son-of-a-bitch who had washed out of cadets in basic flying school. He was going to make life miserable for us because he had the upper hand and wanted to throw his weight around. Our training turned into a complete donnybrook.

The DI's were inexperienced newly assigned PFC's and they were trying to teach master sergeants how to march. The basic training only lasted two weeks for us. During those two weeks we lived in barracks so crowded no one could walk between the beds, wall to wall bunks. There was total confusion. Blankenship operated best in this type environment. When things were hectic and confused he would add the unnecessary bullshit. He would belittle us for no reason and lied to the Tac Officer about our conduct just to put us on report. He was probably the most chicken shit man I'd ever met, save Sergeant Smith, in my Army experience.

Everyone agreed with my evaluation. We were at his mercy because we could be eliminated if there was any trouble. So we took it and didn't complain. Most of the men assigned to our flight vowed revenge, but Blankenship was careful to avoid being alone. He knew he'd be dog meat if we caught him off the base. He was dubbed the "chicken-shit corporal" and none of us would forget him, but we knew we'd get even—our time would come. How his type found positions of authority was an unanswered question. On one occasion while he was passing out some obvious bad information on a subject I knew well, I called him on it. His face turned red and he nearly had a stroke. Needless to say we became immediate enemies. He wanted my butt something awful. I knew he would go out of his way to get me if I wasn't careful. I challenged him to fight in the ring at the gym. He was the larger man and should have accepted the challenge; instead he made a feeble excuse.

The base had spun their wheels for two weeks before it was decided we needed no further basic. They just wanted to get us out of there before all hell broke loose. The program at Sheppard had been designed for new recruits, not a bunch of experienced soldiers.

Before we left Blankenship got me aside and told me he knew I would never become an officer. There was no chance of me making it through cadets if he couldn't. I told him in no uncertain words he had better not be in my area when I got commissioned or he could give his soul to God because his ass would be mine.

We were all shipped to the San Antonio Aviation Cadet Center, better known as SAACC. You'd recognize it now as Lackland Air Force Base. We were to go through rigorous mental, physical, and medical testing. Approximately fifty-five percent of us wouldn't make an assignment to aviation cadets. During my testing I met two fellows who became my best friends. Hal Landis was a muscular six foot two with a blond crew cut from Minneapolis. He'd been attending the University of Minnesota and was a member of the varsity football team. The other was Dave Lewis, a rebel from Mississippi.

We had the Civil War going constantly, mostly through my

19

prodding. It was fun listening to Hal and Dave argue about who won.

Hal, Dave and I passed all the testing and were classified and qualified for pilot, navigator and bombardier. The one hitch was navigators were needed most urgently. The USAAF had enough men qualified for the other crew positions at present. It seemed awfully unfair. If we had qualified for pilot training only we would have gone to pilot school, but we'd qualified for all three crew positions. Navigators were scarce and hard to train so we were selected. My decision was easy, especially after they explained that if I didn't accept navigator training I would be grounded. For me it would have meant returning to the Infantry. No way would I let that happen. At least I could give it the old country try. Dave and Hal also gladly accepted the alternative. All three of us were apprehensive about navigation school because the wash out rate was very high. We would have a tough row to hoe, but we figured if others made it, we could too. You have to be flexible. We decided to meet the challenge and beat it. We would become the best damn navigators in the entire Army Air Force!

Fate had thrown us together because our names all started with an "L" and we would stay together for a long time. After we were classified, all we had to do was wait for our shipping orders. We went to the service club that night and drank to a pledge. We were going to help each other and stick together through thick or thin. We felt reassured to have buddies like each other.

Within a few days our orders were cut for the next assignment. We were going to Ellington Field near Houston, Texas for pre-flight and we would be there for six weeks assuming we didn't stub our toes. The best part was that we were on the same order and our names appeared alphabetically one after the other. The train ride from San Antonio to Ellington was great, but all the fun and games came to a screeching halt as soon as the train made a stop on the siding within the base proper. The upper classmen boarded the train and life became a little tougher. They put us in a brace which was the cadet's version of attention. We had to make many chins, throw out our chest and suck in the stomach until it hurt. They ordered us off the train, we fell in next to it, in a brace again. The upperclassman were in complete charge. No other people of authority were in view. The three of us made sure to fall in next to each other and by doing so we were assigned the same flight. We were able to get our bunks next to each other. Things had worked out just fine, so far. It wasn't long before Dave had Hal and me saying ya'all like it was part of our regular vocabulary. Dave had a favorite phrase, "The south will rise again." My question was against whom? When Dave got a little unhappy with Hal or me he would say, "Do you know that damn yankee is one word?" I told him I was neither rebel or yankee, I was a westerner. That was not good enough for him, you had to be one or the other. Hal's retort was, "Do you know what the rebel's battle cry was?" And without giving anyone a chance to answer he would say, "Aw quits." That always got Dave's competitive spirit alive. You can see we had few dull moments. It was all good clean fun, we never had a serious argument in all the time we were together.

* * *

Our schooling finally started on a stormy day in the spring. The humidity was very high in Houston, but it had to be coped with. We were glad to get started. We were full of spirit and willing to overlook any inconvenience, especially the weather. We were kept very busy, but all in all the academics were not that tough. They kept us drilling for long periods every day and there was plenty of physical training, all of which suited us. The food was much better than I had eaten since joining the Army and we were treated with some dignity. After three weeks we were no longer under the foot of every upperclassman. We now had that behind us. The new cadets got most of the crap just as we'd gotten it before them.

I was selected as a cadet officer due mainly to my real rank of staff sergeant and my experience with troops. It was a good deal being a cadet officer. It included a few extra privileges such as open post on Wednesday night providing the grades were all up to snuff. Pre-flight was great compared to the rest of my time in the Army. We'd wake up for reveille and put on our damp uniforms due to the high humidity. Then came the cattle car, a big box-like vehicle used as a bus to transport cadets to town when on open post. When the van was closed it looked just like a cattle car from the outside and not much better from the inside. It took about thirty minutes to get to town and we were always glad when the trip was over. Houston always looked good to us. It was a real city, not the little town we were used to. You were given

21

Saturday and part of Sunday off, if your grades were acceptable, and if you had not been assessed any tours. One tour would restrict you to the base. Walking tours was punishment for any infraction of the rules. You were free to leave after the Saturday morning inspection and review and were due back Sunday evening. You couldn't go further than a fifty-mile radius of the base.

Getting away really helped your outlook. The bus would stop at the USO in the middle of Houston and generally speaking it was the best place to meet girls. Most of the time if you wanted to get picked up all you had to do was stand in front of the USO and the girls would drive by, give you the once over, and if they liked what they saw they'd ask you if wanted to go with them. Near the USO was a beer joint called the Black Cat. All the cadets used to go there for beer and to play a game called "chug-a-lug." Eight or so cadets would sit around a large table and each would order a pitcher of beer and on signal would chug-a-lug. The last to finish was the one who paid the tab. Since we were always strapped for dough we couldn't afford to lose and we never did. But our uniforms paid the price. I could never figure out why we got so messed up just for a free pitcher of beer that we couldn't enjoy.

Graduation day finally arrived. The time had passed rapidly. During the period I had become cadet squadron commander and I appointed both Hal and Dave as flight lieutenants. We had it made.

After our final parade we received our new orders. The whole class was going to Laredo Army Field for aerial gunnery. The bombardier cadets from the other side of the base were going with us. We really had a train load. Laredo is in south-west Texas on the Mexican border. When we arrived we were dismayed to see so many GI's waiting to start training. There was a great backlog. Since we were cadets, specifically navigator cadets, we had a priority to complete training as soon as possible. The wheels had to handle it very carefully, so it wouldn't cause a riot. Those poor bastards were living on top of each other. It was so crowded and many had been waiting for a long time.

It was decided that we could slip right into the cycle without too much notice if no one knew we were cadets. There was so much confusion about starting dates, it was a mess. We were admonished not to disclose that we were indeed cadets. For the remainder of this school's training, which normally lasted six

22

weeks, we were GI's. We wore fatigues and looked like any other GI but it was the worst kept secret of the war. Some one opened his big mouth and let the cat out of the bag. There was hell to pay! Many fights broke out—the men waiting for a starting date were so frustrated, and you couldn't blame them. It also gave those GI's who had a hard on for future officers an opportunity to get their licks in. Most of the fights never progressed too far before the MP's stepped in or some one on the side lines broke it up.

We started our training which consisted of learning everything there was to know about the fifty calibre aerial machine gun. In fact, in a period of two weeks we were able, while blindfolded, to detail strip the gun, name every part, of which there were over a hundred, and put it back together in less than ten minutes. It seemed impossible but somehow we did it.

We fired on all types of gunnery range which included trap, skeet and stationary machine guns mounted on a tri-pod. There were indoor ranges as well. On the moving skeet range we rode on the rear of a pickup truck at thirty miles an hour and fired at clay birdies being launched from tall houses. The birdies came from all directions. In most cases if we missed the birdie they hit us. Each man had to work in the launch houses when not on the truck. We learned how to place the birdie on the sling arm to hit the pickup truck. It was all a game as far as we were concerned. There were also trucks with turrets mounted on the rear. Instead of machine guns the turrets had two 12-gauge shotguns. The birdie would be launched from the launch house and we had to track it with the turret and fire the shotguns in an attempt to hit them. Great fun!

There was even a penny arcade. Automatic BB guns were fired at targets on a track, all indoors and it didn't cost a penny. We loved it. They also had gun cameras to be fired at projected enemy fighters. More fun.

Then there was the outdoor fifty calibre range. Targets were mounted on the tops of jeeps. The jeeps were on a track behind a dirt wall. As the target came around each gunner would fire at it. The tips of the ammo were dipped with different colored paint to identify who was making hits and thus scored. The worst part of that range was the rattlesnakes. The rattlers seemed to be everywhere. They had jeeps running around the range running over the snakes in an attempt to control them.

23

Aircraft recognition was a big part of our studies. You had to become an expert on aircraft identification or you would never become an aerial gunner. Slides were flashed at 1/100 of a second on a screen and you had to know them all, enemy planes as well as friendly.

We had two hours of physical training in the hot and dusty fields. Each day was a long and hot affair. One day during training the instructor made an announcement to the effect that anyone interested in going out for boxing would be excused from further physical training. There were three immediate volunteers. Working out in the gym beat the hell out of rolling around in the dirt. The only problem we faced was injury because if you boxed and got hurt it could cost you cadets. It was unlikely though, due to the use of 16-ounce gloves. We were so happy to escape the two hours of calisthenics in hell each day it was worth the gamble.

After a few days the instructor informed us we would be part of the base boxing tournament. Although we really didn't want to box in front of the whole base we had no choice. During the tourney I was scheduled to box against a guy from another squadron just as Hal and Dave were. My opponent got hurt and couldn't fight. In the meantime I'd been working out each day with a fellow cadet from Austin, Texas. Carl was a soft spoken guy who was just about the same size as me. To complete the card it was decided that Carl and I would be matched against each other. I tried to get it cancelled because we were all from the same squadron and this tourney was one squadron against the other.

It was no soap. We were scheduled to fight a three round bout. I knew I could beat Carl easily. After all, I'd sparred with Carl daily and Carl wasn't much of a boxer. On the night of the boxing tournament when the time rolled around for the fight to begin, I climbed into the ring feeling quite confident. The big problem occurred in the first round. Carl who had been sparring in an orthodox manner had all of a sudden become a left handed fighter. I had trouble right off the bat. Carl was winning, there was no doubt. Everyone knew I was the superior fighter but someone forgot to tell Carl. It took me a round to figure out Carl's new style and from there on out it was a one way fight. They called it a draw but I'd won the last two rounds easily. Carl and I became good friends. Hal and Dave also won their events. Our squadron won the overall on points and the other squadron had to spring for the beer. It was 3.2 beer and it took a lot of it to make you feel good. The latrines got a good work out!

The last two weeks of our training was devoted mainly to flying. We were flying the B-24 and each cadet was assigned a gunnery position on the aircraft to specialize on. However, we still had to fire from all the turrets. Without a doubt, this was the best part of the training for two reasons; first, we were actually flying and second, we were almost finished with gunnery school.

Our graduation didn't amount to much. We were awarded a set of silver aerial gunners wings and a set of orders assigning us to our next station. We were going to a place called San Marcos AAF, for advanced navigation. That sounded great to us. We waited patiently for word of our departure. Delays were built-in, they had to keep you sweating until the last minute. The whole class of navigator cadets was going to the same school. The bombardiers were scattered to three or four locations. We were packed and ready to go when the final word was received. Departure was set for the following morning. The big scramble was on to find a map showing where San Marcos was.

We had the afternoon and evening off and decided to go across the border for the first time since arriving. A rule had been established that no man could go across the Rio Grande without a buddy. The reason given was that a sergeant had gone across four months earlier and had been incarcerated for that period of time. He had refused to pay a whore, who had pulled him into a doorway and screamed for the Policía. They came and threw him into the bastille and kept him without a trial. All efforts by the U.S. State Department were futile. The Mexican authorities refused to release him. It made us mad as hell to think they could get away with that. We heard he was finally released after we left Laredo.

We took the bus and then walked across the bridge to Nuevo Laredo. It took only minutes to decide we had wasted our time. Tijuana looked clean compared to this place and Tijuana was a cesspool. We promptly made for the north side of the river.

Everyone had been warned of the ninety percent VD rate in Nuevo Laredo but as it turned out most of the GI's were getting infected on the Texas side. The Mexican whores were inspected frequently, the Texas whores were not.

The next morning reveille came early. Everyone was up and eager to leave and it took little time to get the formation squared away and on the train. After the train was loaded, it started with a jerk and headed north. The only sad note was that we had to leave the dog we'd adopted at Laredo. We'd kept him hidden and trained him not to bark. He'd been weaned on beer and was a real lover among the canine corps, even though he was small. He was always getting involved with female dogs and we were pouring cold water over him often. We left him with the next class who promised to give him comfort and love. We'd named him Routstep. He'd be missed since he'd been our constant companion.

We traveled two hundred miles north on the flat wheel express. During the ride we reflected on the training we'd just completed and decided it'd been a ball. The penny arcade and the skeet ranges had taught us something about ballistics, to say nothing of becoming experts with the use and care of the fifty calibre machine gun. The most enjoyable part was the flight portion of the training. We fired at sleeves being towed, at ground targets and fired gun cameras at actual fighters. I'd been assigned the tail turret as my specialty and it was exciting hanging behind the airplane. But the biggest thrill was the ball turrett. It hung below the aircraft and you were hanging in the slip stream while laying on your back and sighting between your feet.

3.

Our trip on the square-wheeled express proceeded north through dismal looking countryside heading for San Marcos, Texas. It seemed we spent more time on the track sidings than on the main line. The trip of two hundred miles took so long it was hard to believe, even then. Troop trains had a low priority. We were in no big hurry, but wanted to get started. We were very apprehensive because of the stories we'd heard about navigation school.

We were met, as expected, by the upperclassmen. They were quite efficient at everything except locating and identifying our luggage, or should I say, duffel bags. We fell in at attention along the side of the train and were kept at attention for a long period of time while they tried to straighten out the mess they'd created. It would have been so simple to let us fall out and identify our bags. Apparently they hadn't thought of that and were just being hard ass for no good reason except to make life miserable for us. They could give it their best shot; no one was going to get me to lose my temper. I had plenty of experience with this kind of treatment. I guess I was getting used to it. As we used to say, "Don't make waves." The best way to handle this kind of treatment was to keep your mouth shut and do as you were told. Everyone agreed that the upperclassmen were fatherless.

An officer, probably a Tac-Officer, saw the donnybrook and called the cadet in charge aside. The cadet officer reported and stood at stiff attention while he was being told something. We could barely overhear his responses of "No sir, yes sir." We had no doubt he was getting his ass chewed out for the delay in getting us to our quarters. It had been a long day and everyone was bushed. The cadet officer was finally dismissed and returned to our formation. He gave the order to stand at rest which allowed us to talk to one another, but it was a good idea not to talk in ranks even when given rest because it could piss off one of the inquisitors and that could only lead to more pain.

27

We spoke very quietly under our breaths but only a few necessary words. Then in desperation, the cadet in charge had us fall out to identify and get our bags. In a matter of minutes we had them and were back in the formation.

The upperclassmen marched us for a few blocks. They constantly yelled at us for not marching at attention. It was impossible to do so with bags in both hands and a duffel bag over your shoulder. No one could march at attention under those conditions but that was no excuse. We finally arrived at our living quarters and were told to put our bags down and to prepare for inspection. We almost laughed out loud. We had been on that dirty train since early morning and the heat and dust had taken their toll. The inspection was made with the expected results. Now you can understand what I said about their alleged parenthood!

With this kind of treatment, navigation school was going to be a test of our fortitude and endurance more than our brains. Things were bound to improve. Maybe the big wheel cadet officer would fall into a deep hole!

After the inspection which no one passed, naturally, we were ordered to enter the tar-paper buildings, called shacks, and find a bunk. We scrambled in and found three beds next to each other. At least we weren't being split up. We figured that was a big plus.

Advanced Navigation School was where you learned all the fundamentals of aerial navigation in sixteen weeks. The course had been designed to take a year to complete but had to be condensed because of the acute demand for navigators to man the hundreds of aircraft produced monthly. No way could the Air Force meet the aircrew training demands or keep up with aircraft production. It was going to be a real challenge. We knew only the stouthearted and the lucky would be around at graduation time. The normal attrition rate would eliminate thirty to forty percent of the class.

Our day started at 0600 hours and generally ended at 2200 hours. There was no time to loaf. When we flew night missions the day automatically got longer. It was a test of endurance as well as aptitude. If you were a little above average intelligence and could take the pace you might have what it took to be an Air Force Navigator.

Air sickness accounted for some of the washouts but most had to do with desire and the capacity to withstand the rigorous academic pace. The discipline, passing inspections, physical train-

28

ing, hours of drill and demanding study was what it was all about.

If you failed an inspection, or got into any minor difficulty, demerits were assessed and every demerit over six cost you an hour on the grinder, marching at attention, sometimes with a parachute strapped to your ass. One tour restricted you to the base for the weekend. Luckily, we never had to walk a tour. You really had to stay on the ball to avoid them.

We were assigned a classroom which would remain the same throughout our stay at San Marcos AAF. Each of us had a large desk where we could lay our maps and charts out to draw our courses and make our calculations.

Our first instruction was in Dead Reckoning, the basis for all aerial navigation. Without a firm understanding of DR you would never understand the more complex mysteries that were to follow. At this point we lost a couple more guys who could not keep up the pace.

When we progressed into Celestial Navigation things became much more difficult. There were many mysteries to try and understand. The fifty-eight navigational stars as well as the planets, moon and sun had to be observed and calculations derived to determine a line of position or LOP's as we call them. The LOP's took the form of a line on a chart and when crossed with one or more became the fix or position.

During the day we shot the sun and at night whatever stars were in our hemispheric location. We would then enter the classroom, make our calculations and plot the LOP. If it crossed over your location, you knew the shot was good. It took a lot of practice to become proficient.

One night we were shooting the stars and plotting the LOP's on our charts. It was a hot night and we were allowed to take our uniform shirts off and work in T-shirts. I was standing next to one of my classmates whose name was Bill Russell. We both had our sextants to our eyes. I'd just completed my observation and was checking the readings on the sextant when I noticed out of the corner of my eye that a full colonel was watching. Bill had no idea the colonel was standing close by because he was busy taking an observation of a star. There was no way for me to warn him.

"Mister! What star are you shooting?" asked the commandant of cadets.

"Sir, I am shooting Polaris," answered Bill as he lowered his sextant and tried to stand at attention.

The colonel then asked, "Fine. What is the pointer system for locating Polaris?"

"Well, sir, you see that telephone pole across the street? Right above it about 30 degrees up is the North Star."

The colonel's mouth gaped open and he started to stutter, but finally composed himself long enough to ask, "How in the hell are you going to find that God damn telephone pole at 30,000 feet?" Without waiting for an answer he continued, "I have heard of some funny pointer systems to locate stars in the heavens but that beats all." He chewed Bill's ass out for a good five minutes straight. In the confusion I slipped out of sight. I didn't want to get involved in a no win situation. The colonel was so pissed off he almost exploded and I didn't want to be near the fallout. The colonel finally ran out of adjectives, turned and left the area, fuming.

I met Bill at the door. "Why the hell did you say that?"

"Beats the hell out of me! It just sorta came out that way. I should know better!"

"I guess! Christ, you know the pointer system as well as any of us in the damn class."

"I'm a dumb shit. We were just naming the stars in the big dipper and using the pointer system to locate Polaris. It just came out without thinking."

"It's a damn good thing you're such a hero or your ass would be mud."

Bill was a real hero. He'd earned the Distinguished Service Cross during action in New Guinea. He'd also been recommended for the Medal of Honor and just missed. Instead, he was presented the DSC and was promoted to technical sergeant. Bill was the only cadet in our squadron who actually outranked me. I had to tease him more because he was always kidding someone for little things. "Bill, it's a wonder that bull colonel didn't have you lined up and shot."

"Not funny."

We all had a good laugh at Bill's expense. About then, the head class instructor came out of the building and said, "Wasn't that Colonel Nevell I saw talking to one of you?"

"Yes, sir."

"I wonder why he didn't come in to see me. He was CO of my old B-17 group in Europe."

30

I knew why he didn't come in but I wasn't going to get in the middle of this one. It was up to Bill to tell. He was still shook up. He knew he might be in big trouble and the axe could fall. I figured Lt. Gaffney would hear from the colonel about the events that led up to his rapid departure, but we never heard another thing about the faux pas. I'm sure Bill had survived because the colonel knew of his war record. It would not do to have a hero of this magnitude washed out for something so trivial. Bill had a very hard time functioning the rest of the night. Who wouldn't have?

Our flying training was the most interesting. It let you put all your ground school training to work. We flew a total of about one hundred and fifty hours. Generally the missions lasted between two and three hours. We flew the AT-7, a Beechcraft twin engine job. It had been designed from one of the popular twin Beeches. It was fitted for three students, an instructor, and a pilot.

The AT-7 was a good trainer, if not roomy. The three student navigator positions were in the main cabin and the instructor rode in the co-pilot's seat. The first seat was designated for the first or lead navigator. The lead directed the aircraft and the two other navigators followed the airplane. If the lead was off the other two should be navigating where the plane actually had been. Hopefully all three would be close when the charts and logs were checked on the ground. Each student rotated and was responsible for a different leg of the mission. We three always flew together, again due to the alphabetical listing of our names. We generally had the same instructor who was a pretty good Joe, but he was tough. We learned plenty from him. He had already flown a combat tour. At times he disagreed with the teaching methods and instead taught us how it was in the real world. We often thought how bad school would have been if the three of us hadn't gotten along so well. When flying, no matter which of us directed the plane, we made sure the lead didn't get too screwed up. We called it "cooperate and graduate." You had to be discreet, because the instructor was so close, but we had ways of beating the system without the use of words. Actually, we had learned our lessons well and needed little prompting. Things in the air were much different than how it was done in the classroom. In the classroom the pressure was not on as it was in the air. You had to stay on the ball to keep from getting your ass in a sling. Mission accomplishment was a strong vote for your continued existence as a student navigator.

The next two cadets were eliminated from our class after we completed the Dead Reckoning portion of our flight training. It was apparent some of the cadets had not learned well enough or were just not cut out to handle the pressures of a navigator. On the ground you were not rushed into decisions but it was a different story when you were flying and real mistakes could not be hidden. Some of the guys would get so rattled when they made a small error it would eat them up. The bad part of the program was if you fell behind the class you had to catch up or you were through. There were no washbacks. You had to get it the first time or out you went. There wasn't time to waste on any one who couldn't progress with the lesson plans and keep up with the rest of the class.

We took written exams every week and believe me they were piss cutters. I studied every spare minute I had which wasn't much. If you goofed off it didn't take long until the instructors knew you had a problem. I went off the base only when I felt secure about my progress. We studied every night and on our days off. We even studied after lights out under a blanket. It was against the rules but necessity dictated the gamble. We three had a good system of study and we were making it through all our exams. Because of our success others in the class asked if they could study with us. We didn't mind if others joined in providing they didn't get into bull sessions. As I mentioned before, my incentive was very strong. I could not even think of going back to the Ground Forces after I once sewed on my first Air Force patch. Being a grunt sergeant with the Infantry did not fit into my plans. I could not look back. My future was in the air. I knew it.

I was again selected to be a cadet officer. It was always possible they would not want me after they found out that I couldn't and wouldn't be chicken shit like some of the cadet officers we had encountered here. After my appointment as flight lieutenant an announcement was made that there would be a drill competition. Since all of us in our flight had been together at pre-flight and had marched the fancy drill there, we had a good chance in the competition. We drilled on new formations and some of the old ones. We were getting quite good, in fact, I would say sharp. It would be a feather in our caps if we won the event, and then we heard the winners would be granted two full days off in Austin and would not have to stand inspection or march in the parade that weekend. The prize was worth the extra effort. Getting away from there for two whole days would be great. We could relax or chase girls or whatever. Just to get the school off our minds would be great therapy. Our extra work paid off. With over twenty flights participating, we won first place. Our reward would start the following weekend.

Saturday morning came and we didn't get rustled out of bed for reveille. I had almost forgotten what it was like not to get up early. Unfortunatly, being used to getting up at the crack of dawn ruined my stay in the sack. We climbed out of bed and cleaned up and headed for the bus stop. We caught the bus to San Marcos and made our way to the Greyhound bus station. There we had breakfast and about an hour later our bus departed for Austin. The ride north was pleasant. We felt free from the rigors of cadet life. We knew Austin had to be better than San Antonio. Anyone who had gone through classification center there would agree. We also knew that Austin was the home of the University of Texas. After walking around and getting nowhere, we recalled that Carl Henning, a fellow cadet, lived in Austin. Maybe he would be home. We called his home and learned his father had gone to San Marcos to pick him up. Carl was the fellow I boxed against in Laredo. We were told to wait at a certain place until they returned and Carl would pick us up.

It was a couple hours before Carl found us. He drove around town showing us the points of interest. During the drive Carl told us he was having trouble keeping up with the pace at San Marcos. We offered him any help necessary to get him through the course. First off, he'd have to give up the trip home every time he had a day off. We explained that we studied instead of going on open post. He was appreciative.

We had a great time that night and a relaxing time the following day. It all passed too fast. Soon it was time to leave and get back to the old grind.

* * *

I noticed as we got further into the course the instructors became a little more human and helpful. I guess they waited to see who they thought would finish the course before they spent the extra effort. Some of the new instructors were returning from combat tours and others were selected from previous graduating classes. I was sure some of our class would probably be selected to stay on as instructors and hoped it wouldn't be me. I wasn't here to become an instructor, I was here to learn to fly as a combat crewman on bombers. There were plenty of cadets who would be happy to stay on but not the three of us. My dreams were of flying the new B-29. From what I had heard not many got that assignment unless they were experienced or a big wheel. The B-29 was known as the Cadillac of the Air Force. I sure wanted to drive around in that Caddy. Looking at the logical side of the ledger, the war in Europe was taking its toll. Most of us would end up in B-17's or B-24's and go to the ETO. There would be no inkling until graduation as to what assignment we would get.

Changes in our curriculum were made due to the returning combat navigator instructors who had seen action overseas and found some of the old curriculum was not used in the real world. The schools were trying to keep abreast of the overseas command requirements, thus we were taught some of the important techniques associated with the combat situation. I enjoyed the approach because it seemed to eliminate some of the bullshit.

We were well into celestial navigation and becoming proficient, but some of the cadets were scared to death of celestial. I thought to myself, if I were in that kind of shape I would find other employment. If you didn't know celestial the chances of you and your crew surviving were nil, especially if you were assigned to the Pacific theater. I was all the more determined to become the best damn celestial navigator there was. I guess I was odd, I liked celestial. The key to becoming good was hard work. You had to build your own confidence before you could expect your crew to have confidence in you. After all they were putting their lives in your hands. It might upset them if you got them lost. If you excelled at celestial your chances of flying the B-29 were enhanced. I am happy to say, the whole task of understanding, learning and accomplishing the theory of navigation came easier for me than for some, and I really enjoyed it. I had forgotten my overwhelming desire to become a pilot for the present. The navigator was known as the intellectual member of the crew. That pleased me. I strived to be a credit to my new profession and I wanted to be a part of my country's victory. If that sounds like a bit of flag waving I'm glad, because it was.

The day finally came. We were to start flying crosscountry missions. I felt we were now going to be able to do something constructive. The flights were the gauge of your ability, however, the days stretched to eighteen hours at times and were always a test of endurance. If you flew past midnight you were allowed to sleep past reveille, but not for long. There were just so many training hours to fit everything into.

We were constantly reminded of the need for new navigators. Navigators had the highest cadet priority, due in part to the grueling pace and the tremendous washout rate. My guess was the Air Force was losing more navigators than other crew positions. I was not discouraged. Actually the need stemmed from the comparably few navigators being trained. It didn't surprise us that there was a shortage of navigators. Otherwise we would have been in pilot training.

As we progressed the washout rate increased. Friends would be here one day and then before you knew it they were gone. It was heartbreaking to see your buddies eliminated. I guess, if you couldn't hack the program it was best to find out now instead of later when the chips were down. Our classroom was now half empty. Actually, we three didn't worry about being washed out. We felt we were getting along just fine and had no bad hangups. I think the guys who were in trouble knew it before they were informed.

We entered the last phase of our training and were within sight of actually graduating. This was no time to get sloppy. The fact of life was that some would get booted in the last week. That had to be a real rough way to go. When we were in our last week we were very confident. Only a terrible screw up would do you in. The big thrill came within two weeks of finishing when we were told to order our officers' uniforms. I almost broke the door down to the fitting room at the PX. I decided since this was such an important event I wouldn't buy anything off the rack. Instead, I ordered only tailor made uniforms. What the hell, you only go this way once. The pinks and greens, as they were called, were good looking and comfortable. When I got my hat, like all the others, I had to get a fifty mission crush into it. In those days all Army officers had to wear metal grommets in their hats. However, that rule didn't apply to hot flying officers which set them apart from the other Army officers. As soon as the uniforms were delivered, we turned in our GI's. We then wore the officers' uniforms without the rank attached. What a wonderful feeling it was to know the end was so close. We were very distinctive wearing officers' uniforms, real class, the envy of all the other cadets.

One morning a week before graduation I had to pick up a few items at the Post Exchange. As I reached to open the door it swung open. Lo and behold, to my surprise, there stood my old tormentor from Sheppard, Corporal Blankenship. The sight of him made hatred fill my heart and soul. He was the worst excuse for an NCO I had ever seen or would see throughout my long career.

"If it isn't the chicken shit corporal," I said, without even thinking.

He stuttered, got red in the face, and then said, "So you're still an aviator cadet. I thought you'd be long gone by now."

"No chance, asshole! I'm here and soon to be commissioned. What surprises me is that you still have those two lousy stripes."

He tried to compose himself but my verbal onslaught had caught him off guard. "Some one really fucked up for you to be wearing that officer's uniform," was the return.

"Tell me, Blankenship, how did you manage to get here? Did they get so sick of you at Sheppard they just wanted you out of their sight?"

"Why, hell no, I asked for this transfer and I got a good job here!"

"I'll bet. Are you still a dog robber for some officer? You're such a kiss ass."

"Like hell, I got a good job in the supply squadron."

"You mean the mess hall, don't you?"

"Go to hell."

"You're still avoiding combat, aren't you?"

"I'm ready to go overseas anytime."

"Bullshit, your kind always finds a way to keep away from the shooting."

He was so confused. But why not? His peewee brain was pickeled in alcohol. He turned to leave, then stopped and said, "You still might not make it through this school and become an officer."

"You had better pray that I don't see you when I get commissioned or you might be a buck-ass-private, not a chicken shit corporal. At least the Army was smart enough not to make you a buck sergeant."

"Yeah, I got fucked. I'll get promoted pretty soon."

"On second thought, if someone did send you overseas, you would probably ruin the war." Without giving him a chance to say another word I turned and stepped through the door. I looked out the window and he was still standing there with a blank look on his face and his mouth open.

I tried to avoid confrontations because a cadet had few rights. You were prone to take crap just to try to avoid any problems. In his case, however, I could not let him off the hook so easily.

The following week I was informed by one of my old friends in the supply squadron that Blankenship was no longer a corporal. He'd gotten drunk and disorderly one too many times and they busted him. It couldn't have happened to a better guy.

Everyone was confident of graduating as we got to within a few days of graduation. The only thing left was the end of course examination, a tough exam which covered everything. We really hit the books and did very well. Carl Henning had studied with us during our cram sessions and we thought he was in good shape. But after the exam when grades were posted, our class had another casualty. Carl had been notified of his elimination with only three days to go. It was heartbreaking. We cried along with him, we were all so sad. It was hard to believe he had failed. We had him right on top of everything we thought, but he had blown the exam badly and apparently that did him in. He had clutched up during the test and the rest was history.

"What happened, Carl? You seemed to know the material pretty damn well," I asked.

"I just went blank, and it got worse by the minute. I never finished and knew I was in trouble."

We helped him pack and he departed that afternoon, a very sad day. Later we all agreed, if he clutched up in the exam room, what the hell would he do when the pressure was really on?

On the other side of the coin, the three of us were assured of being commissioned second lieutenants.

4.

The day we had looked forward to for so many struggling weeks had arrived. It was a chilly day in December of 1943. Soon the new year would be upon us.

Four hundred cadets sat in the base theater, splendid in their new pinks and greens. All looked like officers, however, missing were those shining second lieutenant bars and the wings of silver. We had our new officer serial numbers, the formality of graduation was all that stood in the way of the start of our great adventure.

It had taken months of hard work to get there and we wanted to enjoy every bit of it. We knew soon many of us would be separated from our long friendships and head in different directions. That was the sad part. We had suffered through many ordeals to make it. My mind wandered back to a few days earlier when Carl Henning was informed of his dismissal, poor guy. The tension built among the cadets as the theater filled with families and friends. We just wanted to get this show on the road. The excitement was almost too much to bear.

I knew my folks were in the audience somewhere, but where? I tried my best to spot them. They had saved their gas rationing stamps for months to drive to San Marcos and see me graduate. It had been a long trip in the 1939 Dodge from California to Texas. They had been confident I would make it through navigation school, more so than myself. But you know parents, they think their kids can do no wrong. I wondered what Carl's parents were thinking. My father had made it known that he would have walked here to see me get my wings, he was so proud. They were wonderful parents. I have always felt very close to them even though I was one of six children.

I had hoped eventually to go through pilots' school in grade but for now I was happy to be an Air Force Navigator. I knew the tremendous responsibility that would soon be mine. The training

38

taught me more than how to guide an airplane from point A to point B. It taught me how to grow up and look life straight in the eye and how to go for it.

The curtain finally went up. Seated on the stage were all the brass. There were the usual speeches and other time wasting trivia. In time they got their act together and got on with the program we all waited for. It started with a mass oath of office and allegiance, followed by the presentation of certificates and the silver wings. We each had the two gold bars in our pockets and would pin them on right after we returned to our seats. Everyone was very anxious to get over to headquarters after graduation to learn of our new assignments.

The three musketeers were seated in a line next to each other. I was very lucky to have found two friends like Hal and Dave. I knew we'd be friends for the rest of our lives. We had been together since our names were called at the classification center. We'd done little without each other since. We prayed that again, we would be shipped to the same outfit. It seemed logical to expect that since the service did everything alphabetically, we might be assigned together. But we knew the Army in all its infinite wisdom was seldom logical.

We lined up in the aisle, marched across the stage and received our wings and commissions. It seemed like eons of time passed before they called Lieutenant Harold H. Landis. He marched stiffly to an officer standing in front of the table on the stage which contained the wings and parchments, turned and made a smart salute. His wings were pinned on and he was handed his parchment. The salute was returned and a handshake preceded his rapid departure from the stage. It seemed like an eternity before my name was called. I felt a little weak-kneed but drew in a deep breath and marched as slowly as I could make myself. I had to keep from rushing. It was finally over! I had my wings and parchment and was off the stage. What a relief. Just as I stepped from the stage I heard the name of Lieutenant David T. Lewis called. It was true, we were real officers, I thought as I headed quickly to my seat. At our seats we pinned the gold bars on each others shoulders, they felt kind of heavy. Hal spoke up and said, "God, we are officers and gentlemen by an act of congress."

It broke the tension, we all laughed. The last man passed by the officer in charge of attaching the wings to our uniforms and the proceedings were declared at an end. The response from the new officers was overwhelming. After a few minutes things got back to normal. I started looking for my parents, then decided I would have a better chance finding them outside of the theater. We were met just outside of the door by a fat supply sergeant whose left fist was full of money. He was collecting the traditional dollar for the first salute. He was doing a great business, he knew where to place himself and when. I cared not about who I gave my first dollar to, I just wanted to do it and carry on the tradition. At first it was hard to remember that we really rated a salute, then it sank in.

We crowded our way past throngs of people in search of my folks. We had agreed to meet in front of the theater if we got separated. "Mom, Dad, here I am." My mother reached for me and gave me a big hug and a kiss, then I turned to my father and he had the biggest grin on his face. He gave me a bear hug and a handshake. They had tears in their eyes. I was close.

"Congratulations," they said in unison.

"Folks, these two fly-boys are my good friends. Dave Lewis and Hal Landis, my father and mother."

"We are happy to meet you both. We've heard a lot about you in Johnny's letters," said my father as he extended his hand toward one then the other.

It was great having my folks there on one of the proudest days of my life. We stood talking for several minutes until Dave suggested we go to the officers club and relax over something to drink. The officers club was off limits to cadets. In fact, we were told it was against the law to even look in the direction of the officers club.

"We are officers now, we can walk right in the front door," said Dave in his southern drawl.

We made our way to the folk's car and drove to the club. It was a big building and looked well kept. We got out of the car and walked right up to the front door as Dave had suggested but still felt out of place. I'm not sure what we expected to find inside.

"If someone tosses us out we will know we aren't welcome," said Hal as he held the door open for my parents.

Dave led the way into a large room with tables and chairs. We sat down as a waitress approached.

"Let's have a drink to celebrate," said Dave.

"Good idea, even if it is early in the day, I'm dry," I answered.

"It is a special day in our lives so let's relax and act like real officers," added Hal.

"Christ, Hal, we are real officers," I said.

"Sounds fine to me. Maybe we can have a little lunch with our drinks," added Dad.

"You boys seem to get along well for only knowing each other for such a short time," said Mom.

"Actually, we've gone through four bases together, that must be some kind of record. You don't have much time in the service, especially aviation cadets to meet and stay with people. The washout rate is so high, you make friends and before you know it your friends are gone. We three decided to work extra hard together and it payed off. During our first meeting when we were at San Antonio, we pledged ourselves to do the best we could and to help each other no matter what. We studied long and hard and never gave up, as some did," was my explanation.

Our lunch and the drinks arrived and the appropriate toasts were made. It was wonderful to feel so good and to have my parents with me to savor my achievements and share my glory. We were in a new world and I was really enjoying it.

"We should report to headquarters and pick up our orders soon. In a way I hate to because I have a feeling we are finally going to be separated. Why don't we drive up to the visiting quarters where you can rest up? Then we can go get our orders and start packing. I'm in a hurry to get off this base and act like a human again. We can pick you up for dinner, say, at 1730, to you that is 5:30, Dad."

"Sounds fine to me, Son. Okay, dear?"

"That would be just fine."

We drove to the visiting quarters, checked them in and then jumped in the car and headed for headquarters. When we climbed out of the car we just stood there not moving. We were afraid that our paths were splitting.

"Well, lets get our butts in there and see what Uncle Sugar has in store for us."

41

5.

The car with the three eager new lieutenants pulled up in front of the headquarters and they hurried in to see what fate had decided.

"Aviation Cadet Lea, er, I mean Second Lieutenant Lea reporting for orders, sir."

The captain smiled and returned my salute. "You're not the only one to forget he's no longer a cadet. After all, habits are hard to break."

"Thank you, sir. I feel foolish."

The captain received the salutes of Hal and Dave, then started looking for our three envelopes. He found two envelopes on his desk but had to look elsewhere for the third. He returned and said, "Here you are, gentlemen. Open them now and if you have any questions I'll try to help."

We took our envelopes then looked at each other and waited for the other to open his. I'd heard the captain explaining to some of the guys that this class, unlike some in the past, had many different assignments. That didn't make me too happy, it only made the chance of being separated more likely. He also had said that some classes had gone en masse to one command to fly either B-17's or B-24's, but this class will be flying many different type aircraft.

"Let's all open them together and then we can get on with it," I suggested. We unfastened the flaps and pulled out the sheaths of orders to inspect them.

"You know I'd settle for B-24's right now if we could go together," said Hal.

We all agreed.

"Fat chance, we are screwed and tattoed. I'm all alone on this order. I mean you two are not on it," said Hal dejectedly. "I'm headed for the Troop Carrier Command, C-47's. The damn Gooney Bird," he added.

"Shit, I'll trade you. I'm going no place. I'm assigned to San Marcos AAF, Texas as a damn instructor," said Dave in a defeated tone I had never heard before.

"Christ, I'm afraid to look at my orders. They are probably going to send me to bombardier school or something!"

"Just look, the suspense is killing me," said Hal as if he had overcome his shock.

I opened the envelope and pulled out the orders, scanned them for a few seconds, then let out a yell.

"What the hell is it?" asked Dave with a puzzled look on his face.

"I'm going to Kansas! You won't believe this! I'm going to the B-29 outfit! What did I do to deserve this? It's been my dream ever since we started in the program."

"I'm really glad for you, Johnny, you deserve it," said Dave as he stuck his hand out.

"It's a great break and I too am happy for you," said Hal as he came toward me with a big smile and an even larger hand for me to shake.

"Someone had to get lucky. We all wanted to get into the B-29 program. At least we know we got a third of us in."

"It would have been too good to be true for all of us to go together, especially to a B-29 outfit."

"One good thing for me is that I get a two week leave or I guess it's called a delay en route. That's better because they don't charge you with leave. I'll be heading home as soon as I can make arrangements. I can go home and show off for a couple weeks. The girls won't have a chance. Boy, Christmas at home, I can't believe it! Then report to North Carolina to start training," said Hal happily.

"I too have a couple weeks leave before I have to report back here," said Dave.

"You guys lucked out there. I have to report as soon as possible, not later than two days from now. My assignment is to the 58th Bombardment Wing [VH]. My group is the 444th Bombardment Group (VH). They're at Great Bend, Kansas. The order indicates they're in training status, whatever that means. The one bad thing for me was that I was planning to drive my folks home. I hate to have them make the long trip back to California alone."

"I wish I was going that way instead of Minneapolis. I sure wouldn't mind driving them," said Hal.

"Thanks for the thought, buddy."

"Hey, wait a minute, how about me? I would be happy to drive them out there. I'd love to spend my leave in sunny California. I've never been there but maybe it might be as good as you've been bragging about."

"You mean it, Dave?"

"You bet! I'd love to do it if they'll take me along."

"How about Mississippi? I assumed you'd want to go home."

"You know Johnny, I really don't consider Mississippi my home any longer. If I like California, I may call it home after the war."

"How about your folks, won't they be unhappy if you don't show up?"

"No way, I didn't lose anything there and the only family I have is an aunt. Anyway, I can probably get away later to make a short visit."

"That's great, Dave. I don't know how to thank you."

"Are you kidding? Aren't we brothers?"

"I'm damn lucky to have friends like you two."

"What makes me mad is that the damn yankees split us up. Don't they know we could win this damn war if they would keep us together? Now, it'll take a little longer," said Dave with a sigh.

"I sure hate to think of going to war in a Gooney Bird. Hell, no guns is not my idea of the way to fight," said Hal.

"I'd trade you, Hal, if I could. Teaching a bunch of cadets navigation is not what I went through this program for. I'll be putting in for a transfer after the first class graduates. I sure wanted those B-29's," added Dave.

"You probably will get B-29's if you keep asking long enough. They will have to let you go or you will drive them crazy. If I know you," said Hal with a chuckle.

"Are you sure about driving my folks home, Dave?"

"You bet. Like I said, I can go home another time. The people left down there are old men and women and a few draft dodgers."

We drove back to our quarters, cleaned up, put our new uniforms back on and after we got Hal packed and ready in case his bus left sooner than expected, returned just at 1800 hours to pick up my folks. They were ready. They slipped on coats as it had become chilly.

My Dad knew something wasn't right. We were quieter than usual. He said nothing. He knew we'd tell them the news when the time was right. I pulled up in front of the officers club and let them out and then parked the car. In the club Dad spoke up, "Gentlemen, tonight is my treat. We'll have the best there is."

We made our way into the dining room and were seated. We scanned the menu and all ordered steak. I hoped the steaks were of the regular Texas variety, big. They were. We were hungry now that the excitement had subsided.

We ate in silence until Mother finally broke the mood. "It doesn't appear you boys are as happy as you were earlier. Is there something wrong?"

"We picked up our orders and found we were all going in different directions. We're a bit sad. You can never count on the Army to be logical. We're all heading to different commands. Hal is going to the Troop Carrier Command, Dave is staying here in the Training Command and I am headed for the Bomber Command."

"I wish you were all staying here like Dave. I'd feel better about it," said Mother.

"How much time do you have before you have to report?" asked Dad.

"I have very little time. Both Dave and Hal have a couple weeks, but I have to report to Great Bend, Kansas within a couple days. I've been assigned to a B-29 unit and they're training now. I have to get there as soon as possible. There are only a few lucky fellows going there from here. I feel very fortunate. I wanted the B-29 very badly."

"What's next?" asked Dad.

"We have to get Hal to the bus station in town tomorrow morning. And best of all, Dave is going home with you."

"That sounds just fine. We'll be happy to have him. He can have your room. He can use the car also. It'll be good to have one of you, even for a short time," said Mother.

Dave had a tear in his eye. He was an orphan and never knew his mother and father. He said, "You people are wonderful. I only wish I could have been as lucky as your Johnny to have such wonderful parents."

"Then it's settled. We'll drop Hal off at the bus station in the morning. Then we can drive to San Antonio and spend a little time. I'll be leaving from Kelly AAF, near there. We can live it up for a day and a night."

"I recently read someplace that a lot of big brass were in the B-29 program, due to the glamour of the new bomber," said Dad.

"I understand most of the crew members are dual rated. I don't know how that will affect me, but I am sure they can teach me radar and bombing. They have been in training so I'll probably have to catch up with the others. It should be challenging, especially getting in on the ground floor. I'm very excited about my new assignment and anxious to get started with a new tactical unit. I have a strong feeling that we flyboys will run into each other somewhere."

It was a difficult time for the three of us. We'd been very close. We decided to look on the bright side. At least we were now officers and aerial navigators, a hell of a lot better than we were before. We all agreed not to talk of it any more that evening. It was time to relax and enjoy these last hours together. We did just that. We had a fine dinner and after we had a couple drinks.

A tall first lieutenant, the chief instructor of our section, Tom Ross, walked over to our table. He had fought in Europe and was the one who had taught most of what to expect in combat.

"Good evening, folks, I'm Tom Ross."

We automatically stood to attention.

"Please join us," invited Mother.

"I would be happy to. Be seated gentlemen, there is no necessity for you to stand, especially when you are in the club. Which one of you lucky fellows belongs to these nice folks?"

"These are my parents, sir. Mr. and Mrs. Lea. This is Lieutenant Ross, our chief instructor."

"Not any longer. You're on your own now. However, I was able to retain one of you. Lieutenant Lewis will stay in my section. I asked for all three of you, but the head shed wouldn't buy that. You three were my best students. I know you'll all do well at your new trade. What assignments did you two get?"

"I'm going to the Troop Carrier Command and Johnny is going to the B-29 command."

"That sounds fine. I flew B-17's in Europe and if the B-29 is as much of an improvement as we have been told, you're most fortunate."

"Lieutenant Ross, where do you hail from?" asked Mother.

"Boston, ma'am. But please call me Tom."

"Boston is where we lived before John was born. He was the first member of our family to be born in California. We visit Boston from time to time. We still have many relatives there, but there's no place like California. We love it."

46

"Well, if I had my choice, I'd be living there too. My wife and I plan to migrate there after the war."

Tom spent most of the evening with us. He was trying to convince my mother the B-29 was the best plane yet invented. I appreciated it, but I knew it was new and had bugs. It flew higher, further, and carried ten tons of bombs. Yes, it was my kind of bird. She wasn't convinced. She was a mother who worried about her kids. But war is war and there is nothing we can do about it except win and try to stay alive.

6.

My small alarm clock destroyed a beautiful dream. I looked at the monster and it read 0600. That was late by my usual standards. However, I was now an officer and a gentleman and not on duty. I struggled to get my eyes open and my feet on the floor. This was my last day at San Marcos. Too soon I'd part with my folks and friends, possibly forever. We didn't speak of it.

We shaved and showered and then we stuffed all our worldly belongings into our B-4 bags. They were so heavy and fat, they were difficult to handle. We got the bags into the trunk and drove toward the main gate.

The Greyhound station was in the center of the small college town of San Marcos. Few automobiles were on the streets, a typical Saturday morning. We arrived early to have time for a cup of coffee and doughnuts. We didn't want to part hurriedly. We thought since the bus was always late we would have ample time to talk before we had to say good-bye. Not so. For the first time in history the damn bus pulled in ten minutes early. The station master called to have the bus loaded. We hurried to get Hal's bags on the platform. While they were loading the baggage compartment, we said our good-byes. A quick hug and a handshake followed by a promise to write as often as possible was all there was time for. Hal turned and boarded the bus, and hurried to a seat on the station side as the bus driver started the big bus. I felt a hollow feeling in the pit of my stomach as we waved to each other. The bus pulled onto Main street and disappeared around the corner. Dave and I just stared down the street.

"Hell to have to part with a friend like him, isn't it Johnny?"

"You bet, we've been good as a team. It's a damn shame we're being split up. I just know this isn't the end, we'll get together before this damn war ends."

"That big Yankee is one hell of a good man. Kind and thoughtful. He'll do okay, I am sure."

48

"He almost cried when he turned to get on the bus."

"He wasn't alone!"

"Seeing him go is like seeing your brother leave. I feel as close to him as I do my two brothers, maybe closer."

"I know what you mean. Maybe we'd better get our tails in gear. Your folks are probably waiting for us."

We drove back to the field in silence and found the folks patiently waiting. They had packed their bags and were seated next to them. We threw everything into the car trunk and headed for the officers club for breakfast.

"A guy could get used to this luxury."

"Sure beats the hell out of the swine treatment, doesn't it?"

With breakfast finished we set off for San Antonio. The trip was not a long one and the traffic light. We made very good time. Dad's car was running real good. We had no hotel reservations and I knew little of the hotels in San Antonio. The only one I did know was the old Gunther, affectionately called the Gunner by the cadets. It was a cadet's haven. There were more B-Girls and whores there than family members. It was fun trying to hide the real Gunther from my mother. The place was very different during the day, it looked respectable.

We checked in and put our things in our rooms and then decided on a driving sight seeing tour around the city. The main attraction was the Alamo. I'd hoped this visit would turn out better than my first. I came here during my stay when going through classification shortly before I had met Dave and Hal. I was with a fellow from Brooklyn who was a real loudmouth. We were no sooner inside the Alamo until this boob opened his big mouth and said, "This must be the place where a few Mexicans shot the ass off a bunch of Texicans." He thought he was funny, I guess. Needless to say our exit was firm and prompt. I was extremely embarrassed, to say the least.

"What the hell is wrong with you? This is a national shrine where Texans fought to the end for their ideals. You, my friend, are a slob without a brain. I wonder how the hell you got into this program?"

"Aw, shit, these damn Texans think theirs doesn't stink!"

"For Christ sake, use your head. You're dangerous. As far as I'm concerned, I don't know you." I turned and left him standing there with a puzzled look on his face.

I never went anywhere with the jerk again, and avoided him

until he was eliminated. He was one of the big percentage who never made it beyond classification, and I'm happy to say I never saw him again.

This time the visit to the Alamo was without incident. I was glad to have the opportunity to see the historic fort and mission. Afterward we had a nice lunch down by the river, and then I talked the folks into helping me find a warm trenchcoat. We shopped around at the many military clothing stores until I found a beautiful overcoat which cost me a bunch. I knew I was going to need a warm coat. The reports from Kansas and vicinity indicated it was a cold winter. I used all but a few dollars of my money. I was going to have to draw a partial pay when I got to Great Bend or go hungry.

We enjoyed our afternoon and evening. I felt free of all the worries which plagued cadets. The bad thing for me would be leaving the next day. I knew I'd be lonely and blue as I remembered how very hard it was for me when I first left home for the Army. I'd never really been away from home before, and homesickness was the worst thing I'd ever experienced. Now I'd be alone, but at least Dave would enjoy taking my place and that helped. It would take only hours for me to get to the frozen central plains but days before they reached Los Angeles.

The morning was cool and clear I was happy to see. I didn't want a delay in departing. Also, the folks were going to try and make El Paso in one hop and bad weather would slow them down. I was scheduled to leave at 1200 hours from Kelly AAF. I felt real good about my buddy going with my folks. It sure relieved my worries of them driving alone. After a nice breakfast they were ready to start. I wondered if I'd ever see them again. Tears were in all our eyes as they pulled away from the curb and headed west. I watched and waved until they were out of sight.

My transportation to Kelly was from the hotel. There'd be a couple other officers joining me in the lobby, I was told. When I turned to enter the hotel lobby, I ran right into Bill Russell.

"Hi, ole buddy. What the hell are you doing here?" I asked, puzzled.

"Going to Kelly with you. I've been assigned to the 444th Bomb Group, too."

"You're kidding! That's great! We're in the same group! I'm so damn excited about getting into B-29's it's hard to believe."

"I found out that you got B-29's. I thought you might be here, so I called to see if you were registered and when I found you were, I took a cab here instead of Kelly."

"My orders had only my name on them, so I wasn't sure if anyone else was going. I heard a rumor to the effect that a few guys from San Marcos were going to B-29's but there are four different bases in Kansas where they could go. We're lucky to be going to the same outfit, from the same flying school."

"The last I saw of you was when you walked across the stage to get your wings. Was that your folks just leaving?"

"It sure was! My good buddy Dave is going with them to California."

"Great. I wish you and I could have gone to California for a leave."

"You can't have your cake and eat it too."

"Right after graduation I went to headquarters to pick up my orders. When the captain went to the special desk to get my envelope he mentioned that your envelope was right next to mine. A couple of guys from the other section are going into '29's but just you and I are going together. After I picked up my orders, I headed for Austin to meet my brother who was passing through. I only had a few hours with him, hadn't seen him for a couple years, he's a Navy pilot, flies off of carriers. He's been in a couple big ones, like the Battle of Midway. Now he's on his way to Navy Dallas. If he were assigned there earlier we could've seen each other a couple times."

"That's a damn shame. I'm sure glad you got to see him. You may not have another chance for awhile. Remember that night in front of the classroom when you almost blew your career? I've thought of that many times since. I'll bet that colonel had a hard time not laughing out loud when you came off with that telephone pole pointer system. I almost crapped my pants when you said it."

"I think I did!"

"It's going to be colder than a well diggers ass in Kansas. Too bad the 444th isn't stationed somewhere in California or Arizona."

"True. But we can't look a gift horse in the mouth. We two California boys made the grade. If a guy could sell this assignment he could make a fortune."

We found our transportation for Kelly AAF would not leave for at least an hour and decided to take a little stroll down the main drag. We left our bags with the porter in the lobby of the hotel and started to walk. As we reached the corner, a drunk in uniform was headed our way. He was in bad shape, staggering and almost fell a couple of times. It was disgraceful.

"I'll be damned. It's Blankenship!"

"I haven't seen that son-of-a-bitch since we left Sheppard," said Bill.

"I saw the bastard in front of the PX a few days ago. He tried to give me a bad time. Instead, he was the one who had a bad time. You notice he no longer has corporal stripes."

"He got busted. Let's see if the no good shit throws us a salute!"

Blankenship was too far gone to recognize anyone. He stumbled past trying his best to keep from falling on his face. What a mistake. Bill let him go two steps beyond us, then in a loud and commanding voice, he halted Blankenship's progress. "Corporal, I mean Private Blankenship." He turned slowly and almost fell. He was a mess. His hat was on the back of his head, his tie was pulled loose and hanging limply, his uniform looked as dirty as if he had slept in it. He was in such bad shape I wondered why the MP's hadn't picked him up. San Antonio had more MP's than you could shake a stick at.

Blankenship said in a slurred tongue, "Wada ya want?"

Bill was livid. He sputtered for a few seconds, then shouted, "Stand at attention when you address an officer, and the word is sir!"

Blankenship attempted to stand at attention but failed miserably.

"Where do you think you're going, Private?"

"Just looking for a bar."

"No, that's where you're completely wrong. You are looking for the bus back to the base. And, if you are not back there and signed in within an hour, I promise you'll be standing before a Court Martial."

"That's impossible! The God damn bus takes longer than that to get there," he slurred.

"Tough shit. You be there and I don't care how you do it. You get your miserable carcass back to San Marcos within an hour or your ass will be mud. You can call a cab or we can call the MP's, take your choice. If you think I won't check up on you, you are stupider than I thought."

"Give me a break Lieutenant! I'm sorry I didn't call you sir."

"Just like the break you gave us, huh! You made life miserable for all of us at Sheppard for no good reason."

"Give me a break," he pleaded again.

I actually felt sorry for him. He was a pathetic sight. I was getting a little uneasy standing there. We'd gathered a small crowd, mostly GI's and Aviation Cadets. I didn't interfere with Bill even though I was hoping we could end this. We did have an obligation to see that men in uniform conducted themselves in a better manner while in public.

"You now have wasted one of your sixty minutes. Quit your sniveling and get your ass in gear."

Bill shouted like a Top-Sergeant, but why not? That's what he used to be. He continued, "You're a disgrace to your country, the uniform you wear and especially the Army Air Force. Maybe I will have you court martialed."

I felt sorry for Blankenship. However, my memory of his actions and threats could not be erased. I only hoped he would never be in a position to make life tough for men who are trying their hardest to make something of themselves.

"Blankenship, you will never learn. You get busted for being drunk and disorderly and a few days later here you are out early in the morning drunk in public view. You make my stomach turn. You are a disgrace. Now straighten yourself up. The stockade is waiting for you if you are not back at your orderly room in fifty-eight minutes," said Bill as he turned away. You could tell Bill had had experience with this conduct. I caught a slight smile on his face as he turned.

Blankenship was totally defeated and deflated. He tried to tidy himself as he turned and noticed people watching. The bastard was actually embarrassed. He tried to come to attention as he threw a "high ball salute." He turned and took off in a dead run to search for a taxi. He would have a hell of a bill by the time he reached San Marcos. I silently felt guilty for not helping him get some transportation but what the hell, it was his ball game, win or lose.

"He'll always be a slob, no matter what he does. He'll stay a buck-ass-private, too. You can make book on that."

"Let's get off the street, I feel conspicuous out here. I could use a beer. What do you say we forget about the bus and take a cab to Kelly?" I said.

"Why not? We're supposed to be officers, lets act like it even if I'm not too flush."

We found a little beer joint down the street and stepped into the comparative quiet of the bar.

"Bill, are you actually going to call his orderly room?" I asked.

"You bet your sweet ass. I want that bastard to know he is not screwing around with privates. We are officers and obligated to do our duty as we see it. Now, how about that beer?"

I told Bill about my encounter with Blankenship in front of the Post Exchange and he laughed.

"John, we were both NCO's and we know how important they are to the service but Blankenship and his kind are rabble, they can't lead men. He's just a lush, his small brain is floating in alcohol. He won't have to be embalmed when he dies."

An hour later we passed through the gate at Kelly Army Air Field and instructed the cab driver to take us to Base Operations. He knew the way. We unloaded our bags and paid him off. At the passenger counter we were told our flight would be leaving soon and to be ready when it was called. Bill walked over to the telephone, pulled out some change and dialed the operator as he looked at his watch. He was connected with Blankenship's orderly room, identified himself and queried, "Can you verify Private Blankenship has signed in?"

"Yes, sir," answered the sergeant. Then he went on to say, "Sir, something scared the living hell out of him. He looked like a dog shitting a peach seed. Is there something I should know about?"

"Sergeant, I was a former First-Soldier myself so let's just say I jumped his ass and let it go right there, okay?"

"Yes sir, I understand. He's a troublesome man. He just got busted. I have my eye on him."

"Do one thing, keep him away from San Antonio or he might end up in big trouble."

"I read you, sir. I will restrict him and keep a sharp eye on him, you can bet, sir. Good-bye."

"Thank you sergeant, and good-bye."

Bill walked over to where I was standing and said, "I talked to Blankenship's first sergeant and he'll handle things concerning him. I imagine the ass hole will end up a permanent KP. He'll never make life unbearable for cadets again."

"Permanent latrine orderly would be more like it," I added.

Our names were called for the flight. We grabbed our bags and headed for the C-47 parked in front of Base Ops. I sure felt good having Bill along. We got off the ground and tried to relax in the damn bucket seats.

We turned north and my thoughts were of Dave and my folks heading west. So much had happened since they drove off I had almost forgotten how much I missed them. Well, no use looking back, I was with a great guy and knew we'd never regret missing a leave for this.

I recalled my good friend Hal boarding the bus with tears in his eyes. God, I hope we meet again. He probably has the best assignment when all is said and done. He won't be bombing the enemy but his life expectancy is a hell of a lot better than ours.

"Have you ever been up front in one of these planes?"

"To be honest with you, I've never been in a C-47 before."

"Let's go forward and maybe we can take a look around the forward cabin, especially the navigator's station," said Bill as if he knew his way around. He probably did, after all, he already had a combat tour.

"This bucket doesn't have much more in the way of instruments than our AT-7!"

"You're right. Let's go into the pilots compartment and have a look."

After a short inspection of the "Gooney Bird" we were not too impressed. We were reinforced with the thought we'd be flying the best.

"Bill, Hal was assigned to the Troop Carrier Command and will be flying these buckets!"

"Not as bad as you think. His chances of survival are better than ours. Not too many fighters get close to C-47's and the Gooney Bird's don't have to go across a target and get blasted by flak."

"That's not altogether true. If they have to drop troops in a combat situations they'll get shot at."

"True. What I meant was they won't be shot at every time they fly. We will."

"I think we deserve this assignment, but we're lucky about one thing."

"What's that?"

"We're getting out of Texas."

"No argument there!"

"Bill, aren't you from Frisco?"

"Come on, Johnny. It's San Francisco."

"Bullshit. You call my home L.A. so what's wrong with calling your home Frisco?"

"The trouble with you guys from L.A. is you're not clued in."

"Bill, you're a good guy but you've got your head up your ass. It's Frisco to me no matter what you say."

"Hell's fire, don't get all pushed out of shape. At least we're both Californians. Let's make a pact, I'll call L.A. Los Angeles and you can you call my home San Francisco, okay?"

"You almost screwed up and called it Frisco yourself! I'm sorry, I meant to say San Francisco. You have a deal. After all we have got to stick together."

It was cold in the rear of the airplane. I sure was happy with my new coat, it was real warm. Bill only had his raincoat. He either hadn't thought of getting a heavy coat or he didn't have time.

The flight was taking longer than we anticipated but we were happy knowing that soon we'd be at our new base. We agreed to have a drink to celebrate our assignment as soon after we landed as possible. At just 1700 hours we had the word to fasten seat belts. We were about to land at Great Bend, Kansas.

7.

The plane taxied to a spot right in front of Base Operations. It was getting dark but there seemed to be a glow all around. Then I noticed the light snow on the ground.

A welcoming committee of two officers was waiting as the door of the plane was opened by the crew chief. A blast of cold air hit us and I felt chilled to the bone. I can't say I was used to snow. However, in the winter as a kid I had been to the mountains close by and played in snow. My family had a cabin near Lake Arrowhead which on occasion would be used during the winter. The big trouble there was getting snowed in. I still remembered how cold and wet I used to get every time I played in the snow. I supposed it was old hat to these people. They might not play in the snow, but I'll bet they got wet.

We stepped down the attached ladder and were met by the airdrome officer and an official greeter from group headquarters, a captain. It sure was better than being met by a bunch of cadet officers who wanted a piece of your ass. The two officers escorted Bill and me into Base Ops then the captain drove us to our quarters. He came in and gave us a short briefing of what to expect as well as some general information about the base and the group.

"You will be pretty busy catching up with the rest of the group. We will help you out whenever possible. You won't have a lot of time off, at least in the beginning. Your squadron and crew assignments are: Lea, with Ellis in the 678th Bomb Squadron and Russell with Miles in the 676th Bomb Squadron," explained Captain Jason.

"Damn, I was hoping we were going to the same squadron," said Bill dejectedly.

"You'll hardly know the difference. You'll train together and our group is a very close-knit organization. There is rivalry, true, but it's always clean. It's like one big happy family. We'll take some things within the family but from an outsider, look out!

57

We're mighty proud of the 444th. It's the first B-29 group formed in the 58th Bomb Wing. We also think it is the best group in the wing. This is the only wing of B-29's in existence. Another B-29 wing is being formed on paper. They'll be designated the 73rd Bomb Wing. They're scheduled to replace us here when we pull out.

"Tomorrow is Sunday, and you'll have the day off to get settled. I'll try and get someone who has the time to show you the base. If you want to look around by yourselves, it'll be okay but you won't be able to enter the area marked restricted until we process you for clearance. On Monday morning you'll get a briefing and orientation speech, meet the group commander and his staff, then you'll be released to your squadrons. Why don't you get cleaned up and meet me across the street at the officers club? We'll have dinner and a couple drinks and maybe we can find some members of your crews."

"Sounds great to me," said Bill excitedly.

We were assigned rooms next to each other temporarily, but would later be moved to another building to be with our respective crews.

Things were quite an improvement over our previous situation. Instead of being treated like schoolboys we were now on our own. We were told of events and schedules and we were expected to meet those schedules. In the past we were not given the opportunity to make decisions. I was quite happy with my surroundings and realized the life of an officer was a great improvement.

We wasted little time. No use unpacking until we moved in with our crews. We showered and dressed and in short order were ready to meet Captain Jason. He was our only contact with the base thus far but that would change soon.

As we reached the door of the officer's club I felt a little uneasy. We were brand new shavetails in new uniforms and shining gold bars but before I had a chance to dwell on embarrassment or self-consciousness, Captain Jason met us. When we entered the bar we saw there was a celebration going on.

"What's the party all about?" I asked.

"Nothing out of the ordinary. Most of the guys whoop it up on Saturday night. They work pretty hard during the week and let it all hang out on Saturday. Sunday is usually a day off, that is, unless you are flying or have some other duty. Most of the fellows are very friendly and easy to get along with. Let's take a table near the bar if there's one available. It'll be tough trying to remember all the names you'll hear tonight. After we order I'll look around and see if I can find some of your fellow crew members. I know they expect you this week end and will probably be looking for you."

A slim major arrived at the same time as our drinks. He had followed the waitress to the table from his bar stool.

"I am Tom Jackson, the Group Navigator. You must be Lea?"

"No sir, my name is Russell. This is Lea."

We got to our feet and reached to intercept his hand.

"Happy to see you both. We need good navigators and you both came highly recommended from Advanced Navigation School."

"We are very happy to be here. I hope we can measure up to our advanced billing, sir!" I said as we took our seats.

"We sure have a bunch of questions to ask, Major," added Bill.

"Don't sweat it. We have plenty of time to answer all your questions. Of course, this is all new to you and maybe a little hard to get into perspective but believe me, it will all fit together real soon." He turned to me and said, "Let's see, your first name is?"

"John, my friends call me Johnny. And this is Bill."

"Sir, we are real happy to be assigned here. B-29's are what we wanted to fly. We're the lucky ones. There wasn't a man in our class who didn't want an assignment to a B-29 outfit," said Bill.

"We don't have many B-29's as yet. Much of your training will be accomplished in B-17's and B-26's. We have great hopes the production lines will produce faster and relieve the situation. Now, both of you know your squadron assignments so we won't dwell on that. Both squadrons are fine outfits just as the other two are in our group. We'll give you a formal introduction Monday morning. The Group Commander wants to meet you as he does all newly assigned officers. He'd like to welcome you to the best damn wing in the Air Force, as he puts it. We'll lay out a training program and, believe me, you'll be busy. We'll teach you tactics and techniques, not navigation. You are supposed to know that.

"If your training records are correct, you will have little trouble on that account. I saw your records a couple weeks ago and asked for you both. You'll learn things are a bit different in a B-29 than they are in an AT-7. More instruments and the plane goes a hell of a lot faster. We'll teach you bombing procedures and the fundamentals of radar. Both are very important to you because as the navigators, you're the heads of the bombing teams as well as second in command of the aircrafts. In other words you'll be responsible for the coordination of all activities with respect to getting the planes to and from the targets and the bombs on the targets. That is an over simplification of your jobs. You will not personally drop bombs on enemy targets unless you lose your bombardiers. It's vital that you know and understand how to get there and how to use the radar. By the time we're through with you, we'll have you dropping a pickle in the proverbial barrel.

"The radar portion of your training is secret. No notes are taken in class. You will have to memorize what you are taught except for the checklists. You will get survival training which will prepare you for both sea and jungle survival. We have the best people around for this training. There are subjects, too many for me to remember. I promise you this, we don't give you classroom training just to keep you busy. Those days are over. We must have this wing ready when we get all our aircraft assigned. We have no time to waste. We'll give you some cursory training on the engineering of the B-29. You might be involved with some of your own maintenance, changing an engine, or some other such thing.

"After the briefing Monday we'll process you for a security clearance and entry badge. You won't be able to enter restricted areas without your badge. Oh yes, we'll also process your pay records and other administrative matters. Captain Jason will be your immediate contact and he'll guide you through the maze."

"Speaking of pay records, I'm almost broke!" I said.

"No sweat, we can get you a partial pay Monday."

"Sounds great to me. It's good not to be a cadet any longer," said Bill with a big smile.

"I checked on how much we'll make as second louies when I was back at San Marcos. We'll have money to burn. Our pay is a little under $300. Not bad huh?"

"Yeah, I won't know what to do with all that cash," answered Bill.

"You'll find plenty of ways of spending money," interjected Major Jackson and he knew what he was talking about. We had allotments and other necessities, not including a little gambling.

"I know I've generalized quite a bit but you'll find things will work out. Do you have any questions?"

"I have a couple. First, will we stay with the crews we're assigned to? And second, how long have the rest of the crew members been together?" I asked quizzically.

"The answer to your first question is yes. As for the second, that is a little harder to answer. There are different crew positions missing on some crews. As for yours, John, the radar man and a couple scanners are still to arrive. Bill, your crew lacks a radio operator as well as a radar man. You can see we're still putting crews together. We're expecting a slug of radar officers from Victorville very soon."

"I assume from what you have said, we are replacement navigators. What happened to the navigators we are replacing?"

"You are replacing the two navigators originally assigned to your crews. They were the best of friends. We don't know if they'll ever get back on flying status. Both were injured badly in a serious accident two weeks ago. They are lucky to be alive. They were driving fast on a road south of here when a hay wagon pulled out on the main road, right in front of them. They swerved to avoid the truck, lost control and hit a tree. They were damn good navigators and we felt their loss. Now you can see why you are here. They're at the base hospital. It'll be a miracle if they can return to duty for some time to come, if ever."

Bill was curious about the B-17's and B-26's. He asked Major Jackson. "Why will we train in two aircraft we won't be flying in combat?"

"It's easier for navigators than for some of the others. For you the big difference is that you'll have more sophisticated equipment in the B-29. Until deliveries of the B-29 pick up we will have to be content to fly the '17's and '26's. You will do most of your work in the B-17 and the bombardier's will do most of their work in the B-26. Remember one thing above all others, in this command the navigator has more responsibility than he otherwise would. As navigator you have control over the bombardier and radar operator. You three make up the bombing team. Enough shop talk for tonight. Why don't we go in and have dinner and then we'll try to round up some of your crew?"

"Sounds like a great idea. We haven't eaten all day," said Bill as he pushed his chair back and downed his drink at the same time.

Major Jackson led the way into the dining room and was met by the hostess. He asked for a table and with no lost motion we were seated. We had steaks, but unfortunately they weren't Texas size steaks. We were hungry. However, the food was good and afterwards we relaxed over coffee. It was great to be accepted like this, it made you feel like you were on the team.

Captain Jason suggested going into the bar area to see if any one from either of our crews was there. He looked around and finally, at the end of the bar he located someone he was looking for. He turned to Bill and said, "That fellow at the end of the bar is your aircraft commander. Do you want to meet him?"

"Yes, sir."

We pushed our way through the throng. The noise level was high and there were wall to wall people. It'd be difficult to spot anyone. We squeezed our way through the crowd until we made it to the end of the bar where a good looking second lieutenant sat with a beer in front of him. Captain Jason made the introductions. The pilot's name was Bob Miles. He was a tall dark haired fellow handsome enough to have been in Hollywood making love movies instead of seated here in this noisy bar in Kansas. Bill and Bob hit it off right away. I hoped my pilot would be as easy to talk to.

Captain Jason, after searching the crowd elevated on the rung on a bar stool, looked down at me and said, "We're in luck. I see Bart Ellis is pushing his way in our direction."

A slim lieutenant stepped up to me and looked me in the eye and said, "You must be Lea?"

"That's right. How did you know?"

"I am a good guesser. My name is Bart Ellis, you and I have a lot to talk about. I hear you're from California?"

"Right on target. I'm from the northeastern part of Los Angeles between Glendale and Pasadena, Highland Park."

"No shit! I have a friend who lives up that way. I'm from Huntington Beach, down in Orange County. You should fit right in, we have three more Californians on our crew and all are from the southern part of the state. Let's see, Jim Dawson, the co-pilot, is from Redlands; Rich Ellis, no relation, is from Pasadena; Walt Smith, our flight engineer, is from Alhambra. How's that for a crew?"

"Sounds like old home week."

Bart turned to Jason and Jackson and said, "We have a lot to talk about. Thanks for showing Lea around. I'll take over from here."

They both nodded and I said good night and thanked them for looking after us. Then I followed Bart as he shoved his way toward the perimeter. We got through the big crowd and found a table. Bart got the eye of the waitress and soon we were ordering. I took an immediate liking to Bart. He handled himself confidently, sure of every word and thought. He had a blonde crew cut and mustache to match, he was twenty-four years old. He'd been a flight instructor and was a flying sergeant prior to being commissioned.

"Here come the guys now," Bart said as he looked toward the entrance to the bar. He got up and waved with a circular motion. As the two approached I saw they were both about my age, possibly a year or two older. They pulled over a couple chairs from another table and extended their right hands. I shook them each in turn while we introduced ourselves.

"I'm Jim Dawson, co-pilot, and this is Rich Ellis our pickle dropper."

"Glad to meet you both, I'm Johnny Lea, fresh from nav school. I hear you guys are from Southern California too!"

"That's right!"

Jim was just under six foot, good looking, with sandy hair and a cleft chin. Rich was about the same height and had reddish brown hair and a soft smile.

"There's a good chance of getting another Californian for our radar operator. We checked the list graduating from Victorville soon and if nothing changes we'll get a fellow from San Diego," said Bart with enthusiasm as he reached for his beer.

"It'll be like old home week even if we didn't know each other before," said Jim.

"Maybe, but this is Kansas not California and we can't change that. If they had an ocean here it would be more like home," said Rich with the same soft smile.

"I lived within a few miles of Rich and Walt and not more than fifty miles from Jim and Bart, but the LA area is so vast and spread out it was unlikely we had ever crossed paths.

"The weather here sure leaves a lot to be desired. You're right, it's not California. It's colder than a witch's tit most of the time," said Bart. He was an earthy guy. You never misunderstood his meaning. I was soon to look on these three fellows as my inseparable companions.

"We don't want to give you a big head but you come highly recommended. We hear you are a real hot nav-a-guesser," said Bart as he took a long pull on his glass of beer.

"I don't know where you got your information. All I can say is

63

I'll give it the old college try. I'm delighted to be with you fellows, even in Kansas, and I'm happy to know we're gonna fly the B-29. I've wanted to get in to B-29's from the day I started cadet training."

"We're a crew and we help each other like a family. We do most everything together. If you need help with anything, don't keep it a secret," Bart explained.

"I understand I have some catching up to do."

"No sweat, you won't be much behind. We've only had one B-29 flight as a crew. That was just before our first navigator busted his ass in that damn sports car. He was damn good too." Bart said.

"You're putting the pressure on me but I'll do my best."

"That's what counts! Most likely we won't be leaving here for awhile. The factory is far behind in aircraft delivery and the ones we've received are constantly being modified or repaired. I guess the mechanics need the training," added Bart.

"I shouldn't have too much trouble with the navigation, but I'll have a lot to learn about bombing and radar."

"The bombing will come easy. I'll act as your instructor for the most part. We can work on whatever phase gives you trouble, if any. It'll be no sweat," said Rich as he reached for his first beer.

"Thanks for the confidence."

"Hell, the tables are easy and I can teach you the bomb sight in no time. I'll give you a study guide and some other material, then we can go for it."

"By the way, Johnny, you'll be happy to know that Jim and I moved your things into our BOQ with a room next to mine," said Rich.

"Your room is 123. That should be easy for you to remember and the building number is T-250. It is just a couple buildings down from where you were," added Jim.

"It would be funny if I walked in on another guy thinking I was still assigned the room."

"We do everything together like eating, drinking, sleeping, flying and on occasion, chasing women," said Bart with a big smile.

"That sounds fine to me, but sleeping together is where I draw the line." I said trying to be funny.

"You know what I mean. We need to have coordination to be a crew that plans to survive," he retorted.

64

"I understand. I'll do all I can to enhance that coordination."

"Do you gamble?"

"Do you mean money gambling? Life is a gamble, every day."

"Bullshit! You talk like a philosopher, I'm talking about cards and maybe craps."

"Sure, but I'm flat broke. I hope to get a partial pay tomorrow. Why do you ask? Do you have a game here?"

"You bet your sweet ass. There's a game or two going most of the time. The club stays open all day, so much night work goes on. You can usually find a poker game during the day and craps at night."

"I guess there won't be much time for me to gamble. The way it sounds I'll be too damn busy, except maybe on a Saturday night."

"Every day is the same around here, Saturday and Sunday included," added Rich.

"Anyway, you'd better be careful of hustlers in those games," said Jim.

"Hell, Johnny, you won't be that busy. You'll have time off. Sure, it's a lot of work, but we always find time to relax and so will you," said Bart as he finished off his beer and started looking for the barmaid.

"It sure is great to be with you fellows. After all I just graduated from nav school a couple of days ago and you are all old timers, so to speak."

"Are you kidding? I just got here from bombardier's school the end of last month. These two have been around longer than me. Bart was a flying sergeant and an aircraft commander on B-17's and Jim was an AC on B-24's, better known as the B dash two crash four. By the way, weren't you a sergeant too?"

"Sure was. You guys know a lot about me. What a spy system! The only help it was to me in cadets was that they made me a cadet officer because I was a sergeant from the Infantry!"

"That's not too bad!" said Jim. "I know when I was going through cadets, the cadet officers had it made. Johnny, see how jealous they are of a good airplane. At least it lands on three wheels instead of dragging its tail," Jim added as an after thought.

"Bullshit! The B-24 is no match for the B-17," said Bart indignantly.

"Christ, did I start it again? Our biggest arguments around here are about which airplane is the best, the '17 or '24. Who gives a shit! Our bird is the '29, good, bad or indifferent," said Rich as if he had refereed the arguments in the past.

"I flew in the B-24 during aerial gunnery. We were busy learning how to fire guns and heard little of the pros or cons of the airplane, so I'm not getting between you two heavy weights." I said with a laugh.

"What do you say we order another round of beer and then wander back to the card room and see what the action looks like?" said Bart as he waved for the bar maid again.

"I'll spring for the beer if you all carry your own. That's where the service stops," said Jim as the waitress arrived. The beer came and we all walked toward the rear of the building following Bart in a line as he walked slowly to keep from spilling his beer. As we approached we heard the familiar calls. Seven come eleven and once in a while a frustrated "Oh shit." The noise was exciting. I had not been in a decent poker or crap game since the Infantry. Some of those games got pretty wild. I guess GI crap games are much the same everywhere, except the officers played on a table in a club, the GI's were generally on their knees throwing against a wall. Later, I learned not all officers' crap games were played on a table.

8.

Morning came fast. I'd slept soundly. In fact, I felt refreshed and ready to go. I checked the time and realized I was thirty minutes late. I shaved, showered and dressed as fast as I could, pulled on my overcoat and headed out for breakfast.

When I opened the door to the officers club, the heat was welcome. It was very cold outside but hadn't snowed during the night. My new friends were seated at a table in the dining room sipping coffee and reading the Sunday paper, waiting for me before ordering.

"Sorry to delay you guys. I'd slept so soundly I didn't hear a thing from the time my head hit the pillow until a few minutes ago when I opened my eyes."

"No sweat. We're in no hurry, just got here a few minutes ago ourselves. We looked in on you but you were cutting those 'Zee's and we didn't have the heart to wake you," greeted Bart.

"Let's order now. I could eat the south end of a north bound jackass," said Rich in a very expressive way.

Jim dropped the sports page on the floor and moved over to make room for me.

"What's Great Bend like?" I asked.

"Great Bend is out in the boondocks, so forget about going to the big city. There's nothing to do there. The base has all the facilities we need, which is the reason so many people are at the club all the time. Most guys with families found no place for them to live in town and gave up on the idea of having them near."

"Here comes the waitress. Flag her down," said Rich. We ordered our breakfast and while waiting for our food to come we shot the breeze and got better acquainted.

"I understand pilots on B-29's must first be AC's on either the B-17 or 24. Is that true?" I asked Bart.

"The '17 is a damn good bird, probably the best we have," was his reply.

"Bart is always coming off with that shit! The '24 is in some ways superior. It's faster and will carry a little more, but any damn fool can see that neither the '17 or the '24 can hold a candle to the B-29. He's too damn stubborn to admit it."

"Christ, Jim, don't you get your water hot. This's just a little friendly discussion. Let's face it, the B-29 is still unproven in combat and still has a lot of bugs. If they can work them out we'll have one hell of a bird."

"Maybe so, but we're here to prove it's the plane of the future. No matter what any of us think we have to have a plane that can go a long distance and carry enough bombs to do some damage."

"Don't worry over their ramblings. They'll never end that argument," Rich had heard the same words spoken before.

"Seriously, we're one big happy family. We're always comparing the merits of our past experiences with the present. There isn't a plane to compare with the B-29. True, it does have some glitches, but they're working hard both in the field and at the factories to work out the bugs. Some of the problems stem from overheating engines. We try to hang in there and help with evaluations; that is, whenever we get a chance to fly it."

We finished our breakfast and decided it was time to get over to Al's office for my temporary line badge. Fortunately Bart had his car because it was much too cold to do a tour of the base on foot. At Al's office everything was ready for me to sign. My picture was taken for my permanent security badge while I was there.

Bart started by driving around the base to show me the location of the buildings I'd have to go to frequently. First stop was squadron headquarters where I was introduced to our commander, his staff and other personnel. Next we went to squadron operations, where I met more people. I'd be lucky to remember half of them. Ops was where it all happened for crew members. Next stop was the training building and personal equipment section where flying clothes and equipment would be issued. Rich insisted on going to the hangar that housed the bomb trainer. I was anxious to see how it was set up. There was a large tri-pod on wheels with a bomb sight on the platform high above the floor. On the floor was a small box on wheels which was moved on command from the instructor. The bombardier's job was to intercept at a point where he could hit the moving bug, as it was called, with make-believe bombs. Hits were scored by markers attached to the bottom. When the release time was up the marker made colored marks on the top of the bug, assuming your calculations were correct. It looked difficult but it also looked like fun. It reminded me of the penny arcade at gunnery school.

"Now you guys are in my domain. That overgrown tri-pod, as Bart calls it, is where you become proficient at bombing before ever dropping a bomb from an airplane. You can see the Norden bomb sight attached above is exactly like the one in the airplane. We'll teach you the fundamentals of bombing right here on this bomb trainer. You won't feel out of place in the nose of the aircraft when we're finished here," Rich explained.

I could tell from the way he spoke that he knew what he was doing. The best way to learn something is from a guy who knows the score. Rich was easy to talk to and had a great sense of humor so I knew we'd hit it off just fine. Jim had previously told me Rich was considered one of the very best bomb-aimers in the entire wing.

"Looks like fun. I've always said if you enjoy what you're doing it comes easier and you do it better."

"True. It's fun but it's not a toy. Bart thinks it is."

Bart laughed out loud. He had a little of the devil in him. I knew we'd have few dull moments with him in charge.

"When are we going to see a B-29? I'm eager to take a look inside."

"I thought you'd never ask!" Bart said. He'd been waiting for me to say something.

We drove down a street headed toward the flight line, parked, and walked to a gate guarded by an armed MP. The sign printed on the fence read RESTRICTED. At the gate the MP looked me over because he didn't recognize me. He checked all the line passes carefully and asked for my AGO card to check against my pass. Finally he was satisfied I wasn't an intruder and let us enter.

In front of the hangar was a shiny new B-29. Apparently it had just arrived from the factory. The plane was a giant with smooth lines. You could see at a glance this machine was fast and efficient. We entered the wheel well and climbed the ladder to the flight deck. I looked in wonder. The expanse of glass in the nose gave great visibility and the navigator's position was well planned out with all the necessary instruments, plus some instruments I'd never seen. To say I was thrilled was putting it mildly. "Okay, I'm ready to take off," I said from the navigators seat. "It meets my standards."

"That's good. What would we do if you weren't pleased?" asked Bart, bringing a good laugh from the four of us.

We crawled down the tunnel to the rear and inspected the two large bomb bays and the rear section before the tour was over. As we walked toward the gate I turned and looked once more at the plane. We hoped this was the one that would get us through the war in one piece. If not we'd die together. I congratulated myself for being assigned here. I wished Hal and Dave could have been as fortunate. I was indeed lucky to fly in this beautiful airplane with these fine fellows. We'd be together for a long spell. I'd found my place in the sun.

After lunch I told the others I had to write a few letters to let my family know what was happening. I wasn't really in the mood but I knew starting tomorrow there'd be little time. As I wrote, I mentally calculated how far along the folks were on their return home and wondered how Dave was doing.

I finished my letters and was relaxing on my bed when Jim came in and asked, "How'd you like to take in a movie tonight?"

"What's on? I haven't seen a show in ages."

"*Casablanca.* I hear it's a damn good picture. Bogart and Bergman are the stars."

"Count me in. How about the other guys?"

"They've seen it and don't want to sit through it again. We'll have dinner together before, okay?"

"Great."

The dinner and the movie turned out just fine. This new life suited me. I was more content now than at any other time since I'd enlisted. My newfound friends and I had similar needs and enjoyed each others company. I declined an invite to have a short beer. I needed to hit the sack in order to be fresh for the events of the next day.

I walked into the group headquarters a little before 0800 hours and found Captain Jason doing some kind of coordinating. I also noticed Bill Russell sitting against the wall. I walked over and asked, "Am I late?"

"Hell no! I just got my wires crossed. I thought we were supposed to be here at 0700. I've been sitting here cooling my heels."

"I hope they get this show on the road soon, the hurry up and wait we were used to in cadets gets old. I want to get started with the training."

Bill agreed and told me about meeting his new crew the night before and how much fun they were.

"The only thing wrong is there isn't another Californian on our crew."

"You won't believe what I'm about to tell you. I'm the fifth Californian on my crew and there's a good chance we'll get another from radar school. The best part's they're all from the south."

"Christ, you can really pick em, can't you?"

I was about to continue when Al Jason came over to us and said, "It's 0800. Lets go in and meet the group commander. He likes to give a short welcoming speech."

We followed Al to the commander's office, a big room with a large desk and a table pushed against the front forming a "T". Seated at the table was the group staff. We saluted smartly which impressed Colonel Harry Baker. His name was carved on a large piece of Philippine mahogany. He was in his early forties, straight and tall, obviously a man of great experience. A small smile seemed to be his predominant feature.

"I'm Colonel Baker and this is my staff." He introduced each officer and explained his function. "You'll probably never see this body assembled at one time again, but from time to time you'll undoubtedly run into one or more of them. They're kept pretty busy but never too busy to help you in a time of need."

The colonel outlined the short history of the 444th and then turned the meeting over to Major Tom Jackson, the group navigator. I'd liked him the moment I'd met him that first night at the club. We would see him more often than any other staff officer of the group. However, most of our training was to come from the squadron training people. Major Jackson briefed us on the training and told us we'd have to work a bit harder to catch up with the others. He went on to say, "Our departure to some overseas location is unknown at this time as is the departure date. However, we must be ready for any event. That is why we have to accelerate your training schedule." He added, "You'll be given all the help you require to accomplish your task."

After the briefing concluded we were instructed to report to our respective squadron headquarters for further processing.

Lt. Colonel Mitchell, squadron commander of the 678th Bomb Squadron, seemed to be one damn good guy. He made me feel right at home. He explained that he was happy to have me in his squadron and expected me to fit right in. Then he took me to the personal equipment section to be fitted for a parachute, oxygen

71

mask and other flying equipment and clothing. I had a hell of a load. Next I was sent back to group to get my clearance finalized and to be issued a permanent line and restricted area pass.

By 1700 I was all in. I'd been running my tail off since 0800 with no break, so I was glad when Bart came driving up and asked, "How's it going? You look beat. Jump in and I'll run you back to the quarters."

"Thanks for the lift. I'm bushed and I think I could use a drink!"

"No sweat. We'll drop by the club after you get rid of all that shit you're carrying. What'd you think of the people at group and squadron?"

"They all seem quite competent. The guy who really impressed me was Colonel Mitchell. You can tell he knows the score and acts like he wants me. He's an okay guy."

"He's the fairest guy you'll run into. He has a good handle on what the hell is going on. He loves to gamble and be around the guys. You'll probably see him in a game or two. We have a damn good squadron. Most of the guys are fine troops. Of course, there are a couple assholes and candy asses in our squadron like most outfits, but damn few. You won't have any trouble finding out who they are."

"It looks as if I'll be in ground school the whole first week, and just think, I won't have to march to class like an aviation cadet."

The week of ground school was very interesting and the time passed rapidly. My average school day was twelve hours, either spent in the classroom or in one of the trainers. They threw material at me fast and furious. I was used to that so it was no big deal. After all I was young and tough and eager for my first flight. It was not in a B-29 as I had hoped, but in a Martin B-26. No matter, I was finally flying in a real bomber. It wasn't long before the whole crew was preparing for our first cross-country flight, it would be a long one, and best of all, in a B-29.

The mission was a three-thousand mile flight and included simulated attacks on three large metropolitan areas, one of which was Los Angeles. To think I would be right over my hometown! Too bad I couldn't stop over and see the family.

Take off was scheduled for 1000 hours returning around 0300 the following day, a long haul. I'd really have to work my ass off to make sure all went as planned. I did and the mission went very well. My instructor was pleased with my work and knowledge of the equipment and procedures. I was happy to have items signed off in my training folder. All the squares had to be filled and there were a bunch. Bart told me he was mighty proud I was his navigator and, further, that I was a hell of a lot better than the first one he had.

"I heard he got hurt."

"He busted his ass in a car wreck. He was a crazy bastard."

He said no more and I never asked him any questions. It was obvious Bart had not been too happy and was relieved to have a new navigator. I felt Bart was a good leader and pilot. He held a heading as I'd never figured a pilot could.

The flight had been a real test of my endurance. I loved the airplane. It was everything I hoped it would be. It was very stable to take celestial shots from, not like the AT-7 leaping all over the sky. She was a real smoothy. It was great to fly at 25,000 feet without an oxygen mask on your face, and because the plane was pressurized and heated we wore summer flying suits in the middle of winter.

As we drove back to the quarters Bart reflected on the mission. "I understand our next mission will be a bomb training mission, for you," he went on to say.

"Yeah, I have to navigate and then set up and do the bombing. Rich will be my instructor. We've been working hard on the bomb trainer. It should be interesting. Hope I hit the range, let alone the target!"

Training progressed for the crew and for the most part things were fitting together nicely. I'd caught up with the rest of the squadron and the crew acted as if I'd been with them from the beginning.

Bombing was a lot of fun for me. One night we were on a training mission dropping practice bombs from a B-17, my first actual drop. The bombs were the 100 pound practice bombs filled with sand and powder. They were painted blue and were affectionately referred to as the "blue devils." I navigated the plane on the proper heading down the bomb run toward the drop zone and prepared the bomb sight by entering the proper information into it. I reset the cross hairs and then was ready except for moving the indices. When you locate your target and kill the drift and ground speed the crosshairs are over the target, the indices move, and when they come together the bomb is released automatically. In my excitement I turned on the switches prematurely and as I rolled the indices to the starting position I brought them

73

together. Before I knew it one of the blue devils was on its way to terra firma. I knew I'd goofed when I heard the distinctive click as the indices passed over the crosshairs. I'd dropped the damn thing. I felt like jumping out and trying to catch it. I wondered how I would ever live it down. At least we were over the start of the bomb range and not over some town or oil field. After that faux pas, I managed to do a reasonable job. It did take some time to live it down, but I had it coming so I took it like a man. Actually, that mistake taught me a great lesson: follow the check list and keep your head out of your ass.

As time passed we were allowed to fly the B-29 more. We all felt at home in it. One day I had a bright idea and decided to try it out. As long as we would all be flying together from then on, it might be a good idea to teach the scanners how to navigate by pilotage or map reading. On long cross countries they could assist me and it would give them something to do. An error in judgement. After spending hours with them teaching them to read an aerial map they were excited about the prospect of helping me navigate. I figured when I was busy with other activities they could keep me current with certain points on the ground. The problem came when I was engrossed with a delicate reading which required my undivided attention. That was the time they called on the interphone to tell me they'd spotted something or had a question about something they didn't understand. After using my new multi-navigator invention on one cross-country, I withdrew their maps and told them in the future they wouldn't have to help me. I've often wondered if they had outsmarted me by bugging me, knowing I'd withdraw their maps if they got to be a pain in the ass. I thanked them one and all for their efforts and told them that one navigator was all that was required from then on.

New crew members were needed to fill the void. Some of the crews kept trickling in throughout the end of 1943 and early 1944. By the end of January all the crews were in place in our squadron. We were at full strength. A crew consisted of eleven men, usually five officers and six enlisted. Occasionally, the fifth officer would be a flight engineer. Normally the fifth officer was the radar operator. In our case it was the latter.

The last man assigned to our crew was Orville Dudley, the radar operator. He'd arrived from Victorville AAF where he had finished his training. We were a bit disappointed. There had been a deletion of one man on the shipping order, and instead of the

Californian we'd expected, we got a little round second balloon from Southern Illinois. Dudley came from a farm and was not accustomed to the friendly harassment he received. He was short, round and had sandy colored hair and a pale complexion. I was amazed he hadn't worn off some of the groceries at Victorville, but I soon learned his two pleasures in life were eating and sleeping, especially sleeping. He was twenty years old and when asked, "Have you ever had a sun tan?" replied, "Not if I could help it." His pale complexion flushed rosy red when he was teased. He was quickly nicknamed "Roundy." He violently rejected the new moniker. We tried in vain to convince him that no one would call him Orville, it was too hard to say. When we referred to him as the "Chicago Kid" he reacted even worse than he did to Roundy. He said maybe if he'd come from California we would've left him alone. After a few days of heckling him the novelty wore off and his life was a little bit easier. He was a damn good radar man, a welcome completion to our crew.

Sergeant Walt Smith, the flight engineer, was thirty-five and the oldest member in our crew. He stood six feet even and had the kindliest expression a man could have. He was very soft spoken and unless asked a direct question, seldom said anything. He was very knowledgeable and we considered him the best engineer in the entire squadron, if not the group. Of all the enlisted men I felt closest to Walt. When flying we had to work in harmony. His position was behind the co-pilot and he rode backward. My position was on the opposite side and a little to the rear. We could look at each other by just turning our heads. When he discovered I was from a section of Los Angeles only a few miles from his home, he was happy. He, too, was a native. Walt was the senior EM and he was NCOIC. In an emergency he was on top of the problem rapidly.

A young fellow from Omaha, Nebraska, was our radio operator, Ray Siverson. He had curly blonde hair, a light complexion, of medium height with a ready smile. He was known for his exceptional knowledge of the radio.

The central fire control man or CFC, was nineteen, built like Ray, with light brown hair and a much rounder face. Roy West was from Kentucky and like his ancestors was a dead shot, except Roy did it with a fifty caliber machine gun. He was a fun-loving guy with a seemingly permanent smile. His crewcut was not the stiff variety because his hair was so fine. His job was to supervise the gunnery system and to direct aerial defense. The remote-controlled turrets were assigned from his position located atop the rear cabin. The CFC had a control panel from which he assigned gunfire under attack. The CFC could fire any of the guns himself or assign them to gunners. There were five gunners on the crew including the bombardier. At that time this was the most advanced gunnery system yet devised. It incorporated a 70-mil radius sight which had a large red dot in the center circled by smaller dots adjusted by turning a knob on the gun sight. With the center dot fixed on the enemy aircraft and the outer dots adjusted to fit the size of the plane, a hit was assured, providing the navigator fed the proper information into the computer. The system would compensate for ballistics. The system had to be good because the B-29 seldom had fighter protection.

The last three members of the crew were the two scanner gunners and the tail gunner. The thirty-two year old tail gunner was the second oldest of the crew. Affectionately called "Pops," he was from North Carolina and had a drawl which made him sound as if he was from the deep south. His name was Carl Reed and he was a former newspaperman. He had a light complexion and unruly light brown hair and was the slightest built man on the crew. I guess that's why he was the tail gunner.

The left scanner was Art Long, a Bostonian with black hair, of average build and height. When Art and Pops got into a conversation it was something to hear; they had such different accents.

Last but not least was the right scanner. His name was Ron Ellis. Yes, another Ellis, but not related to Bart or Rich. Ron hailed from Tennessee, was tall and skinny, and had honey colored hair. His crewcut was like a bristle brush. He reminded me of a mountain man minus the coon skin hat and buckskin clothing. Regulations called for him to wear khaki but I was sure he'd have rather dressed as I pictured him.

This had to be a unique crew, three men of eleven with the same last name and five from Southern California. We became a family and only official functions precluded the association of all eleven men.

A B-29 crew member had to have at least two skills. Enlisted men could have had training in maintenance, radio repair, armor or any of a number of skills akin to flying. The same applied to the officers except for the bombardier and the pilots. Both pilots, however, had to be qualified first pilots on one of the heavy bombers to be acceptable. The radar man had been to navigation school prior to radar school, and as for me, I got a rating change due to my training which made me triple rated. That is, as navigator, as radar man and as bombardier. Rich and I had also gone through aerial gunnery.

I was very proud to be with this assemblage and was confident that together we would survive combat. We each got to know how the others thought and reacted accordingly. Most of our training took place in trainers or flying. The B-29 we flew as a crew but in the B-17 or B-26 I often flew with other people. Although we tried to stick together regardless of the type plane we flew, it was not always possible.

After I'd been at Great Bend for two months I felt we were ready. The crew had reached its peak. There was little doubt our superiors were aware of it, too. We were declared combat ready and knew the time was growing short before our departure to places unknown.

9.

The time passed rapidly at Great Bend, due mostly to the pace of activity. I wrote letters whenever I had a few minutes to spare. Some weeks ago I'd found time to get letters off to both Dave and Hal, and by some strange miracle, I'd received a letter from each of them on the same day from widely scattered areas. Hal wrote of the bitter cold and how he had almost frozen his ass off in Minneapolis. He went on to say the girls were mighty impressed with his uniform and silver wings. I envied him briefly, but I wouldn't trade his leave at home for my assignment. He'd have said the same if he were me. The letter from Dave told he had finished his course and was now a full fledged instructor navigator. He said he wished he were with me and the hell with the instructor assignment. Also, that he'd had a wonderful leave in California taking my place with the family. Reading their letters left me painfully homesick. I used to get homesick frequently, like once a day, but I learned to live with it. Reading their letters about all the girls and other friends and relatives left me depressed and feeling sorry for myself.

It was then that Bart walked in and said, "Come on Johnny, stop the daydreaming and let's go win us some money. I'm getting low."

"I really don't know if I'm up to it right now."

"What's up? Did your girlfriend back home send you a Dear John letter?"

"Nothing like that. I was just a little homesick, I guess."

"Well, the best thing for you is something to take your mind off it. Get it in gear and let's go kick some ass."

I grabbed my coat and walked out the door behind him. He wasted no time with small talk, he just headed across the street to the officers club. As we went into the game room I asked him, "Where are the other guys?"

"Fucking off! I guess they wanted to write home or something, but that's not important. What's important is that you concentrate on gambling and nothing else."

"What's wrong, Bart, losing control of your flock?"

"Bullshit. Let's not worry about them, let's get in a game."

"You're right. One can't afford to mope around. We have to stay fresh and flush."

"Do you see an opening at any of the tables?"

"Not yet, let's look around and see what the hell's going on before we jump."

"I told the others to be here by 1800. We can eat when they get here. In the meantime lets try to get into a game."

* * *

You could have set your watch by Jim, Rich and Roundy. They came through the door together at exactly 1800 and when they got within talking distance, they said in unison, "We're here, Mother!" I had to laugh.

Bart frowned, turned and said, "Come on, you smart asses, let's get some chow."

We found a table for five and sat down. Roundy tried to be funny asking, "What can I order, Daddy?"

"Keep acting like a child and that's the way I'll treat you. So don't be a smart ass. Order!"

Roundy knew he had been upstaged again and complained, "Christ, I was only making a little joke, you don't have to get so abusive."

Silence fell over the table while we looked at the menu as if nothing had been said.

After a few seconds lull Jim said, "I sure would like to know where and when we're going overseas. I'm sick of this hell hole."

Things were back to normal. We all took part in the speculation. As a matter of fact, it was always the main topic of conversation, even bets were made on when and where. Everyone's mind, too, was occupied with the question of how the B-29 would fare in combat. No conclusions were reached from the discussion, each opinion was kicked around. The end of February was near and the 444th Bomb Group had few of its assigned aircraft.

On delivery aircraft were immediately sent in for seven major and fifty minor modifications. The problem was compounded with the bitter cold weather and the fact that most of our maintenance and ground echelon people had been shipped to the port of embarkation. The remainder of our maintenance people along with factory technicians had to make the mods. The Battle of Kansas was on. It was called that by General Hap Arnold. He was most unhappy over the lack of progress of deliveries to the four groups of the 58th Bomb Wing. Our deployment as a wing was dependent on getting our assigned aircraft.

The 444th Bomb Group and its three sister groups were to receive 150 B-29's. Each group would be a formidable striking force, together a mighty military weapon. But the bottle neck had to be broken or this mighty fighting force would remain impotent.

When the ground echelons had started pulling out the beginning of the week we knew the time was getting short. The consensus at our table was that we'd be going to India, and it would be possibly a month or longer before we got all our aircraft. We were eager to get the show on the road. To stay sharp meant you had to keep in the groove and keep the training going. Rumor had it that we'd be going to a beautiful base with outstanding facilities. It was described as out of this world. We were skeptical, but hoped it was true.

"Each of the four groups will have a separate base just as we have here in Kansas. It'll be one hell of a sight to see 150 B-29's moving to the other side of the world," said Jim breaking the spell at our table.

"Just think of the flow plan someone will have to work out with the 40th at Pratt; the 462nd at Walker; the 468th at Smokey Hill and us here. It'll probably be one hell of a mess," speculated Bart.

"No doubt they've been working on the move up at the wing. Hell, they have to have something to do," said Rich adding his two cents.

Let's not worry about it. There's nothing we can do to change it. All I know is that we'll be ready whenever they are," Bart said as he dug into his steak.

"Well, as for me, I'd like to get some more time on the bomb trainer. How about it Rich, would you set up a couple practice missions for me?" I asked.

"No sweat. It'll help keep me busy. I'm available tomorrow, are you?"

"You bet."

"Now that you've got that settled, let's finish our dinner and see if we can get you into a poker game. We might need extra money for our future long trip," Bart said as he pushed himself away from the table and got to his feet.

10.

Everyone on our crew was eager to get overseas and get the show on the road. The big hangup was still aircraft delivery and the task of making each aircraft combat ready. All supervised instruction had ended, it was our ball game. Survival would depend primarily on our skill and training but luck could not be discounted.

We were flying formation missions as well as gunnery, bombing and long overwater navigational missions. We had reached the point where we were confident that nothing we'd have to face in the future would be beyond our expertise.

Gunnery missions were simulated combat missions. Our best fighters attacked and we countered with gun cameras instead of live ammunition. The gunners, the bombardier, and I participated and were scored.

Most bombing missions were flown in formation. On the missions we flew alone I generally participated as bombardier. Our great bird was a real war machine, a steady platform which accounted for the excellent bombing and gunnery results. The B-29 was sure to shorten the war.

Overwater navigation missions were flown mainly over the Caribbean, some landing in Cuba. These were what I really needed. I knew very soon I'd have to guide a B-29 halfway around the world and the responsibility for my crew's safety would depend on my knowledge and judgment. I was eager to fly the long missions putting to work all the training that had been heaped on me. The experience was a great confidence builder.

The last 3,000 mile training mission was designated as a night cross-country simulated bombing mission. We were assigned three different cities to attack and drop simulated bombs. The navigations log and the 35mm camera for radar scope pictures were to give evidence of accuracy. The camera was built with a hood which fit over the radar scope, pictures were taken at intervals from the IP to the target. Later the film was developed and a critique held.

The mission was planned in detail to insure success. We had a game plan and would follow it to the tee. The important part of the mission was getting to your target on time and then getting your simulated bombs within a certain radius of the intended target. I had pored over weather reports as well as maps to be certain of all terrain features which could affect the mission. I'd worked closely with both Rich and Roundy and explained what I expected of each of them. We had to work in close harmony. The three cities we were assigned to attack were Salt Lake City, Los Angeles and El Paso. I had drawn my course very carefully and had prepared my pre-flight information with care. I was under the gun and my performance under pressure had to be determined. I created most of the pressure myself. I wanted to do a good job and show everyone I knew my business. The only way to gain crew confidence was to be confident and do a good job. Most of the crew were unaware of the science of navigation. They expected to be taken someplace and returned. It just wasn't that easy.

When we were alerted for the mission I was happy it was finally on. After the last minute details and briefings were held we left for our plane to start the important tasks of pre-flighting the equipment and its systems. We completed our tasks and were ready for our great adventure. We'd found but one minor discrepancy and carefully noted it on the aircraft forms. It was not a grounding item. We started the engines and taxied to the runup spot. All systems go. As we rolled down the runway I felt the same excitement I'd felt during the big poker game a few nights back. Yes, I had another winning hand.

Takeoff was uneventful. We climbed on course and headed west toward the first target, Salt Lake City. I hoped the citizens of that fine city would never feel the sting of such an attack for real. They were completely unaware of our presence as we passed over at 25,000 feet. At that altitude the outside air temperature was forty degrees below zero, but the fine heaters of our B-29 kept us comfortable in our lightweight flying suits. We crossed the snow covered peaks of the Rocky Mountains and soon I saw Grand Junction ahead. We were over Provo in approximately thirty minutes more, then north to our IP some twenty miles south of Salt Lake City. Our aiming point was be the tower of the Mormon tabernacle. Overcast weather necessitated a radar bomb run. Just prior to reaching Provo the clouds covered the entire city and we experienced some turbulence from the mountains to the east of the city. Once past the higher mountains the air again was smooth. We turned north using the new radar known as the APQ-13. It was state of the art. It clearly showed our target. The first target was hit. The crew coordination practice had paid off. After the simulated bombs had cleared the bomb bays the doors were closed and I ordered a hard turn to the left. We headed south west toward our next intended victim, the wonderful city of Los Angeles.

The flight was routine as we flew further west. The clouds which made our last target unseen had cleared and we were flying in clear beautiful skies filled with bright stars and a half moon. The desert below was void of lights until we came within view of Las Vegas, the lights could be seen for a distance of a hundred miles. Flying in the B-29 was unlike flying in any other airplane. It was nearly silent and much easier on the occupants. I felt odd using my hometown for a target but I had had no choice in the selection. Nostalgia at being so close to home and family gripped me for a few brief seconds. I wondered when and if I would ever see them again. I knew there would be no leaves granted before our departure. I snapped out of my daydream and got back to work. As we closed on our unsuspecting target I wondered how well defended the sprawling metropolis which lay below us was. Could they defend themselves against a real air attack and how would they endure? I was sure ground defenses were tracking us for practice. I tried to concentrate on the job at hand. Distractions like that could cost a man his life. After all I was now a professional military officer, not a schoolboy.

My planned attack of Los Angeles was to approach from the northeast using Mt. Wilson as the IP and the city hall as the aiming point. No great loss! The night was clear and bright but the city below could only be seen on radar. The blackout was effective. The moon was the only light and it didn't provide enough illumination for visual bombing techniques. Radar was good to bomb by but never as good as being able to see your target. I gave the order to get the radar on the line and to make preparations for the radar bomb run. With all our practice it wasn't very difficult. We approached our target and soon had simulated dropping ten tons of bombs on my city. We continued on our escape and soon were over the Pacific ocean headed toward Santa Catalina island, one of my old playgrounds. Approximately half way across the Catalina channel I gave the pilot the new heading and the big plane turned smoothly toward our final target, El Paso. As we turned I looked north across the great basin and could visualize my home in the hills to the north. I had a strange sinking feeling in the pit of my stomach. What would it feel like to be ordered to bomb your home town? I shook my head and came back to earth. I had to control my emotions and get back to work.

We winged our way to the southeast. The next attack would be made at a lower level. We skirted the Mexican border and when we passed the mountains of the Southern California desert, we reduced our altitude gradually and leveled at 12,000 feet. I was busy with navigational duties and forgot the nostalgic mood of a short time before. We were traveling at 250 knots and expected to arrive over El Paso in less than two hours. Daylight would be breaking by then and we'd have no trouble seeing our target. Our latest weather report indicated strong surface winds, but it should have no effect on our mission.

The crew worked like a smoothly oiled machine, we set up in a short time for the attack. We passed abeam of Phoenix. I could see it plainly off our left wing. Soon we'd pass over Tucson and then a straight in run to our target. We were still flying close to the Mexican border. I was sure they were asleep and unaware of our presence. The mission would be completed for all intents and purposes after the third simulated attack. Then we could relax and head for the barn. The beauty of the rising sun sent rays streaking across the dark skies. It was going to be a beautiful day. Ahead we saw our target. As predicted, the sky was clear. I set in motion the bomb team and we worked unhurriedly with an almost casual approach. We passed over the IP and I told Rich it was all his. I then unfastened my seat belt and went forward to watch him work over the bomb sight. He was so cool it was scary. He found his target and opened the bomb bay doors and in a matter of seconds our bombs had raced toward earth. As the bomb bay doors closed I ordered a turn to the northeast and reported to the crew, "We should be home in two and a half hours."

Bart called all the crew members on the interphone and said, "Congratulations on a job well done. You all performed like veterans. Now I think we are ready. Let's go home!"

At that moment the flight engineer called the left scanner and said, "Make a scan of number two engine and report back."

Art Long called back, "Left scanner to engineer, over."

"Go ahead, scanner."

"I'm sorry, Walt. I just took my eyes off the the engine a few minutes ago. I didn't see the smoke then."

"What color is it?"

"Black. Oh shit, there's a flame streaming from the engine. It's trailing under the wing."

"Hit number two bottle, Jim," ordered Bart.

"How 'bout it, Art? Did it go out?"

"No way Walt. It's burning like hell."

The other extinguisher was activated but the fire burned on unabated. Things didn't look good.

"Nav, this is the pilot, over."

"Go ahead, pilot."

"Johnny, get everyone down the tunnel and take charge in the rear. Jim, Walt and I will stay for awhile and see if we can put the fire out. When you get back there get on interphone and I'll keep you posted. Make sure everyone has his survival vest on with his parachute. We may have to go in a hurry, any questions?"

"No sir. I'm on my way."

I followed Rich and Ray down the tunnel. The tunnel was located over the two bomb bays and was the only connection other than through the bomb bays from one end of the plane to the other. Ray wasted no time. After he sent the distress message he moved like a mole down the padded tunnel. All I could see was his butt wiggling ahead of me. I gathered all the people in the back and explained what to expect and to get ready for the worst. They all responded to my instructions and within seconds I was on the interphone calling Bart, "Nav to pilot, over."

"Go ahead, nav."

"We're all set back here. How's it going up there?"

"I'll call you back. I have a radio call. Over."

I felt the heat from the fire and saw the flame trailing behind. I ordered everyone to line up at the rear door and to waste no time when the order came. "When you jump, make it fast so you'll end up close to each other when you hit the ground. Any questions?"

Some looked anxious about jumping. I didn't have time to worry about the jump. I wished for someone to help me out the door when my time came but, like the guy said, "It's lonely at the top!"

"Johnny, Bart here. Get them out right now and you follow. It's not getting any better. We'll try to get her down, but we may

85

have to jump, too. Good luck."

"Okay, let's go." I pushed them ahead and Rich led the way into the void. Roundy was last and froze in the door. "Get your ass out right now."

He turned and looked at me, he was scared shitless. I put my boot in his back and gave him a hell of a push. He flew out into space and I heard him yelling for a split second. I still had the headset on and was just pulling it off when I heard Bart's call.

"Johnny, are you still there?"

"Just ready to take a walk. What's up?"

"We may get this down okay, but it may get hairy before we get to Biggs AAF. Get your ass out and we'll see you on the ground."

I ripped off the headset and stepped into the door. I looked straight ahead, not down, and took the long step. I tumbled toward earth 10,000 feet below. I lost sight of the plane as I sped earthward at terminal velocity. I arched my back and was falling feet first. I could see the ground coming up at me. I wanted to free fall until I was down to three or four thousand feet. I could not get the last sight of the B-29 diving with the black smoke trailing from its engine out of my mind. But now I had to pay attention to my own plight. I could see the dust blowing and knew I had to be sharp or the chute would drag me all over the desert. Who was it who said, "It's not the fall that kills you. It's that sudden stop." I strained to see if any other chutes were visible. None were.

I estimated my altitude as 3,500 feet and decided it was time to open my parachute. I pulled the D-ring and the pilot chute snapped out into the slip stream followed by the main chute, a wonderful sight. My speed of fall decreased from 124 mph to much less. It felt as if I was in slow motion. I can't tell you what a nice feeling it is when you see all that nylon overhead. I was floating down and realized I still had the D-ring in my grip. I let it fall and watched until it was out of sight. I lined up a rock on the ground by sighting between my feet to determine wind drift. Then tried to turn my body so I would have the wind at my back. I didn't want to land backward. That could really get you in trouble. I pulled the shroud lines and turned in the right direction. I estimated the wind to be at least thirty knots and it was gusty. I didn't like it. I went through my landing procedures rapidly and just before my feet made contact, I pulled the clip out of my quick release and turned the knob so that if I needed to I could let the chute separate from me. I wanted to keep my chute if at all possible. It might come in handy out here in the middle of nowhere. The last few seconds I recalled the cliché "If your chute doesn't open we'll issue you another!"

I bent my knees slightly to cushion the shock and all at once I was on terra firma. The wind caught my parachute and I ran with the canopy trying to keep my balance and at the same time spill the air from the chute. It started to collapse. Then a gust caught it, pulled me off the ground and spun me around. I had to let the chute go. I hit the quick release and fell back to the ground. The parachute seemed to climb out of sight. I stumbled forward out of control and fell on my back in a large patch of cactus. I hit flat and the spines pierced my clothing. I felt the pain from my shoulders to the top of my boots, my body had been violated and there was no help in sight. I tried to get to my feet without being impaled on more needles, to no avail. I could feel new punctures as I lifted my body. I was a mess and there was nothing I could do. I staggered out of the cactus and looked for some shelter from the elements. There was none in sight. I had to stand or the spines would break off or work in deeper. I had never been more miserable in all my life. Every move, however slight, caused great pain. To think just minutes ago I was serenely on my way home. I tried to pull some of the thorns out of my legs and arms but they broke off, I decided to let the doctors remove them once they found me.

I had forgotten about the rest of the crew, especially the three left on the airplane. I made a silent prayer for their safety. I'd been lucky. At least I made a good landing under extremely bad conditions. Well, maybe up to the time I landed on my ass in the cactus. My instructors would have been proud.

Two hours had passed since my untimely entrance into the cactus patch. The pain and discomfort had not waned. "Where the hell are the rescue people?" I said out loud. I knew they were looking for me. I felt warn liquid running down my back and hoped it was just perspiration. "Where the hell are those guys. I need help," I yelled at the top of my voice as if someone could hear me over the howling wind.

Three and a half hours of agony passed and the sun was almost at its highest point before the ambulance and jeep finally found me. I saw the dust before I saw the vehicles. I was so relieved to see them my spirits rose rapidly. I tried to wave but that hurt too much. They drove right up to the cactus stump I was leaning against. Four men jumped from the vehicles. They handed me a cup of cool water which tasted like the nectar of the Gods, then pulled a stretcher from the ambulance and helped me on it face down. "You'll be fine now, Lieutenant. We'll have you back to the base hospital in no time. Try and stay as still as you can so you won't further aggravate your wounds," said the medic in charge.

I lifted my head and said, "Captain, I mean doctor, how does it look?"

"I won't lie to you, you're a mess. But not to worry, we'll take good care of you. Now take these pills. They'll help the pain."

I took the pills with more cool water. I was thirsty and had dirt in my eyes, mouth and nose. I felt the strain of my ordeal and lack of rest. I'd been going for over twenty-four hours without sleep.

I barely heard a sergeant ask, "How many others were there with you, Lieutenant?"

"Eight bailed out and three stayed with the plane, unless they too had to bail out."

"Good, I wanted to be sure. The B-29 made it into Biggs with an engine smoking. We picked up all the rest of your crew. You were the last. The short lieutenant was separated from the others some distance, about half way between you and the other six," the sergeant explained.

"That's great. Thank you for your efforts." My eyelids were getting very heavy as the ambulance bumped over the uneven terrain to the nearest paved road. The pills were working. I felt no pain, only relief. Without another word I drifted into a deep sleep.

The next thing I knew I was being lifted from a stretcher to a surgical table. Then the lights went out again as I breathed deeply into the rubber cup that was put over my face. They had decided to give me general anesthesia. I swirled into a confused unconscious state and then it was over. It had only taken seconds to take care of me. At least that's what I thought. Actually I had been on the table for more than two hours. I came to in a comfortable bed feeling very groggy and soon fell asleep again.

I entered the conscious world that evening some hours later. I opened my eyes and was delighted to see some of my comrades seated nearby. A good looking nurse came to my bedside, maybe not Florence Nightingale but I'll bet she was better looking. She called the doctor and he came in.

"How do you feel?"

"Like a pin cushion, I think."

"No wonder, we pulled a lot of thorns from your body and some were quite deep. You may feel a little discomfort for a few days but you should be able to leave soon provided you get no infection."

Before I could say anything he turned and left, leaving the nurse standing at my bedside. That suited me. She was looking better by the second.

"Your dinner will be here in a few minutes. I'll help you when it arrives. Is there anything else I can do for you?"

There was, but I doubted she would get in bed with me.

"How the hell are you?" asked Bart as he came to the side of my bed.

"I think I'll make it. I feel like a target for a bunch of Indians with bows and arrows."

"Christ, if I thought I could get that nurse I would go out and jump in a cactus patch. If I were you I'd stay sick for a month," said Bart excitedly.

"Yeah, when I woke up and saw her smiling at me I thought I'd died and gone to heaven."

Jim and Rich came to Bart's side and Jim asked, "What the hell happened to you after you hit the ground?"

"First of all, when I told you I was going to jump I had to push Roundy out first and that took a little time so I landed some distance from the others. When I got my nerve up and stepped into space I free fell to three or four thousand. The wind had really started to blow and gust. It caught my chute and I went into the cactus. That's the short and the long of it. The worst part was waiting with all those damn arrows in my back."

"Well, it's all behind you now. No pun intended. I called the base and they are sending a bird down here with an engine and a crew to work on it. We're in no hurry," said Bart with a grin on his face.

"Hey Rich, you look no worse for wear. How did you make out?"

"John, you wouldn't believe this. I hit the ground and was trying to spill my chute as it dragged me across ground. The wind pulled me right into a big mudhole that cattle had used for drinking. It broke my fall, but I was a mess."

I laughed, then decided I didn't want to do that again. It made me ache all over.

"They tell us if all goes well you'll be up and around as early as tomorrow. You have some stitches in your back to close the holes they had to make to get the spears out."

"I thought I could feel something pulling back there. Damn, I'm hungry." My nurse heard me from down the hall and came in with a big tray of food. I was ready. I hadn't eaten since lunch the day before. I dug into the food like a wolf after the lamb. The nurse helped me as required. I made it look harder than it was. Boy, a guy sure could go for her.

"The way things turned out, you could've stayed with the plane, but I couldn't take that chance. It's a lot easier to explain why you jumped than why someone was hurt in a fire. We put out the fire after you bailed out. We drove at a steep angle and blew it out. We made it to Biggs in no time. There was no structural damage to the plane. We can't afford to lose a bird now. We need to get them ready for our move. After they hang the engine we'll test fly it in the local area and if all's okay we'll head north to Kansas," announced Bart.

My three buddies stayed until the nurse ran them out. She told them she had to give me a bath! The look on their faces was priceless. They headed back to the BOQ and told me they'd be back in the morning. My nurse laughed after they left and said, "I thought they'd get a kick out of me telling them you were going to get a bath."

"Aren't I?"

"No, they gave you one before they operated."

"Oh, hell."

She just smiled, picked up the food tray and disappeared out the door.

That gal really turned me on. What a dish. I'll bet everyone at this base was after her. She really had class along with the looks.

The next day about mid-morning the doctor came in and looked me over. He examined my backside and pronounced me nearly fit and signed my release. He told me the stitches would have to come out in a week or so and added that they could be removed at my home station. I was really disappointed when a different nurse came in that morning. I'd forgotten they worked on shifts. She was nice, but no doll like the night nurse. She helped me into the uniform the guys had bought for me at the PX. My flying suit was ripped to shreds and was thrown away. I was instructed to take asprin for relief of pain. I was as sore as a boil but I met my buddies in the hall and soon forgot about the pain. We walked away from a place I hoped never to visit again, but if Laura was to be my nurse I could have a relapse real easy.

"You're walking a bit stiff, Johnny," said Roundy as we headed for the BOQ.

"You would too if you were sewed up like a rag doll."

We got to our rooms and I felt hungry again. "Anybody in need of some chow?" I asked.

"Sure thing. Let's go to the officers club and eat like gentlemen," said Bart as he led the way out the door.

"I sure need something soft to sit on. My ass is so sore."

"Damn, Walt took a soft cushion out of the plane and I forgot it in my room. Roundy, run back and get it like a good fellow," requested Bart.

"As usual, I'm an errand boy."

"Don't piss and moan, just get your little ass in gear. We'll see you at the club and if you're a nice boy we'll let you sit with us."

Roundy took off in a dog trot.

"Bart, after I jumped I thought you guys were going to buy the farm with all that smoke streaming behind," I said as we walked to the club.

"We got the fire out and feathered the prop and landed here. They had all the emergency equipment including the meat wagon out but we were fine."

Roundy returned and we had our lunch. After lunch we called for transportation and were driven to the plane. The maintenance crew was getting ready to remove the bad engine. They were disconnecting all the plumbing. They needed to install an engine stand and a new engine. We could tell we'd be there for another day or two.

There was nothing for us to do but wait for the plane to be repaired. I felt tired and wanted to rest. However it was painful to sit for any length of time and lying down was worse. They all laughed at me leaning against the wall reading a pocket book. Someone wanted to play penny ante poker and I finally agreed. If I could stand, the game might take my mind off my smarting wounds.

The next morning I felt much better. I heal pretty fast. It was suggested a trip across the border into Juarez for some booze might be a good idea. We found a bus to haul all eleven of us to

91

the border and to wait until we returned. We went across into Mexico and bought as much booze as the law allowed. It'd come in handy when we left the states.

One more day passed and finally our plane was ready for a short test hop and then the return trip to Great Bend. I sure was ready to go. We had an uneventful trip back. We were content having had all the excitement we needed for a while. Bart asked me to sit in the co-pilots seat so we could talk. Jim headed for the coffee pot and sat behind.

"Johnny, you qualified for pilot training and got caught in the squeeze of needing navigators and I know you had a few hours flight training in cadets. In fact, if I'm not mistaken you soloed in light aircraft, true?"

"I sure did, and loved it. I was all set for pilot preflight but it was navigation or back to the Infantry. I have to be honest, I'm very content as a navigator and enjoy the work. Maybe someday I'll get a crack at pilot training. It would be a lot nicer going through in grade rather than as a cadet."

"You'd make a good pilot. As a matter of fact, you can start being a pilot right now." He reached over, disengaged the autopilot, and said, "It's all yours. Try to hold your course and altitude."

"This is great. I do appreciate the instruction."

"By the time you go to pilot school you'll have plenty of four engine time. It should really help."

He was right. I did get plenty of flying time and I logged it in my log book.

"It's always good to have a spare pilot on board in case of trouble," said Bart as he leaned back and lit a cigarette.

After landing at Great Bend we were greeted by our squadron CO and his Ops officer. Colonel Mitchell was happy to see us and the aircraft. "It's about time you returned from your vacation. Seriously, we were glad to hear you had no serious injuries and the bird was okay. Ellis, you did a damn good job."

"Thanks, Colonel. All the crew deserves credit. Our only casualty was Lea and he'll be okay in a day or so."

"How's the plane?"

"Fine sir. It's running like a watch," answered Bart.

"Colonel, anything new about us leaving?" asked Jim.

"More rumors is all. They have us going to India, but we had that figured out. Rumor has it we'll end up in a damn nice place. I think it was said, it'd be a place out of this world! There will be a debriefing and the old man will be there. He was happy you brought your crew home safely and of course, the plane."

By mid-January 97 B-29's had been delivered from the factories, but only sixteen were ready to go. Most of the others had to be sent directly to modification centers. Some stayed at the centers for sixty days. Hundreds of engineering changes were made: the radar, fitting new bomb bay tanks and changing all the engines from the training engines to war engines. Slings and dollies were being made to carry extra engines. As a result the XX Bomber Command did not have one B-29 that was completly combat ready.

Seventy qualified technicians from the 58th Bomb Wing were sent to Marietta, Georgia after General Hap Arnold made a visit there and found the depot was in need of help.

On the first of March there was a classified briefing for the pilots and navigators. We were eager to get there and were sure we were finally going to get the word. We were informed the first elements would depart on 10 March and details would be completed soon. We learned our destination was a place called Charra, near Calcutta. It was emphasized that the new base was to be one of the super bases. When the briefing concluded we were jubilant. We were finally going to war.

However, on 9 March, the day before the advance party was to depart, things got screwed up. General Arnold and his staff had arrived to watch the B-29's leave. What they found was that not one aircraft was ready. The modification program was in complete chaos and in the general's words, "Void of organization, management and leadership." There was no agency coordinating the work at the centers, depots or sub-depots, or even at the squadrons. The shit was going to hit the fan.

The situation was so chaotic that no one at Bomber Command could tell General Arnold where or when the missing B-29 parts would arrive. He was so angry he had to get away. He left a major general behind to work all night with his staff to get all the answers and report directly to him at Smokey Hill AAF. The staff prepared a chart on every B-29 on hand and a list of every part necessary to put that aircraft in combat ready condition. When the report reached General Arnold he realized that not a single bomber was ready for departure. He ordered an all out crash program to get the job done and assigned it the highest priority, above every Air Force program. The Battle of Kansas was on. Some of us called it the Kansas Blitz. The general put out an order that 150 B-29's were to be ready to leave on 15 April for the CBI.

The red tape melted and a lot of help was provided to meet the target date. Boeing and other aircraft companies supplied a great wealth of talent to get the job done. Sub-contractors were ordered to stop everything until they provided the necessary parts. The flow of material to the Kansas bases was endless, by every conceivable type on transportation. It was hell on the aircraft employees, due in part to the exremely cold weather. Workers had come from warm climates in the United States and were not prepared for the harsh weather. In late March the first B-29 was certified complete and turned over to Bomber Command. It took off for India almost immediatly. Others followed in a stream. The remainder of the 150 B-29's were readied and all of them departed as scheduled.

In the month it had taken to complete the project our squadron continued flying B-17's and B-26's. We had little free time. Many had requested leave and were denied. The group didn't want to get caught short. No one was sure of their departure date. We just sweated it out.

The "War of Kansas" was over.

11.

The long wait finally came to an end. Orders for the 444th Bombardment Group (VH) to move to an overseas location came through. There were no surprises. The group was to be based at Charra. Charra was located at the foot of India's central mountain range, approximately 100 air miles northwest of Calcutta and fifty air miles north of Jamshedpur, the steel producing center.

Each group of the wing had a deployment plan which contained routing, departure times, dates and other pertinent data. Each of the four groups based in Kansas would start their departure to insure that all assigned aircraft would be on their way on or before 15 April 1945. Some aircraft would arrive at the final destination on that date. The deployment plan was arranged so that each group would have approximately the same number of aircraft arriving at their designated base each day. This was to be the longest and biggest move of its kind in the history of aviation.

We left Great Bend early in the morning of 15 April, one of the last of the 444th Bomb Group. All aircraft were loaded to maximum allowable weight. Most carried cargo. Others carried a mix of cargo and personnel. We departed with the firm belief that we were to occupy one of the large well equipped bases rumored to have been built for the B-29's in England, China, India, Russia, Siberia and elsewhere. We'd been congratulated by the elite on being privileged to go overseas with such an organization as the 20th Air Force. We were to have nothing but the best. Our bases were to be located with access to large cities for recreation and relaxation. We knew it could not be all that great but figured we were damn lucky.

The 20th Air Force came into being on the activation order of 4 April 1944. It was established for the purpose of taking into action a single type aircraft, the still unproven B-29 Superfortress. It was activated in Washington DC and after much political in-fighting and haggling about who would control the 20th AF, it was decided that no other than the Commander-in-Chief of the entire USAAF, General Hap Arnold, would be our boss. The 20th AF was the first of its kind in military history and was considered the World Air Force. This was even depicted on the shoulder patch. B-29's would be deployed from many different locations. At least that was the theory.

Our scheduled trip was more that 11,500 miles routed through Gander Lake, Marrakech, Cairo, Karachi to the specific bases in the Calcutta area. Our first leg took us across the eastern United States and on to Gander Lake, Newfoundland, a distance of 2,600 miles. The field was on the east coast of the large island.

The flight went without a hitch and our aircraft performed perfectly. We hoped it would give us the same service all the way to our destination. When we arrived in the area of Gander and the deep snow was visible I couldn't help thinking of how different it would be on all the other stops along our route. We were cleared for a straight in approach and were advised to expedite as a snow storm was expected. We came in right on course and on time. The "Follow me" truck escorted us to our parking place. There were at least twenty B-29's of the wing parked, taxiing, or getting ready for departure. It was a breathtaking sight, all those beautiful planes lined up shining in the partial light and with such a beautiful backdrop. I'd met my first challenge successfully.

After parking we went in to base operation to close our flight plan and heard of the first of a series of mishaps. One of the B-29's of our wing made a forced landing at Presque Isle, Maine. There was no immediate news about the occurrence. We were told further information would be available as received. We hoped, after the fiasco about the modifications, that no serious trouble would come to light. We were lucky because we had no sqwaks to write up in the maintenance forms. Here they had a first in, first out rule which made it apparent we'd be here for a couple days. The good news was that thirty-two of the B-29's had arrived at the new bases on this day. I thought to myself, others made it, and my theory was, if some one else can do it I can too.

We were tired after a long day and decided to get our quarters assignment and hit the hay. We had to be in good shape for the officers club that evening.

We were shown to the BOQ and it wasn't too bad. We'd seen worse. We dumped our bags, got undressed and hit the sack. Sleep came fast for all of us.

I awoke in the early evening and waked the others. A good shower and shave made me feel human again. When everyone was ready we headed for the club and the night life. At the club, Bart received a message to call base operations for instructions. The duty officer told him all B-29's were grounded until further notice. Further word would be given at a scheduled 0900 meeting the following day at operations.

"What was that all about, Bart?" I asked as he hung up the phone.

"He wouldn't say why the grounding except that something of an undetermined nature had happened."

We entered the bar and spoke to some of our buddies who'd heard the rumor that a plane had crashed at Marrakech and until the cause was detemined all B-29's in the system were grounded. The bad news had a dampening effect on us all. Later in the evening confirmation of the crash came from base ops. Also that there were no serious injuries. This news started speculation in all areas of the bar. It sounded like a huge bee hive.

All four groups were represented at the club, and to get our minds off of the lost airplane, each unit was trying to convince the others that their base in Kansas was the worst,—same old bullshit. There was one common agreement. We had more than enough training due to delays in the delivery of our aircraft back in Kansas. In spite of arguments to the contrary our group was sure that our base at Great Bend was inferior to the others. Everyone agreed that no matter how rough the Battle of Kansas was we would have it a lot better in India.

No one was closing the bar and there was hardly a sober man to be seen. Many had fallen by the wayside earlier. We five decided we'd had enough and it was time to go home. I hoped we could find our way. We had a fun night even with the bad news, and all agreed we were with a great bunch of guys.

I'd run into a couple classmates from San Marcos who were assigned to different groups. We'd discussed how they rushed to catch up with the training as I had. The laugh was that there was really no rush. They had heard of my big adventure in the cactus patch and thought that at least I had something to talk about instead of the old routine we had all become accustomed to. I also found that they'd covered the same ground I had and now we were standardized.

While we were living it up in the club it'd snowed so heavily the area looked like a winter wonderland. The cold flakes hitting our faces seemed to cure the effects of the alcohol, and certainly made us walk faster to escape the cold. By the time we reached the BOQ we felt no effects of the drinking. It took us little time to get into bed and to fall soundly asleep.

I awoke with a start as I heard someone scream,"Oh, shit, we're going to be late for the meeting at ops. We have to be there in twenty minutes."

Bart was right. We'd have to skip breakfast but they were sure to have coffee at the meeting. There was no way to do anything but get out of the warm sack.

"Let's get our asses in gear. Rich, you and Roundy can stay in the sack if you like. Pilot's and nav's are the only ones who have to be there. We'll see you after the meeting."

We rushed out into the cold foggy morning. The cold went right through my flying jacket. Kansas was warm compared to this deep freeze. We just made it prior to 0900, but many straggled in late. The operations officer sort of expected it after the party the night before at the club. Anyway, there was no great hurry. We weren't going anywhere soon. People dragged in for the next thirty minutes. We gave them hell. After all, we'd made it on time and we could act "holier than thou." It was all a big joke to us. The base commander was very patient and understanding and made no mention of the unmilitary entry of some.

"That must have been one hell of a party you all had at the club last night. I'd hate to see you when you got good news," Colonel Henry said as he arrived at the dias.

There were groans and snickers at that statement. The colonel went on to say, "Gentlemen, it looks like you will be our guests for a time. I'm not sure what the outcome will be nor am I sure how long it will take to complete the investigation. The forced landing at Presque Isle was a precautionary landing. Apparently they had a high cylinder head reading on one of the engines and had to cage it. They had no further incident and that certainly didn't cause this delay, I'm sure. We expect a report soon from the maintenance people we sent up there. The more important incident causing this delay was the accident at Marrakech. The message we received was not all that clear, but apparently the plane didn't develop enough power on take off and crashed at the end of the runway. Whether it actually got airborne or if the accident was a ground abort we don't know as yet. The important thing is that we lost no crew members. I'm sure you are anxious to know which squadron lost the aircraft, but I can only give you the group. The message went no further. It was from the 462nd Bomb Group."

There was an immediate groan from some of the people seated in the room.

"I know you all want to know more about the crash, but that's all I have on the incident. I promise to keep you posted on new information as well as the outcome of the investigation. Till then you'll be with us. I hope you're confortable and have a good stay. If you have any other questions now is the time and I will try to answer them."

The colonel was a good guy. He established a time of 1800 for posting new information each day at Gander. He also stated, "If important news becomes available it'll be immediately conveyed. I recommend you stay on base in case we get orders for you to depart immediately. The natives are friendly here abouts, but I recommend you not try to shower affection on any of the ladies. Most are married to local fishermen who don't like the competition."

We all had a good laugh because we knew what he was saying. Each aircraft commander instructed his crew of this edict. Only special reasons would be accepted for passes to town. The meeting broke up and everyone headed either for chow or more sleep. That evening we checked in at base operations at 1800 to see if further word had been received. The TWX indicated there had been another crash the day following the one at Marrakech at Cairo, Egypt. The only information available was the plane was lost to fire and that it was also from the 462nd. They had lost two aircraft and it was like a hammer blow. We all felt very bad. We expected losses in combat, but operational accidents prior to arriving in the combat zone were hard to take.

Four more days passed without any firm word about our departure. This had an adverse effect on crew members. Morale, however, was still good. We survived by planning the rest of the trip, playing cards and reading. Almost everyone found time to get some letters written. The air crews made frequent trips to the flight line to check the parked aircraft. We decided to take advantage of the cheap prices of booze and soap for future use and barter. Shortages of both had been rumored. The problem was finding room on the airplane for all our purchases plus what we'd picked up in Mexico.

The days dragged by and morale was sinking. Something dynamic was needed to shake the troops back to life. Instead, another bulletin was received aggravating the morale problem. Two more crashes enroute were reported. Apparently both occurred at Karachi, India. Disasters seemed to be working in two's instead of the old superstition of three's. The 468th Bomb Group had lost both planes and this time there were some fatalities. Four of the 150 B-29's which had started out were lost without a shot being fired in anger. The guys lost the desire to party or even talk about it. To get their minds off of the bad news, some of the crews found ways of keeping busy working on or around their planes. I decided to go down to mission planning and work on our next overwater hop. I was very surprised to find a number of navigators working on charts and fuel planning and such. I joined right in.

Our next leg on the journey, if they ever released us, was the longest overwater flight of the trip and certainly the longest overwater flight any of us had made. We all figured when the word did come through we'd be ready for immediate departure. We knew it was going to be one hell of a gaggle. We were told departures would be as close as possible. We had 2,700 miles of ocean to negotiate and the only land was the Azores, some 2,000 miles downstream. We needed this challenge to keep us from thinking of the lost planes.

It remained cold. The season had extended longer than expected, but the snow had quit and for that we were grateful. I kept thinking it would've been better to be stuck in Cairo where at least you could take in the ancient historical sites and not freeze every time you stepped outside.

Two full weeks had passed when at the 1800 posting the word was that the grounding had been lifted and all aircraft would expedite their departures to their next destinations. That same night the aircraft from Presque Isle arrived. They would be the tail end of the stream of planes making their way to India.

It was great tonic. The news spread like wildfire, and spirits rose. The departure schedule was posted at 2000 hours at base operations. The plan was simple. The first to depart would be the 40th, followed by the 444th, 462nd and the 468th. Takeoff time was established to begin at 0600 hours and the interval would be every twenty minutes to give necessary separation. Briefing was held at 0430 hours and crews were to be at their aircraft one hour before departure. Altitudes were staggered and cruise control had to be maintained so we would not stack up at Marrakech. The briefing had concluded with a hearty good luck wish from the base commander. We were sure he was glad to see us on our way and also relieved there had been no misadventures in the town of Gander.

When our alert came at 0800 the following morning we'd been up for some time. We were to depart at 1030 hours and that made us ninth in the string. Everyone was excited and we had slept little waiting for the call to briefing. We felt fresh and just wanted to get the wheels in the well.

We did the pre-flight inspection and found the aircraft ready. Bart, Jim and I attended the final weather briefing. The others stayed at the plane and waited impatiently. There was no significant change in the weather. Some ground fog, then broken layers of clouds up to 10,000 feet and clear above. Our cruising altitude was 20,000 feet. The worst was the ground fog, however. It hadn't delayed any of the earlier departures.

I was impressed with the traffic management. We took the active runway and were rolling at precisely at 1030 by my stop watch. We lifted into the air and quickly disappeared from the view of all those below as we entered the first deck of clouds. The weather aloft was better than briefed and soon we were climbing in crisp clear weather to our assigned altitude. An exciting time for all of us, some more than others, but as for me, the great adventure had started anew.

I was very busy as we headed toward North Africa many hours away. We leveled off at 20,000 feet and I was able to get an accurate fix from radar and loran. Our first position report would come in one hour and at hour intervals until arrival at Marrakech. With so many planes flying so close strict adherence to the flight plan was a necessity. It was a good feeling winging our way across the Atlantic. A few thoughts came to me as I looked at the water four miles below. I'd never imagined I'd be in an organization that was making history. My daydreaming was soul satisfying and helped pass the hours. I relaxed until it was time to get my first position report ready. The controlling agency wouldn't be happy if I were late. My main concern was to always be accurate for more than one reason, not the least was to keep the air sea rescue people informed of our whereabouts. There was one hell of a lot of water out there, and if we went down survival depended on rescue knowing where to look.

All was going well. We were right on flight plan and Bart flew my headings within a half degree. He was good and we were lucky to be his crew. He was also a good leader.

"How's it going back there, Johnny?" asked Bart breaking the silence within the plane.

"Just great. What's up?"

"How about a little lesson in celestial? After all, if I'm going to make you a pilot, you have to teach me to navigate."

"Come on back, I have time. We can do some observations on the sun and work out the solutions to see how you do."

He was back at my desk within minutes, eager to start. I readied the sextant and got him up at the head of the tunnel where the astrodome was located. I gave him the rudiments of the sextant and he started shooting as I worked out the mathematic solution from my tables. After two minutes he slipped down to the desk and said, "Well, how the hell did I do?"

"We'll know in a couple of minutes. Let me get the reading and I'll finish the solution and plot your shot." While he was shooting I had taken a loran fix to be sure of his accuracy. We plotted his shot and it was damn good. "Have you ever taken a shot before, Bart?"

"No, why?"

"Your shot was right on the button, within allowable limits. Now I'll show you what you did and then teach you how to solve the problem and how to plot the line of position." He was so eager it was hard to turn him off. I told him I had to work up a position for the report and if he liked he could take another sun shot and I'd use it with my other findings to get the postion. His enthusiasm and skill astounded me. The other qualified navigator on the plane had yet to offer to help. Roundy was a damn good radar operator but I was unsure of his navigational skills. He was lazy and had to be pushed. Rich, on the other hand, was always interested and was a damn good DR navigator and helpful when I needed it. I knew I'd need him when we flew over Asia.

Time passed rapidly. Everything had gone well during the first nine hours and we were right on our flight plan. Being twenty minutes apart made radio contact the only way of knowing other planes were in such close proximity.

My personal feelings were that this flight above all others had proven to me and my fellow crewmen that I was competent and would keep them from getting lost.

"Radar, this is the Navigator. Over."

Roundy was off headset and had to be awakened by one of the gunners. When he finally got his head set on, "This is radar, go ahead."

"Sorry to wake you but it wouldn't hurt for you to take part in this little adventure."

"Okay, what can I do for you?"

"You can do your job for the crew! Now, crank up the radar and give me the 100 mile scan, I want to pick up the Azores."

The radar position was in the aft portion of the ship, aft of the gunners compartment, near the camera hatch. He was required to drop chaff when over targets where there were radar controlled anti-aircraft guns. The metallic rolls made an unholy mess on enemy radar screens and made it difficult for gunners to fix on the bomber. Radar was very helpful in the B-29, especially over water. When land was visible the contrast was better.

I adjusted my radar scope and lo and behold, dead ahead at fifty miles was the Azores. A thrill raced down my spine because I knew that I was exactly where I was supposed to be. "Navigator to crew, we are fifty miles from the Azores. You should be able to see the islands shortly."

We passed over Lajes field, made our report, and got our weather update for enroute and destination. Everything looked perfect. We were told that one of the earlier departures from Gander had landed for mechanical reasons, no emergency.

Two and a half hours later we made land fall over the dark continent. We reduced altitude to 8,000 feet and we saw all the land features, nothing but desert. It sure looked dismal. We contacted the tower when we arrived in the area of Marrakech, received landing instructions and within minutes we landed and taxied to our assigned parking place. We deplaned into sweltering heat. From the freezer to the frying pan was the way Pops, our tailgunner, put it. He was right, it was hot as hell.

We were parked next to seven B-29's which had arrived ahead of us and within a few minutes we turned and saw another beautiful cigar shaped aircraft land and coast to the end of the runway. The B-29 was the most cleanly designed plane that had ever been built. As I stood there I felt good about our future.

After the usual debriefing and closing of flight plans we were advised that we would be here a minimum amount of time. It was getting dark fast and the heat of the day was still hanging on. It was most uncomfortable, hot and dry. However, we could suffer a little, knowing we were one step closer to our luxurious base.

Departure was scheduled for 0800 hours and we would take off in the order of arrival. Our priority was getting some chow and a shower. Then to hit the sack.

The quarters were adequate, but too hot to rest. Fans provided the only air conditioning. Early in the morning Bart and I headed for ops for final weather and route briefing and then I completed my flight plan as Bart looked on. We met the rest of the crew at the chow hall and had breakfast. The mess hall was so hot we made it brief and ate little.

"Surely Cairo will be better than this hell on earth," said Rich as he wiped his brow.

"Let's all hope so," said Bart.

Our next leg to Cairo was a distance of 2,350 miles straight across the Sahara desert. It was like flying over water because of the vast uninhabited areas. Our route of flight took us across Libya, then we skirted the southern tip of the gulf of Sidra, then over the great desert again until we reached Egypt, and on the river Nile was Cairo.

Climbing into our plane in Marrakech was like stepping into an oven. All hatches and windows were opened as well as the bomb bay doors to allow as much air as possible to flow through the plane before take-off. Soon we were airborne climbing on course to our assigned altitude of 17,000 feet. This leg proved to be the most dificult part of the journey. There were very limited navigational aids, so close attention to the instruments was required. Rich's assistance in map reading from the nose of the plane proved to be very helpful. Landmarks, however, were few and far between. The flight plan was for ten hours and meant hard work for me all the way. I had the sun and coupled with DR that was all there was except radar when near the coast. I thought this vast nothing was the most miserable land I had ever seen.

As I looked at the Air Almanac to work up a sun shot I realized my twentieth birthday was the next day. I'd forgotten about it in the excitement. I'd be spending it in ancient Egypt. It sure would be great to celebrate by taking in the Pyramids and the Sphinx.

The hours passed quickly. We were getting close to our destination and as usual, I had to get Roundy out of the sack to get the radar cranked up and on the line. I needed the radar as a cross check. We continued toward the Nile river valley and soon vegetation and huts were to be seen. We reduced our altitude and people everywhere stopped to look skyward at the silver monster. I saw the telltale lines which represented the Nile on the radar scope. We were almost there. The Nile valley was such a contrast to the shapeless land we had just traversed. Water and vegetation looked inviting. We found the airport and were on the ground within minutes.

The heat was still with us, but not like Marrakech. At least there was a slight breeze coming off the river which provided some relief. The B-29's which had departed prior to us were neatly parked alongside of the runway and we took our place in the parade. We got the word that Wing was anxious to get us all to our operational bases ASAP; so much for the delay for sightseeing.

Bart said, "I knew we wouldn't get a delay. You know how Wing wants to get right to work punishing the enemy."

One of Bart's favorite sayings, and he had many, was, "It's like escaping from the asshole of the world and arriving at the bosom." He said it as he led the way to our quarters.

I didn't think it was all that good, but next to Marrakech Cairo was heaven. We were scheduled to leave in twelve hours, barring any maintenance delay. It was midnight and we were pretty tired. We had flown two long missions without much rest and on top of that were fighting the time zones. By the time we had something to eat it was 0200 and I was sagging. The quarters were an improvement over Marrakech, but it wasn't everything! Sleep came easily, but not before I thought of my family once more, I missed them so, especially on my birthday.

We were alerted the next morning at 1000 hours be ready to buzz off at noon. Preparations were completed. I was ready and we were airborne on time. Just after we broke ground, Bart said, "Since it's your birthday and you wanted to see the Pyramids, we'll just take a little detour over the area and do a little sightseeing. We may get our asses chewed out, but what the hell, it's worth it. It's your birthday."

"Thanks loads, I'm looking forward to seeing them, even from the air."

A little later we flew over the land of the Pharaohs at Giza, a sight never to be forgotten. To think they had been there for 3,000 years. "I'm going to come back here someday and take a closer look at all the wonderful sights. Thanks again, Bart."

"No sweat. I thought about breaking the airplane so we could stay awhile, but on second thought they may not have let us off base anyway, so I decided we'd take an aerial excursion. Now, lets get our asses in gear. What's the heading?"

I set him up with the necessary information and we headed for Karachi 2,400 miles to the east. This leg took us across Jordan, Saudi Arabia and skirted the Arabian sea to southern Iran and finally Karachi, India. This leg was an interesting flight. There were changes in the landscape. Unfortunately, we arrived late at night as we had day takeoffs and day flights for the most part.

We headed away from the magnficent scenery and crossed the Gulf of Suez and the Sinai desert. We climbed to 20,000 feet and completed this leg in about the same time it took for the last. Time went rapidly. It was 2300 hours local time when we arrived.

On landing we received instructions for the next leg and were driven to our quarters. We cleaned up and headed for a decent place to eat. Few were operating at this late hour but soon we found a nice cafe. We ordered a rack of lamb for eleven and some of their best wine. There was a toast in my honor. "For the birthday boy," as Bart put it. Not home but not bad under the circumstances. After dinner we returned to the quarters for some much needed shuteye.

"Just think, tomorrow we'll be at the plush base waiting for us across India," said Roundy seriously.

"If I were you I wouldn't believe all that bullshit. I just hope it's comfortable and has a good runway," commented Bart.

"Well, at least we'll have a place to hang our clothes. That'll be a plus," added Jim.

How wrong everyone but Bart was. We had asked about Charra and though no one had been there all agreed it wasn't much. We were told that it was built by the British and leased to the US. Everyone knew the British didn't build fancy bases like the Americans.

We rose at 0800 and got ready to go. Our flight was 1,500 miles to the Calcutta area. Then we would have to find our base. Calcutta was located in the eastern part of India close to Pakistan on the Ganges river. A shorter flight was welcomed. We flew over some interesting country, but I was already forming a bad opinion of India. It was dirty and dusty and looked like all the life had been extracted. Maybe I was wrong and Charra would be much better than the folks at Karachi had painted.

We were over Calcutta in six and a half hours and were given instructions on how to find Charra. We contacted the tower when we got nearby and received landing instructions. We found the runway and took our first look at the desolate ugly place. "Hell, we must be at the wrong place! This God damn place is a hell hole," I said over the intercom.

"No, we're at the right place. It's just the wrong place period," added Bart.

The single runway sloped. There were no buildings. It was so damn hot you had a hard time getting your breath. The "follow me" directed us to our parking revetment. We shut down and climbed to the ground unbelieving. We were met and welcomed by all the group and squadron brass. Quite a reception! Later we found out there was little to do here so it wasn't surprising so many people greeted us. I heard some yell, "you'll be sorry!"

"Welcome to Hell's Half Acre," said Colonel Baker, our group CO.

We got the meaning real fast. It was hell all right. "How could those sons of bitches lie about this place! It would have been better if nothing had been said. Then we wouldn't have expected too much. There are no words to describe this piece of shit," I said as I looked around.

"This is the real anus of the world," said Bart. He modified his opinion of Marrakech. "Marrakech was a place of beauty compared to this piece of shit and that's giving the benefit of a doubt to a lot of shitty places."

Colonel Mitchell said, "Bart you've always been descriptive and what you said is absolutely true. Nothing I've ever seen in my career has been as bad as this!"

We unloaded our belongings and were driven first to ops then to what was laughingly called our new home.

"So this is what was meant by the best in the world for B-29 crews. I only hope the other groups' bases are better than this one," said Jim as he pulled off his shirt.

"This place has got to be an enemy prisoner of war camp. No one would do this to us on purpose, at least not friendly forces," said Rich as he looked around the dilapidated building that was to be our home.

"It makes a guy wish he were fighting in Europe. We really got screwed!" said Jim.

There was a lot of truth in the original observations of our crew. We'd get more shocks as time passed.

12.

CHARRA—CHARRA—CHARRA. Hell's Half Acre, yes, the names were synonymous. No place on God's green earth could compare. Anus of the world was as close as any description available. The 444th had been royally rued, screwed and tattooed. The personnel were so down it would take a miracle for morale to get up to ground zero.

We inspected the base and found the lack of facilities appalling. The damn British had done it to us again. Everywhere we went turned our stomachs. "What the hell do they expect us to do for recreation, play with ourselves?" asked Bart.

After a few days at Charra the group CO called for an officer call to brief on the current situation. Colonel Baker always looked immaculate in the dirtiest place in the world. We could never figure it out. We were always dirty and sweaty looking, how could one not be in this heat and dust?

The colonel entered. Attention was called, rapidly followed by, "Please be seated, gentlemen. I have called you here this morning to bring you up to date on the current situation. We'll look at what has transpired to affect the events coming about and talk some about the abominable conditions under which you all must work and live. I've heard questions concerning why things change so fast. You must remember we're new to this hostile environment and command. As most of you know the XX Bomber Command which is part of the Twentieth Air Force has as its boss General Hap Arnold. We're in a melting pot here. It seems that we're part of the old political football game and we're the ball. I'll go back and briefly explain what I'm driving at. Last November an advanced party of five officers was sent out here to get construction under way with the help of Admiral Lord Louis Montbatten and the Central Public Works Department for India. American aviation engineers began work on several existing runways near Calcutta, one of which you are occupying. Two officers flew to

Kunming, China to talk to General Chennault on various operational matters and arranged to procure escape and evasion information and such indispensables as money belts, silk maps, local currency, Chinese-Burmese bloodchits, and other items needed by our downed air crews. After, the commander of XX Bomber Command was sent by General Arnold on a whirlwind tour of bases in this area and in China. He completed arrangements to have three runways in the Chengtu Valley of China extended and completed for use by B-29's. A fourth was to be built at Kwanghan. Actual work on these projects started last January with General Stilwell's people. The priority was very high. Stilwell had to pull people from the construction of the Ledo road. There were 6,000 working on the runways. Half were aviation engineers, plus over three hundred thousand Chinese laborers so that each bomb group would have its own staging base. Each field has an 8,500 foot runway, built mostly by hand. The runways are nineteen inches thick, made of rounded rocks and gravel and covered by native concrete consisting of crushed rock, sand, clay and water. They built fifty-two hardstands also. You will be briefed further on the China situation and how you will operate out of there at a later time. The politics got very sticky. It seems that each theater commander wanted operational control of the B-29's for his own use. To prevent this from happening, the 20th Air Force came into being under direct command of Hap Arnold."

The colonel stopped, took a drink of water, wiped his forehead and then went on. "Our operational plans have been finalized. We will attack targets in Southeast Asia as well as Japan and occupied China and Manchuria. We'll have to fly support missions over the Himalayas, better known in this area as the Hump, to help supply the forward bases with the items of war. I understand there's a meeting for the pilots and navigators a little later to get more details." He reached over and pulled a piece of paper from his briefcase and continued. "Some day in the near future the 73rd Bomb Wing will be deployed to the Marianas after those islands are secured. This addition to our striking force will undoubtedly bring more pressure on the enemy. Now, for the good news. Plans are being completed for a move of our group from Charra."

The very quiet officers who had been listening so intently all yelled as Indians. "I don't blame you! It appears we should leave here within the next few months. I can't lie to you. It won't be one of those super deluxe bases we were promised, but it should be heaven compared to this rat hole. The new base the 444th will call home is a place called Dudkhundi. I am told it will be a great improvment over Charra. We all know the limitations of this base for operations and how miserable the living conditions are, but please bear with us and hopefully this situation will improve. Thank you gentlemen for your indulgence. Good luck and may God look upon us with favor."

Attention was called as the colonel and his staff left. The noise level in the large room was pretty high. All I wanted was to get out into the fresh air. I was steaming with perspiration. Everyone else was, too. The humidity was getting so high, it was hard to breathe.

We made our way to our quarters and all we could think of was the good news about getting out of this hellhole. No matter where we were sent, we were sure it would be a great improvement.

The Permanent Second Lieutenants Club, known better as the PSL had limited their membership to second lieutenents with over a year in grade. They wrote a group theme song called, "Down in Old Charra Where Shaftin Was Born." Needless to say, the song fit this place to a tee.

It was such a blow because we'd from the beginning heard how lucky we were to be in the B-29 program, and of the fine bases we would be assigned to. If nothing had been said about the great facilities, we wouldn't have expected so much, and we wouldn't have been so unhappy or shocked at what we found.

The priority of making the war hot for the Japanese was full-filled by our arrival in India. All we had to do was to get on with war, so back to Charra. Charra had been built by the British as a medium bomber and fighter base. It consisted of two runways, one 4,000 feet and the other 6,000 feet and they were constructed at right angles. The runways sloped with the lay of the land and the land did not lay too well. The short runway sloped about four degrees and the long runway resembled a sine curve. If you didn't touch down at the beginning of the runway or landed a little long you would hit the slopes and would be in trouble. Our lack of runway accidents was only because we had the best pilots in the USAAF.

The physical setup was typically British, everything scattered all over the place. The buildings near the the runway were small, a tower and an outhouse used for the weather station. No hangars or shop buildings of any kind. A few revetments were scattered around the countryside in camouflage fashion. The administrative buildings and the living areas were divided into three distinct areas. The administrative area consisted of two long buildings approximately one mile from the field. The two living areas were one and two miles from the administrative buildings. "Living areas" were barracks and mess halls with outdoor latrines and wash houses. All buildings constructed in India were of similar pattern and material, concrete base and floor, pole or log framing, bamboo siding with plaster, straw thatched roofs, and wooden swinging doors and windows.

The advanced echelon of supply personnel arrived on 4 March and found the base abandoned. No personnel or supplies. They contacted missionaries, the only source of information about the country and its people. Supply channels were established with the quartermaster depot at Asansol, thirty miles to the north. The base took on the look of a boy scout camp in early April as Air Transport Commmand started delivering personnel. The days were spent meeting new arrivals and using the old Air Force cliche of "you'll be sorry." The phrase was well used at all new locations. New arrivals seemed to have at least one bottle of spirits in their B-4 bags. They needed it, and consumed it without delay. We had to get used to the weird sounds of the night in India. The combination of jackal's calls with native drums was anything but soothing to the dreams of civilized men. The more fortunate had lanterns and insect repellent and could brave the bugs for a game of cards. No one ventured forth without both. Medical lectures and the largest leper colony in the world a mile away made everyone disease happy.

A team was assigned to keep the sacred cows off the runway. The water supply was initially maintained by use of fuel trucks from the refueling section. The gasoline taste was eliminated by pumping the water into lister bags and allowing it to mellow. The executive officer was our ambassador of good will. He soon had the cooperation of the Anglo-Indian officials and British administrators in a kind of reverse lend-lease to make the base more livable. Pumps were installed in wells for showers and furniture locally manufactured was provided for living quarters and day rooms.

The hottest month of the year was June in this part of India. The monsoon rains would soon come and they'd be welcome. The sky was generally clear and the scorching wind was off the Indian desert to the northwest. The only precipitation came from afternoon thunder showers. Squalls were preceded and accompanied by thick blowing dust, better known as blowing mud, and strong gusty winds. The normal average maximum daytime temperature was 120 degrees and at night it got down to eighty-five degrees. The work day was established from 0700 to 1500 hours.

Extreme heat caused a decrease in lift and an increase in engine fires on takeoff, so the times of flying were limited by the heat; 105 degrees was established as the cut off, which meant no flying between 0900 and 1700 hours daily.

We settled in to our new quarters and soon discovered we were running short of clothing. "I don't know about you guys but I'm running out of clean clothes. What the hell are we going to do?" asked Rich.

"Do some washing. We have the soap. All we need is water and a pail," I answered.

"Hold on, I just heard there are some natives who will wash our stuff," declared Jim.

"You gotta be kidding. Have you seen what natives look like?" I asked.

"They look pretty scroungey, but we do need clean uniforms," added Jim.

"I don't know about you guys, but I'm for letting them do our laundry. I sure as hell don't want to be a scrub maid," added Bart.

It was mutually decided that we would hire a native to do our laundry. We put our clothes into separate duffle bags and gave them to the laundry workers.

We headed for the chow hall to eat, and were told an operations meeting was scheduled.

"Another hot meeting. I'll sure be happy when it cools off, if it ever does!" I said as we found a table. We ate in silence and then left as fast as possible, but there was no escaping the inferno.

"Maybe we'll get used to it," observed Rich.

"Don't hold your breath," said Roundy as we reached our hut where our fan was working very hard and getting nowhere.

Later that afternoon Bart, Jim and I attended the ops meeting. We were anxious to find out the bottom line. The big question was when, where, and how. We hoped soon to be flying. When you were airborne you could cool off. The groups waiting for the meeting to start were speculating on a multitude of subjects: the

112

move, flying missions, and other things that effected all of us. In a few minutes Lt. Colonel Bill Bixby, group operation officer entered from the rear door and asked us to be seated.

"I know it's hot so I'll try to make this meeting fast. Hold your questions until after the briefing. I may answer some of them as we go," Bixby said. He was a West Pointer and a damn good pilot and leader. A pleasant fellow and good looking too. He looked like Robert Taylor, the actor. He was about thirty years old with dark hair and a small mustache. Not one hair was out of place. He continued, "I will try to bring you up to date on the operational picture. We have much to contend with operating from Charra. Many difficult decisions had to be made. Here is how we plan to accomplish the task. Our problems include a lack of storage facilities. Another is the short runways and hot temperatures which make takeoffs dangerous or impossible. Therefore we will have to conduct our operations from another base. Charra will remain our maintenance and administative base, and all transition flying will still operate from here. All bomb training, Hump missions and combat missions will stage out of Chakulia, the 40th Bomb Group's base, fifty miles from here. I anticipate no major problems with this arrangement except the inconvenience of getting there."

He then said, "Now, we'll get into more pressing business. Please make notes and check the operational directive concerning our operations into China via the Hump. The code name for this operation is MATTERHORN. Each group of the wing will have its own forward base, however. I will give you the names of the others in case you have to use them for emergency or otherwise. Radio frequencies will be in your mission flimsies and will give you required information for each mission. The 40th at Chakulia will use Hsinching or A-1, the 444th flying out of Chakulia will use Kwanghan or A-3, the 462nd at Piardoba will use Kiungiaim or A-5 and the 468th at Kharagpur is assigned Pengshan or A-7. It would be a good idea for each of you to become familiar with the code numbers and if you can remember the names, all the better. Also, mark your charts with the locations of each base. There's a master copy at each squadron ops. The Chengtu valley where all these bases are located is over twelve hundred miles away over the roughest terrain known and has some of the roughest flying weather you will ever encounter. Make no mistake, after you have flown your first hump mission you'll wonder if combat flying can be worse. I'm not trying to frighten anyone, but

I must warn you to be on your guard and ready for anything. The terrain goes up to almost 30,000 feet and the valleys are not much lower. If you have an emergency, evaluate it rapidly and get rid of your load, if necessary. You will be on your own for the most part, at least until better communications are established. One of your worst enemies will be the weather, don't take anything for granted or you might be part of the granite, if you get my drift. All of us will participate, some more than others because of scheduling problems at times. Instrument flying will be the standard. If you have not logged much lately, I suggest you get some hood time. The navigators will have the worst job. This area is uncharted for the most part. You will have to correct existing maps and help us make necessary changes. I want you all to know that I do not take flying the Himalayas lightly. We will be getting help from ATC. They will be flying C-46's and C-47's. If they can make it so can we! There will be rotational people at the forward bases and from the looks of the weather and dust around here we will get plenty of volunteers. The China bases will be supplied with fuel, bombs, and other items necessary to run combat operations from there to Japan or occupied China and Manchuria. We can't stockpile too much up there because of the precarious situation. We could lose one or all of these bases if the Japs decide to make a big push. I overheard one of you fellows say it looks as if we are going to be truck drivers, and you're right, but ATC can't at this time handle it alone. Each squadron will have one of their aircraft stripped and made into a fuel tanker. It's a shame we have to take our new bombers and make tankers out of them, but again, we have no choice. Those aircraft will be taken out of our hides, they are lost to us for combat operations. Now, the good news. Our first Hump mission will be on the 24th. We will be sending out at least one aircraft from each squadron. Security has been too lax. Tokyo Rose seems to know more about our operation than I do! If she can get the information about some of our plans, we can expect plenty of future trouble, so keep your lips buttoned. That is about it for now. Hang in there and get as much flying time as possible. Maintenance tells me we're in pretty good shape. More info will be coming out soon. When we know something of value you will get the poop through your individual squadrons. Now, if you have any questions, come forth." The colonel was almost swarmed under with the surge of people trying to get next to him at the podium. We had no questions at present and wanted to get out of the steam filled hall.

Just as I was about to get to the door I ran into my old buddy, Bill Russell. "Bill. Over here."

"Hey Johnny, how the hell are you?"

"Hot and pissed off. How about you?"

"The same. They sure threw a fuck into us shipping us here, didn't they?"

"Sure as shit. This place is like an open cesspool."

"You're right. This is worse than that hellhole, New Guinea, and believe me, it was bad. What pisses me off is that they kept promising us super bases with all the fine facilities and recreation as well as being near large cities. What bullshit. I should have known better."

"Well, Bill, that's all true, but still we're lucky to get into the B-29 program. Things are bound to get better. They can't get any worse."

"I guess we'll survive somehow. Let's go outside for a little air."

"Bill, I just missed you coming across from the states. I was one or two jumps behind you. Did you have any trouble?"

"No more than anyone else. It was a bitch, huh?"

"It wasn't too bad except being stuck at Gander."

"That was a bitch! I was at Marrakech for two fucking weeks and I was pissed off. Still am."

Jim and Bart had walked ahead when I stopped to talk to Bill and were now out of sight. We continued to talk.

"How do you like your crew by now?"

"Great. We have one other guy from California, Bakersfield. What are you doing tonight? Maybe we can get together."

"Sounds fine to me. Where do you live?"

"Down on skid row. Come down to my squadron area. We're in hut number 13, a real mansion. If you have any beer bring it along. We're fresh out, but we do have hard booze."

"What an invitation. Come see me and bring you own beer."

We both had a good laugh for a few minutes then I saw Jim and Bart approaching. "Hey guys, over here." They came over and I asked, "Do you know Bill?"

"Sure, we met back at Great Bend, don't you remember?" asked Jim.

"I have to shove off and meet my guys for chow. I'll see you tonight after the sun goes down."

"Good show."

"What happened to you guys? I thought you headed back to the quarters."

"No, we went over to squadron to get some more poop. We will either be flying a combat mission or a Hump mission within a week," announced Bart.

"That suits me. Anything to get away from here" I answered.

"Wasn't it clever of the Air Force, sending us to Hells Half Acre knowing we would beg to fly combat just to get away from Charra?" asked Jim with a big grin on his face.

"What a philosopher. But he could be right," I replied.

"Let's get our asses back to the hut and open a bottle, before this place drives me nuts," said Bart.

"You're the boss." We caught the shuttle and climbed up the tailgate. It was so hot the metal burned your hand when you pulled yourself up on to the rear of the 6X6 truck bed.

The war situation in the India-Burma area was mostly unfavorable. The Japs were driving through northern Burma and northeast India. The battle lines were within easy fighter range of the B-29 airfields. Tokyo Rose kept us posted each night. She was even announcing the arrival of new B-29's and their crews and the dates each B-29 base would be bombed. What concerned us was there wasn't enough revetment for all the planes. Our aircraft were parked on the short runway, wing tip to wing tip. This made the group very nervous, so they instituted a plan for evacuation and defense in the event of an air raid. The planes were to scramble and to remain airborne until all the enemy planes cleared the area. The planes not airborne were to man their guns and fire at the attacking enemy airplanes. Picture if you can, forty B-29's scrambling to get in the air all with a maximum of two hours fuel aboard. Transportation would have to be provided for the crews to be available. It would be like a French fire drill. The zero in the statistical column of losses from enemy raids was only because there were no enemy air raids. Those of us involved in that bit of stategy were hard pressed to understand the idiot who thought up the plan. I will admit there were few options, but using a B-29 as a ground firing weapon or trying to get all those aircraft airborne and not lose most to enemy action was just plain crazy. What was needed was fighter protection and anti-aircraft guns to protect us, not some hair brained evacuation plan. Later some of the obvious defense plans were instituted.

Group came out with a training directive and we started flying. Most of the training was spent on formation flying and practice bomb missions to Halliday Island in the Bay of Bengal.

We knew we'd soon be flying for keeps. The wing put out a frag for our first combat mission which meant the first B-29 was committed to combat. We were sure the airplane would show itself well. It was a matter of getting the experience of flying in big formations and getting the coordination down to a science while being shot at.

On 24 April the first airplane was assigned to fly the first Hump mission. Major Bailey and his crew, one of the oldest, were assigned. Things were bound to start humming around here. Major Bailey's plane was loaded and took off. Two days later two more aircraft were designated to fly the China Express. The Hump mission usually started with an aircraft with an over grossed load flying 1,200 miles at altitudes as high as 30,000 feet. The crews stayed in China two days and then without refueling returned to home base. All in all it was a demanding mission, but had to be done if we were to bomb Japan, and that was what the whole show was about. The second 444th plane to fly the Himalayan Mountains into China was piloted by Captain Shelby. He too was one of the charter group members. Shelby and his crew became the first twentieth Air Force crew to engage in combat in a B-29. They were over the India-Burma border when they encountered twelve Japanese fighters, their newest design. Six took up position around the Superfort and looked it over for fifteen minutes. Then came the first attack, firing as they came in. Eight shells ripped into the B-29's mid section wounding one of the scanner gunners. Three turrets went out of action due to malfunctions and the 20mm cannon in the tail jammed. However, the two fifties in the tail were enough to hit one of the enemy fighters coming in and send it down in flames, the first enemy aircraft to be claimed by a B-29 crew. The enemy fighters became very cautious, and made twelve passes in all and then departed after engaging for thirty minutes. The B-29 continued to China and landed safely at Kwanghan and unloaded their much needed cargo.

13.

The haphazard life of the 444th Bomb Group continued until 1 June 1944. It was then that the first battle order was issued from headquarters 58th Bomb Wing (VH). The four groups were to ready a total of 100 B-29's for the first combat mission.

On 3 June the group attended its first combat mission briefing. The target selected was the Makasan railway workshops at Bangkok, Thailand. Excitement was high. The men of the 444th had trained long and hard to be sitting in this briefing room. Facial expressions reflected realization of the seriousness of what lay ahead. The briefing advised that the 444th would take off at 0545 hours the following day as part of the 98 readied B-29's. One phase of the briefing was obvious by its absence. No one could predict what enemy defenses were at Bangkok. The impression given was that it shouldn't be too concentrated. However, one gun would represent a challenge as far as the crews were concerned.

All groups were flying from their home bases except the 444th which had to fly to the three other bases for combat support and then take off at the end and form up at a predetermined rendezvous point. All groups were off at the proper time and were carrying five tons of 500 pound bombs on each plane. The 40th, 468th and 444th carried general purpose high explosive bombs and the 462nd carried incendiary bombs. The first major mishap occurred on takeoff. One of the 40th Bomb Group's aircraft lost an engine, became airborne then crashed back to earth with a tremendous explosion that killed all aboard except one. Fortunately this was not known by the other combat crews until after completion of the historic mission.

The planes slowly climbed, formed up in formation and headed toward the southeast. Seventeen aborted for a variety of mechanical reasons. The weather deteriorated as the 58th Bomb Wing's aircraft winged their way toward the target. Before the formation reached its halfway point more planes had turned back reducing strength to seventy-seven planes. The four groups were stacked from 17,000 to 27,000 feet and all would have to bomb through a thick overcast which blanketed the target. The results of this first strike were classified as poor. Much work had to be done to perfect techniques of radar bombing. A number of enemy fighters rose to challenge the B-29's, but few pressed attacks. No damage was sustained by any of the B-29's and one crew claimed one probable destroyed fighter. On the return trip there was more trouble. The 40th lost two aircraft to ditching in the Bay of Bengal. Four men were lost. One of the two aircraft actually floated to shore the following day. The crew made shore two days later near the Hooghly River. Meanwhile, one of the 444th's planes ran short of fuel and headed for Kunming, China. The tanks went dry prior to reaching intended destination and the crew bailed out, luckily, in friendly territory. A fifth plane failed to return from the mission.

"I don't know what to think after this mission," said Bart.

"As far as I'm concerned it went well, but I'm only speaking for our crew. I'm not surprised at some of the screw-ups. After all it was our first wing mission. There are a lot of bugs to work out," was my comment.

"Oh, don't get me wrong, I expected things to get dicked up, but somehow I hoped they wouldn't," answered Bart.

However, history was made that day in June when the Twentieth Air Force completed its first combat mission, and we were part of it.

We made a safe landing back at Charra and went directly to debriefing. The intelligence people had to learn from our observations as a crew. After the debriefing we were treated to a free shot of booze to calm us down; what it did was get us high. We returned to our hut to re-evaluate our crew performance among ourselves. Things had been confused at times and now was the time to get straightened out.

"I won't keep you but a few minutes but I do think we need to open up a few areas to examination. Over the target there was confusion and most of it was due to excitement; however, we'll have to keep the chatter down. At times when Lieutenant Lea was coordinating his bomb team there was chatter. I know you were excited about seeing your first enemy fighters. So was I, but it could cost us our asses. Now remember, gunners, the central fire control man is in charge. All you need to do is to call off

119

attacks by the clock and guns will be switched over to you by CFC. The target today will be considered a milk run in the future. We are in for some tough sledding from here on out. You all did a damn good job. Lt. Lea's navigation was right on and I am sure Lt. Ellis' bombs found their mark and you gunners must have scared those fighters because they left us alone. I'm proud to be aircraft commander. We'll have a good chance of making it through this damn war if we work together. Any questions?"

"Yeah. Who's buying?" asked Pops.

"Need you ask!"

Everyone was tight during the mission. I tried to evaluate my own feelings and it was difficult to remember how I felt. I know I was excited, apprehensive, frightened and relieved when we turned for home. I didn't want to ask the others if they had similar feelings. In the future it would be a lot easier to discuss it.

After a few drinks we located transportation to get the enlisted troops back to their huts some distance away and then collapsed completely, I just wanted to climb into my sack and forget it all.

Immediately after the first combat mission was history plans were underway to strike Japan proper. A whole new dimension came into focus and resupply of the China forward bases had to be accelerated. We were assigned our first Hump mission on 6 June. We were to leave for Chakulia at 1500 hours 5 June to get our load and be briefed.

There were only seven cargo missions flown in the month of April. In May things were different. A total of 238 sorties were flown. ATC's C-46's and C-47's assisted with fifty-four aircraft committed to the airlift. The crews and planes were attached to the Twentieth Bomber Command to help carry the cargo into China. In all, twenty of the precious Superforts were stripped of armament and converted into tankers to supply much needed fuel. Most of the tactical B-29's were assigned cargo missions.

Our crew assembled at our assigned aircraft at 1330 hours, the preflight inspections were completed, and all readied for the short flight to Chakulia. Chakulia was so superior to Charra it was hard to believe. No one comprehended how the USA could have bought a location with Charra's restrictions and lack of facilities. The haunting song written by the PSL made sense when you saw the difference between Charra and Chakulia. We had been shafted. Maybe it would come out okay when we moved, if we ever did! Morale would surely fall apart if someone threw a screw into us and we didn't leave soon. One of the enlisted men said, "If they don't move us we can go on strike."

We took off without difficulty, the plane was so light, and almost before we had the gear up and locked we were in the pattern of Chakulia. We landed and taxied to the loading area for loading and fueling during the night. We were scheduled for an 0800 takeoff the next morning. We would've liked an earlier departure to get away from the heat but the delay gave us a chance to look up some of our pals assigned here and have a beer or two. The Chakulia club wasn't much, but a thousand percent better than what they laughingly called a club at Charra. It was refreshing being on a base that resembled an army air field. There was blowing mud and excessive amounts of dust and dirt but that was India. We were pleasantly surprised to find the quarters assigned us for the night were an improvement over our permanent quarters. After dinner we hit the sack to get as much rest as possible before alert. Our first Hump mission was a new challenge. After talking with those who had made the trip I knew I'd be busy as hell. I never griped about the amount of work I had to do while most of the others were lying on their asses. Better to be busy, less time to think about the many dangers that lurked ahead. A properly planned mission made things easier as it progressed and I tried to cover every possible eventuality. In the morning I took Rich and Roundy with me to mission planning to make sure they understood the problems and to instruct them in how I expected them to assist. I knew in my mind I could depend on Rich, but keeping Roundy on the ball was another thing. He would rather sleep than screw. Navigation required intensified attention because existing maps were inaccurate and the mountains so high. The sun would be my main navigational aid. There was no loran to assist, just old basic navigation dead reckoning. The radar would help guide us in the mountainous terrain. Navigators were required to make corrections to the maps on their charts and submit them for new and better maps to be prepared.

I was up at 0500 and by 0545 had finished my flight plan. The crew met at the chow hall for a breakfast of powdered eggs and greasy bacon washed down with hot strong coffee.

"It's a damn good thing we have strong constitutions. That food was like eating shit," moaned Roundy.

"You're always bitching. Christ, you'd bitch if you were hung with a new rope," said Bart.

121

"Hell, just because you found a home in the Army," answererd Roundy.

"Don't be a wise ass," snapped Bart.

"At least he didn't fall asleep while he was eating!" I added.

Roundy's reaction was to pout. We'd hurt his feelings.

"Let's get our gear and get over to base ops for our weather briefing and get this show on the road," Bart said as he led the way.

Bart, Jim and I went into briefing. After the short session we waited outside operations for our transportation which gave us a chance to discuss the mission. Bart understood about all the crew positions and knew the importance of a good navigator. He thought he had the best and I couldn't agree more. Bart was regarded as one of the best instrument rated pilots around and to my relief I knew I could rely on him to hold course and altitude as I gave it to him.

Our plan was to climb to 30,000 feet for part of the mission and drop to 25,000 for the rest. The trip would take about six hours depending on weather and winds. Reporting of winds aloft was an educated guess, not the exact science weather people would have you believe. No matter, we had plenty of fuel. Fuel was conserved if possible to make the return trip without using the precious supply at the forward base. In fact, at the forward base we figured total fuel required to return and off loaded excess which augmented the base supply and enabled us to return lighter.

When we started our pre-flight checks to be ready to go on time the first thing we heard was Roundy bitching. He was pushing his luck. I decided it was time to have a little talk with him about his actions and took him aside.

"Look Roundy, I'm a bit fed up with your constant bitching. You had better shape up. I expect you to stay awake and on that radar set from takeoff to landing. This mission is dangerous and we're not going to buy it just because of your laziness. Do you read me?"

"Why is everyone on my ass?"

"You're kidding! If you're that thick I guess I'll have to clue you in. You're always lying on your ass instead of getting involved with the rest of the crew. Most of all, as far as I'm concerned, you lack ambition and responsibility as an integral crew member. You seldom do your job without me being on your ass and I'm sick and tired of it! I'm telling you you'd better stay on the ball and be at your console this whole mission. Is that clear?"

"Okay, I got you, but you never answered my question of why everyone picks on me."

"I thought I just did! Do your job and don't whine and then you'll see that people won't give you a bad time, okay! Now, let's get your pre-flight done. I'll need the radar to avoid mountains."

I informed Bart of the conversation I had with Roundy and he said, "It's your ball game."

"All I can do is give him a chance. I need a good radar man but I'll be damned if I'll put up with any more bullshit."

"Your problem. If you decide to shit-can him. I'll take care of it."

"Good enough. But for now I want to see if he can cut the mustard. If not, maybe a firing squad would be in order," I said with a smile.

"Christ, you play for keeps, don't you?"

"I was only shitting you. I'll get him squared away or I'll let you replace him."

We both had a good laugh as I followed him up the forward ladder to the cockpit. The hatches were closed and we were ready to go. The interphone check was made. We started the engines and headed for the run up area. As we completed our run up we got our clearance to depart. The aircraft was very heavy and took the entire length of the runway to get airborne. The plane struggled under the load and slowly climbed to our assigned initial altitude of 20,000 feet. The stifling heat of the morning gave way to the coolness of the upper layers of air, quite a relief.

We climbed at a steady rate of 500 feet per minute and expected a clearance to a higher altitude at any moment. The turbulence was moderate. For the sake of those in the crew who had weak stomachs I hoped we would soon find smoother air. In this mountainous area the air currents did strange things to aircraft and instead of getting smoother, it got worse. Two of the gunners had to use their barf-bags. The turbulence reached its worst, then rapidly leveled off. There were still occasional bumps, but when we reached 28,000 it was fine.

Our previous discomfort was forgotten when we saw the spectacular scenery below. The snow was dazzling in the morning sun. The peaks were completely covered with snow and most of the valleys too. Our aircraft started to pick up ice. Icing was one of the enemies of mountain fliers and if you didn't stay ahead of the problem things could get very sticky. No rest for the wicked. If it wasn't turbulence, it was icing. I didn't even want to think what would happen next. As the deicer boots worked, chunks of ice came loose and slid over the wing with an unnerving noise. I'd heard how turbulent air could be at a target area which had been fire bombed. Heat thermal rise could cause severe turbulence and made control of the aircraft difficult, if not impossible. Rather like a kite in a heavy wind on a summer afternoon.

We had been briefed to guard against enemy air attacks. There had been previous encounters and no reason to believe it wouldn't happen again. We were alert. We had two false alarms but were not shot at. Apparently the enemy fighters wanted no part of us that day.

During the course of the flight I called Roundy from time to time and to my surprise he was at the radar console each time. Maybe I'd gotten through to him after all.

I struggled with my navigation due largely to the lack of aids in these mountains and the effort to update the poor maps. We passed over the highest mountains going around the worst clouds and as the terrain lowered so did we. A big buildup of clouds made a trip longer circumnavigating.

"Bart, it looks like clear sailing now. You can let down to 18,000 if you like."

"Good show, heading for eighteen."

"Sure would be the shits if we lost an engine up in this high country carrying the load we have." I offered as a casual thought.

"Don't even think about it, a guy could bust his ass real easy if that happened. Only skill and cunning could get you through," answered Bart.

As the war progressed the allied offensive in Burma drove the Japanese further to the south and enabled the B-29's and the ATC planes to fly more southerly routes than usual without being fired on. They flew at lower altitudes and avoided the more severe weather and turbulence and the flight crews were more comfortable as they winged their way north to China. Turbulence extended the flight because speed was reduced to prevent structural damage.

I informed Bart to let down to 10,000 feet as we neared the Chengtu valley. I expected to break free of the clouds before we reached that altitude. As planned we broke into the clear and found it was raining heavily. The rain was a welcome respite from the stifling heat of India.

After landing and taxiing to the unloading area we were warmly greeted by friends assigned there TDY. A small amount of maintenance, operation, and support troops were here on a rotational basis. No permanent assignments were intended since this would never be more than a forward operational base.

We found the weather to our liking. It was cool, even a bit chilly as the rain soaked our summer flying suits. The change was delightful. We had a grand evening with some of our squadron buddies. They were happy to see us, as well as the beer and booze we delivered, but the thing that made them even happier was the mail we brought.

As time passed more and more planes with cargo to stock the four forward bases with the necessities of war arrived. The China bases had changed from slow, out of the way stops, to thriving bee hives of activity.

Our stay in China was different than the life we'd led in India. The weather and lack of dust were major improvements. The Chinese were for the most part friendly, courteous and above board. They had big grins on their flat faces constantly and appeared to be appreciative of the American effort to stem the tide of the invaders. They looked clean and neat in their old and tattered clothing. The Indians, even though dressed in white, never appeared to be clean.

Two days later we accelerated down the runway at 0700 hours on our return to home station. As we lifted into the air we observed the ground activity in preparation for the first mission to Japan. We were much lighter on the return trip and the plane reacted to maneuvers without effort and of course burned much less fuel.

Our crew was jelling. It was quite noticeable that we'd become a team. The team spirit was apparent and each had confidence in the others' ability. We had done two things which proved our combat readiness. One, we had flown a successful combat mission, and two, we had made a successful crossing of the great Himalayas. Our biggest challenge lay ahead, Japan and the targets far to the southeast over forbidding terrain and long expanses of water, that would be the real test. No information was documented about how the Chinese communists in remote areas would react if we were forced to land. Whether they would turn downed airmen over to the Japanese, imprison them, or help them evade the enemy and escape safely were unknown factors. Each incident as it occurred would be evaluated carefully on its own merits. We were getting used to doing things in an environment of the unknown.

We landed at Charra after an uneventful trip of five and one half hours and were met by our transport. It was hot as hell and dusty in Charra, our own Hell's Half Acre, our home. I knew I'd never get used to living in India.

"Let's get together in the squadron briefing room and go over the mission to see if there are any comments. I have a couple things I'd like to get across," said Bart as we arrived in front of our operations building.

We all jumped from our seats on the rear of the big truck and dragged into the briefing room for the meeting. "I'm only going to keep you for a few minutes. I know it's hot and sticky. In the future we're going to have to fly many of those devils and we can make out fine if we all stay on the ball. Lieutenant Lea and his bomb team worked their asses off to keep us from getting lost and hitting one of those monster peaks. No mean task. I was happy with your performance, but I can't impress too much the importance of keeping the chatter down on the interphone. If you have something necessary to say don't hesitate to let us know. However, small talk interferes with the communications. I understand the excitement of your first mission but many things take priority, such as enemy attacks. There's another thing I want to get across to you gunners since we didn't have a chance for discussion after the combat mission. A lot of crews had trouble with turrets and guns. I want each of you gunners to dig into the tech orders and make sure you know everything about the turrets and your guns as far as malfunctions are concerned. I sure as hell don't want to get knocked off because we couldn't fire back at an enemy fighter. Coming through this war in one piece depends on team work and being prepared. You all did damn good on this mission and I'm proud to be flying with you. If you have anything to bring up, now's the time." No one said anything. "Okay, I guess we're all on the same wave length. We should be leaving this hell hole in the near future. We'll just have to suffer through it until that day comes. See you all later." Bart gave off with one of his big smiles. He was happy with his crew.

The meeting ended. Everyone climbed aboard the truck and off we went with the red dust swirling behind sticking to our moist flying suits.

"I sure as hell hope our laundry will be waiting. I'm out of everything," said Bart as the truck pulled up in front of the ugly hut.

Sure enough, our laundry was lying on our bunks. The clothes looked clean but my shirts and trousers looked like they'd been worn for months rather than days. All our uniforms were almost threadbare. We called in the house boy in charge of laundry.

"What made our uniforms look so old and worn?" I asked as he stepped into the room.

"Sahib, is it not true your clothing is clean?"

"That is not my question. I want to know what the hell happened to our new uniforms?" I asked again.

"Sahib, best laundry boys in India. Laundry good."

"It's no use asking this little bastard any more questions. He isn't going to tell us," said Jim.

The mystery was too much to let lie. If this continued we'd have no clothes left and replacements were hard to come by. We were too dirty and tired to argue with the house boy so we dismissed him. His white teeth gleamed in a big grin. He slowly turned and ambled out. He was a funny little guy not much over five feet tall, with a very dark complexion and pearl white teeth. When he smiled all you could see was teeth. His clothing was clean and neat and all white as was his turban.

The mystery was eventually solved. Our friends in the hut next door had the same problem and had gone to the river to see how the natives washed the clothes. They were dumbfounded to find the natives disrobed at the river and dressed in our uniforms, then stepped into the water and rubbed the uniforms with a flat stone. Whether or not they used the soap we sent with the soiled clothing no one knew. Small wonder our uniforms looked old. They were being literally worn out during the first washing. I decided to do my own laundry by more conventional means.

On 12 June we were notified we were to fly on the first Japan mission. We were to depart the next afternoon for Chakulia to be loaded for our trip to China, as were other 444th combat crews who were flying the combat mission. We would load there and proceed to our forward base far over the Hump. Ninety-two Superforts were assigned the mission. Each of the four bomb groups input an equal number of planes. This put an extra strain on the 40th at Chakulia because the 444th staged from there in addition to their own planes.

After our aircraft was loaded and ready we took off. The sooner we got to A-3 the more time to relax before the big mission. The flight across the great mountains was much more comfortable than the last trip. The air was fairly smooth. It usually was better at night from the weather standpoint. Personally, I would rather fly during the day and be able to eyeball those damn mountains.

Final briefing was held at 1000 hours the morning of 15 June and takeoff was scheduled for that afternoon. We'd hit the target late that night. The target was the Imperial Steel Works at Yawata on the north coast of Kyushu, a distance of 3,200 miles. Intelligence reported the steel works was producing an estimated 2,260,000 metric tons of rolled steel annually. This amounted to twenty-four percent of the total Japanese production and this target would be heavily defended. The assigned altitude for the 444th was 18,000 feet. The B-29 was designed to carry ten tons of bombs. This mission, because of the distance, would require extra fuel and use of the bomb bay tanks reduced the bomb load, so each B-29 would be loaded with eight 500 pound frag bombs.

Of the ninety-two planes dispatched to China, one was lost enroute and twelve others aborted. Seventy-nine reached the forward bases.

During the final briefing we learned from wing staff representatives, who were dispatched to each forward base, the present war picture. All aircrews were kept informed of the progress of the war, especially in their theater of operations. In China things weren't going well. The 58th Bomb Wing was struggling to get supplies and gasoline into China, but things were tenuous. The big Japanese offensive called "Operation Ichi-goon" had begun on 19 April and the initial strike by General Hada's army was aimed straight into central China against Chinese forces in Honan. The goal was to capture the Peking-Hankow railroad. General Hada was successful and assembled at Hankow and Canton, in secrecy, a 400,000 man army, the largest Japan had ever thrown into a single campaign during the entire war. The main attack was launched on 26 May on two fronts, to the south and east. The Chinese were unable to slow the Japanese army. Changsha fell. American General Chennault, commander of all Air Forces in China, committed his fighters and bombers, but in the end the allied effort to stop Hada was lost. Apparently the Japanese did not know we were operating out of China's Chengtu valley or

128

they didn't believe we had the range to strike Japan. In any case, we were here and knew we could hit Japan. During all this time Generalissimo Chiang Kai-shek and General Chenneault were trying to have all B-29 stockpiles turned over to General Chennault's Fourteenth Air Force. Orders from General George C. Marshall, Chief of the Joint Chiefs of Staff, to General Stilwell were that no B-29 supplies were to be used by the Fourteenth Air Force unless specifically authorized by the Joint Chiefs of Staff. It was JCS's opinion that early bombing of Japan was required to relieve the Japanese pressure on China and to coordinate with American landings in the Marianas, set for mid-June.

This mission was a milestone. The first planes to strike mainland Japan since the historic Doolittle raid back in 1942 from the aircraft carrier Hornet.

Departures commenced at 1616 hours with 68 B-29's airborne. One of the 468th Group's planes crashed right after takeoff without serious casualties. One of the 444th B-29's crashed outbound near Kiangyu killing all aboard. Four more aircraft aborted, and the rest continued toward Japan. We were now down to sixty-two aircraft out of a possible ninety-two. The weather people briefed a five-tenths cloud cover over the target area. We were prepared to bomb by radar if necessary. Each group flew toward Japan in a loose formation until they reached the coast of Japan.

"It is as dark as the inside of a whale's stomach up here. The Japs really have a blackout in effect," reported Bart.

"Roger, but we have a damn good radar picture," I answered.

"Makes for a little pucker time!" said Jim in a casual way.

"Okay, everyone keep on your toes. I expect night-fighters to be up here looking for us," cautioned Bart.

The sky was partially obscured by clouds in the immediate target area. As a result, fifteen planes dropped visually. All others bombed by radar. Bombs were scattered with few hitting the main iron and steel works. Greater damage was done to the adjacent industrial area. Six planes jettisoned their bombs on targets of opportunity due to mechanical troubles. Forty-seven bombed the primary target, two bombed secondary targets, and five more bombed targets of opportunity. All other drops were unrecorded. The first bombs were dropped at 2338 China time.

One aircraft of the 468th was lost to flak and six others were hit including our plane. Our damage was slight and caused no problems on the way home. This was not the case for some of the others.

Japanese night fighters made sixteen weak and ineffectual attacks on the B-29's. Twelve passes were pressed to within 500 yards. However, no claims were made by either side. As we turned off our target we dove to 5,000 feet in an attempt to avoid further attacks by the Japanese flak batteries and soon passed out of their range.

"Those damn Nips were ready for us. I thought we were supposed to take them by surprise," said Rich as he relaxed from the strain of the target.

"Christ, Rich, those intel people should have known with all those damn islands between China and Japan the Japs would have some early warning devices," I answered.

"It could have been a lot worse. I didn't think the fighters were too sharp; their flak was better. But they'll get better as time goes by and they'll be ready for us," added Bart.

"The thing that shook me up was the damn searchlights stabbing up through the clouds and blackness," said Jim.

We had a long trip ahead of us. I gave Bart a new heading and we settled back and headed for home. One after another the B-29's left Japan and scattered as they flew southwest across the East China Sea and passed to the north of Shanghai on their way back to the Chengtu valley. One of the planes of the 444th had engine trouble and was forced to land at Neishsiang, China. While the crew was working on the stricken plane the following day Japanese fighters and bombers appeared and promptly destroyed the B-29. Two other aircraft were lost from the 468th. Both had hit mountains. Losses to enemy action were expected but wasting planes and crews to a mountain is sad. I had explained to Roundy what could happen if we weren't on the ball all the time and these accidents proved my point. Crews get a little too relaxed and think they left the danger back over the target. That kind of thinking could be fatal. I only hoped they didn't crash because of navigation error.

We came within view of the Chengtu valley and were all elated to know the worst was over. Our fuel was low.

When we landed we were told there was not sufficient fuel in the storage tanks for all. Some would have to wait until additional fuel was flown in.

We weren't in a hurry to get back to Charra but were among the unlucky ones to be fueled, and arrangements were made to get the last leg of the long and hazardous mission over. We launched in the early hours and headed across the mountains to India. No further mishaps occurred and all planes returned to their home fields. We landed and spent little time at debriefing. We entered our hut, pulled off our flying suits and boots and hit the old fart sack. As soon as my eyelids slid down, I was in never-never land.

The debriefing prior to my exhausted entry to the sack was conducted by the intelligence people and many things were recommended to help us in the future. They were gaining experience just as we were and we made our recommendations. The mission to Japan was one of the most demanding and tiring missions anyone was asked to accomplish during World War II. Each segment was an ordeal, crossing the Hump twice, flying across the great expanse of China twice, and bombing a well defended target.

The following day it was announced United States forces had landed in the Marianas on an island called Saipan. The big plan was working. The discussion immediately changed to the new events and how they would affect us. Speculation centered on how long it would take to win control of the island, how long it would take to build runways and how long it would take the 73rd Bomb Wing to be in place.

We felt well rested after a good sleep and after cleaning up were ready for our next assignment.

"Let's go down to the line and get the plane cleaned up after breakfast," said Bart as we walked back from the wash house, then added, "Christ, we don't know when the next mission will be laid on and we'd better be ready."

After breakfast we found transportation and were on our way.

"Isn't it amazing how the cooks can destroy breakfast," complained Rich as he pulled himself up to the truck bed. Safety straps were on the rear of each of the trucks and we had learned to board using the staps as if they were ropes tied to a tree.

"I'll never as long as I live get used to powdered eggs and powdered milk. I don't know if I'll even recognize real food when I eat it again," agreed Jim.

"Even when the cooks get good chow they manage to destroy it. I'll bet the Navy eats a lot better than we do," I added.

"Christ, everybody eats better than we do," said Roundy.

We arrived at the plane and climbed to the ground, thanked the driver and turned toward the airplane. We wanted to examine the hole in the fuselage. It could not be repaired while we were at A-3.

"That baby tore one hell of a hole. Lucky it didn't get the pressurized section or we would've been on oxygen the whole trip back," said Bart as he put his head into the hole just forward of the bomb bay doors on the starboard side.

"I felt that hit, it was right under me," said Walt.

"I'll bet it even woke up Roundy," kidded Bart.

"Ah, come on. I wasn't asleep on the combat mission. At least not in the target area," Roundy retorted.

"I'd rather he slept over the target than over the Hump, but in any case I think we have an agreement on your sleeping habits, right?" I asked.

"I'll do my job."

"You're probably one of the better radar men in this outfit, but you're also lazy," I said.

"Do we have to go into that again"? he asked.

"Let's drop it. Like I said, just check in with me before you hit the sack and all will be fine."

We cleaned up the bird, hailed a truck and headed for ops to check on the training schedule.

Things were happening fast and furious in the global war. News had just been received that the Allies had invaded Normandy and were pressing inland. They had been hung up on the beaches but finally made a breakthrough. The JCS must have sweated that one out. The Twentieth Bomber Command's first raid on Japan had not inflicted great damage, but had proven to the world that Japan was not a sanctuary, or untouchable. The mission had got the attention of not only the Japanese, but the rest of the world. In the halls of Congress all halted to hear the news. General Hap Arnold declared the strike by the B-29's had made this a "truly global war."

We were scheduled to fly a training mission the next day. There was much to be done if we were to improve our attack strategy. I thought we'd sink that damn island called Halliday in the bay of Bengal, but it didn't sink and we kept bombing it with our practice bombs. Some of the initial problems were resolved and the B-29's continued to be modified. The extreme conditions in which this plane had successfully operated was a tribute to its designers, but the engines were still the big problem.

We flew three training missions and were being upgraded to

lead crew status, a great honor. I hadn't known that while at Great Bend my training folder had been annotated to indicate that I should be trained as a lead navigator as soon as practical. It read, "Lieutenant Lea performed his training in an excellent manner and had a fine grasp of tactics and all facets of navigation." The training was more than just for me. The bomb team as well as the pilots had to be lead qualified. Our lead crew training was conducted by flying instructors and on completion of all the requirements we would be given a check ride. It was a great deal more responsibility without promise of promotion and meant extra study as well as additional flying.

On the last day of June 1944 we were given our check ride and were certified as a lead crew. On the same day the good news of our leaving Charra was announced, Our new home would be at a place called Dudkhundi located near the city of Kharagpur. The announcement was received with enthusiasm and everyone seemed to find a bottle and extra beer which had been saved for the celebration. The party started immediately and lasted well into the night. We knew anything would be a great improvement over Charra, because it was truly the "anus of the world."

14.

July came in as June went out, hot as an inferno. The big difference was that today was the day we'd leave Charra for the last time. We were moving to our new base fifty miles away. We were lucky. We were assigned to fly the short distance. We would carry all the equipment that we could and still take off on the short runway. The troops not flying would join the motor convoy. Buildings were stripped of everything. We were going to leave old Charra just the way we found it—empty, dirty, and hot.

It took until the fourth of July to complete the move and not a man looked back as he left. The only good thing about Charra was leaving. The new base would make the air crew and ground crews happy, and we would now be able to launch missions from our own base and not have to stage from Chukulia. The odd thing about our new situation was that we were only a stone's throw from Chukulia. We settled into our new quarters and to be honest they weren't that much better; however, the base layout was definitely a great improvement and it also had better facilities.

Dudkhundi had been an operational air base before it became the home of the 444th Bomb Group instead of an abandoned re-treaded base like Charra. Dudkhundi was another British masterpiece of planning which had to be rebuilt, but it was a 100 percent better than what we'd left. Our thanks went to the 87th Service Group and the thousands of anonymous natives who got the base ready before the advanced echelons of the 444th had arrived. A bar had been built, another plus.

We were soon to find the town of Dudkhundi was off limits to American forces, but no great loss, it wasn't much anyway! The reason was that the inhabitants were Hindu untouchables, proud in their caste. The caste system makes life unbearable for the lowest caste. The untouchables even make life miserable for themselves.

The important thing for the men of the 444th was to be as

134

happy as possible in their surroundings. For many there was little to do for recreation. One of the favorite pastimes for the ground troops was to lie beneath their mosquito nets at night and listen to the ever-lasting "crunch, crunch" of the Dudkhundi aborigines, better known as termites.

Most of the Indian natives didn't like Americans, especially after we got wise to their ways. It was a stand off; we had no love for them either. The natives continually begged, borrowed, or stole whatever they took a liking to. They were excellent thieves. A favorite target was GI shoes which would be passed on for generations. The people most happy with the Americans were the owners of Carews Distilleries. Their slogan was, "Carews Booze for Combat Crews." You cannot imagine how many pairs of native feet were employed crushing grapes for consumption by the men of the 444th. It was known to cause mild gastric disturbances, especially when flying.

July 4th brought more than a national holiday. It brought the news of our next combat mission. We were to strike Japan on 7 July. In the meantime available aircrews would fly Hump missions to assure the necessary supplies would be in place. Our crew was scheduled for an early morning departure so after dinner we returned to our quarters to get as much rest as possible in that climate. The weather forecast indicated rough weather all the way. We had hoped this passage would be as routine as our last but there was little chance with the forecast. Our load was fuel, bombs, and other essentials for the coming mission. In the morning after chow and final briefing we were at our aircraft at 0500 hours scheduled for a 0600 takeoff. The essential aircraft inspections were completed and we boarded and awaited word to start engines. The radio cracked with the order to start and soon we were taxiing toward the runup spot for takeoff. We were loaded to maximum takeoff weight. It would require a long takeoff run. I always considered the takeoff one of the most critical parts of any mission. The max load and the heat, even at the early hour, presented us with a precarious departure. All would be fine if we didn't lose an engine before, during or after lift-off. We dodged the bullet and lifted cleanly into the sky and slowly climbed, turning toward the Himalayas. Conversation amongst the crew dealt with the comparison of Charra and Dudkhundi. We were unanimous in our opinion. Charra was the pits.

We reached cruising altitude in a nearly clear sky. The Ganges

River could be seen far below and to the east. The Ganges is the sacred river of India. It was hard to understand why a muddy river held such a spell, but after spending three months in northeast India I realized why. Without the river this area would be like the great desert to the north.

I was surprised to see my radar scope aglow and sharp. Roundy was on the ball for a change. Maybe our little talk produced positive results. We had climbed at a standard rate of 500 feet per minute which provided our best fuel economy with the heavy load. The terrain ahead was ominous and yet beautiful; snow covererd peaks and deep valleys. These mountains were to be feared and respected; they had already claimed the lives of two B-29 crews. We were approaching the area of maximum turbulence which would cause great discomfort to those with weak stomachs. I had never been airsick, not even in cadets so I was sure I was immune.

Flying over this rugged expanse of mountains and peaks was always critical. Mechanical problems or too much icing could be fatal. If forced to bail out chances of survival were slim to none. At 30,000 feet the sky was dense blue and the snow below gave off a bluish-white glare, which made you squint when looking out. I was busy with my navigation and discovered to my delight we were a little ahead of our flight plan. Being ahead of flight plan always made the crew happy, just as when behind they felt unhappy, so I usually told the crew when we were ahead but avoided telling them when behind. Winds up to this point were of less velocity than briefed resulting in less turbulence than anticipated. The flight engineer had pressurized the cabin to 8,000 feet and a comfortable 70 degrees so summer flying suits were adequate and oxygen masks unnecessary. This bit of convenience had set apart the B-29 from its predecessors. I completed my calculations and handed my log and chart forward for the pilots to see what the mission looked like to this point. Bart was always interested in all details of a mission and understood the chart and log. After reading my log he instinctively looked at the outside air temperature gauge and let out a little whistle. "It's colder than a witch's tit out there." Those of us on interphone laughed. It broke the tension.

It was more than pressurization and heaters which made this plane so much better than all other bombers. The B-29's speed, range, gunnery system, and bomb load, were the other assets. The drawbacks were apparent too. The plane was new and untested until now and we were up here finding out for ourselves. But it's speed ranked high. We were faster than most of the Japanese fighters and able to out-distance them in most cases.

The mission was progressing without incident, so I pulled out my paperback pocket book to relax between position reports. Then without warning the plane lurched and a loud bang was heard. Backfire of one of the starboard engines signaled an emergency. The flight engineer could not see the backs of the engines from his crew position; therefore, it was the duty of the scanners to spot irregularities. A rapid call from Walt broke the silence. "Right scanner from engineer, over."

"Go ahead, engineer," came the immediate response from the scanner, Ron Ellis.

"Scan the starboard engines and let me know what you see."

"Walt, there's a lot of black smoke trailing number three."

"Sir, we've lost number three. I recommend we feather the prop and shut down the engine at once."

The prop went to full feather, thus decreasing drag, but we had trouble on our hands.

"Nav, this is pilot."

"Go ahead, Bart."

"Johnny, get us a good position and ETA. I'm not sure what our options are right now. And scanners, keep your eyes peeled and report any unusual occurrences, understood?"

"We're on top of it, sir," answered Art Long.

"I'll have a position report in a matter of a couple minutes. What happened to the engine?"

"Probably swallowed a valve," answered Bart calmly.

It took only two minutes for me to update my last position and I had all the necessary information. "Nav to pilot, over."

"Go ahead."

"Roger, I'm passing the info up and you can transmit it on the frequency I have listed."

"Good show. Figure out how long we can stay at this altitude."

"Will do," I answered and then called Roundy, "Nav to radar, over."

"Go ahead, Nav."

"Roundy, we'll have to keep our heads out of our asses, so stay on the scope and report to me anything out of the ordinary. I don't want to tangle with the "cumulo-granite.""

137

"Will do."

I removed my headset and went forward to talk to Bart without the rest of the crew listening in. "Bart, what is the immediate plan? Are you going to dump the load?"

"Not just yet. I want to see if we can keep this altitude for a while and then I want you to look over the situation real good and let me know when I can reduce altitude. The other three engines are pulling more power than I like. I am not sure how long we can last without overheating the other engines."

"I understand, but I would rather gamble on the other three engines than bail out over these god-forsaken mountains. It would be a miracle to get out alive."

"True, but we may not have a choice. For now we're going for it. We will give it our best shot," Bart said with confidence.

"Good enough, I'll get back and see what we can do about getting down to a lower altitude," I said and walked back to the navigator's table.

I scanned all the charts of the area, especially those which had been modified by our own navigators to determine the exact height of the mountains along the route. After careful calculations I came up with the best possible route of flight and minimum altitude we could fly to avoid the granite cliffs. "Nav to pilot, over."

"Go ahead, John. I hope you have good news," Bart said seriously.

"Could be worse. Hold this heading and altitude for seven minutes, then start a slow descent to 25,000. I'll give you the word. Just make sure you have the right altimeter setting and do not, unless you let me know, go below the altitude I give you. I'll calculate the height each mile along the route. You can reduce some power when we start our descent and give the engines a chance to cool down. Our ETA is still good and I'll keep you posted on any change, over."

"Great, just give me the word when you want me to let down and then try to give me a new ETA if anything changes."

His voice gave hope to the crew as they listened. Bart had a way of keeping panic to a minimum just by the way he spoke. I wished I could be as calm. I tried. Things looked a bit better than when we caged the engine, but there was no relaxing. We all had to stay alert to any danger. I called Roundy to let him know the current situation and what I expected of him. To my delight he did an outstanding job. He recommended a slight course correction and he was right on the ball. Roundy had joined the team.

"Nav to pilot, over."

"Go ahead."

"Come right three degrees to a heading of zero-two-five and start your descent to twenty-four, five. That should keep us out of trouble."

"Righto, coming to 025 and 24.5 grand. Let me know when I reach altitude, over."

I watched the altimeter slowly unwind as I monitored the compass and airspeed. Bart made the plane do exactly what he wanted. He never wavered from the exact heading. At the speed we were moving and the rate of descent I figured we would be level at two-four-five in twenty minutes. I put my dividers on the chart and found the intended position of level off, then made calculations to be sure of the best flight path. In this kind of a situation your best effort sometimes was not enough, but I was going to give it my best shot.

We had been descending slowly and were close to the level off altitude when I heard another loud bang. My heart jumped a beat. "Nav to pilot, we are now at level off. Our heading will remain the same, and what the hell was that noise?"

"That was number one clearing its throat. It's still running a bit hot though, the damn cylinder head temperature is right on the red line. Any chance of reducing more altitude?"

Before I could answer there was another loud report from number one engine. Then Walt Smith called from his engineer position, "Engineer to left scanner, over."

"Got ya, Walt, but I can't see a damn thing," called Art Long from his position at the left bubble.

"Okay, keep a sharp eye. I don't want it to get away from us," answered the flight engineer.

"Nav to pilot, we have to stay this altitude for a bit longer. How is it going up there?"

"I'm hanging on the props with this reduced power," answered Bart.

"I'll let you know. In a few minutes we can go down to twenty-one five."

"Good show, keep me posted."

Fifteen tension filled minutes passed and a deadly silence had fallen over the crew. I was as busy as a one-armed paper hanger, trying to figure all the angles and stay ahead of the events and keep this plane on the right path toward our destination. Every minute got us closer to leaving these unforgiving mountains. I made another sun observation and plotted all the information available and I was happy to see we were exactly on course, but a little behind our new flight plan. That wasn't the big worry because we had plenty of fuel. The important thing was to stay as close to course as humanly possible. There was little room for error. We were lower than most of the peaks in the area and that wasn't comforting.

"Nav to pilot, in five minutes we will clear that ridge dead ahead and then we can let down to 21,500. I'll give you the word for the let down and level off. Our new ETA is later due to the reduction of speed. It'll probably change again, no sweat."

"Good show, Johnny. I'm glad you're on top of things."

"Pilot to CFC, over."

"Go ahead, sir."

"Roy, how much weight could you dump if we needed to?"

"Sir, we could salvo everything if you'd like and that'd be somewhere around 20,000 pounds."

"Okay, thanks, stand by and we'll let you know if we have to start getting rid of the cargo, over."

Bart had told Rich to go aft and look over the situation as far as the feasibility of dumping the load. If we did we'd probably make it; however, I hated to think of coming this far and not being able to deliver our cargo. Rich passed my navigation table. I had to lift the hinged part to let him pass between it and the big four gun upper turret, and I could see the concern on his face. A bit unnerving, but I forced a smile. Rich looked into the forward bomb bay porthole to see what the load looked like, then crawled down the tunnel to the rear. We would have to depressurize and go on oxygen if he actually went into the bomb bays. I was not looking forward to the prospect. It was difficult to work with that damn mask on your face. He came back with the news that we could dump the load but we'd have to depressurize to get out the items stored in the pressurized portion of the plane.

"Nav to pilot."

"What's up Johnny?"

"At our present speed and assuming no big wind changes we have two more hours to Kwanghan." I released my mike button and another backfire resounded throughout the plane.

"Bart, start your let down to two-one-five. I hope it helps."

"It sure will, John. Keep your fingers crossed. I'm reducing power on number one to just above idle cut off. Let's hope we don't get any icing on the props and wings. So far so good."

There was silence on the plane for a few minutes. Then we heard still another blast and this time the plane shook as if given a push sideways.

"Walt, what does your panel look like?"

"Not good, sir. We're losing number one. I can't keep the cylinder head temperature down," answered the engineer in a calm, grim voice.

"Sir, I see black smoke trailing from number one," called Art from his position in the rear.

An immediate call back from Walt, "Sir, she's coming apart internally. It may freeze up any second and then we may not get the prop feathered."

"Okay, Walt. Shut it down, now." Bart ordered. "Johnny, we are in trouble. I'm afraid we can't hold this altitude. I'm going to salvo the load and we'll have to depressurize to get rid of the internal cargo."

"Okay. You are now at 19,000. Level off, we can't go down another foot," I responded.

"WILCO,"

I recomputed with the loss of the second engine and reduction of weight. With one hell of a lot of luck we might make it, but I wouldn't have made a wager on it. Every minute we stayed airborne meant we were closer to escaping the mountains and increased the odds of rescue if forced to bail out. Bart was in full control. He had made all the right moves. Jim was on the radio sending out a MAYDAY. Rich had supervised the release of the load. Walt worked to get maximum power from our two remaining engines and the rest of us did our jobs as best we could.

We had to dump the remaining cargo stored in the aft compartment and the loads in the bomb bays. My ears told me we were depressurizing even before we were told to get on oxygen. Rich had gone into the bomb bays and with the help of Roy West they were cutting the straps and removing chains to release the cargo. There would be some natives on the ground who would think they were under attack. Within minutes Rich and Roy emerged from the bomb bays and the load was salvoed. The plane reacted like a kite and actually started to climb. The men in the rear wasted no time in dumping the remaining cargo from the rear door. Walt pressurized the cabins and off came the oxygen masks. We were now a twin engine B-29, two engines out and the props stationary with their blades forward.

"Sir, things back here are looking better, both props feathered and the two other engines look okay for now," reported Walt.

"We need all the breaks from now on." Bart then called the crew on the interphone and said, "Get your survival gear on and keep your chute at the ready. We look okay for now, but if anything else happens, we've had it. If we have to bail out I want you all to get the hell out in short order and remember this is mountainous terrain so you'll have to be sharp. Stay together when you hit the ground. One last thing, we have a good chance of making it to A-3 so a little prayer wouldn't hurt."

It was scary looking out the window seeing two engines not working and praying the other two kept turning. We were still flying, not very fast, but still flying. Bart was holding our heading as if nothing had happened. Then the radio came to life. One of the planes which had taken off from Dudkhundi behind us had heard our call for help, and with our reduced speed, had caught up with us. They told us they would stay with us come what may. They were flying direrctly above us to avoid going into the side of one of the peaks. According to my maps and radar we were no longer in danger. It gave us a lift to have one of our fellow B-29's with us even if they could do nothing but watch.

After a silence of ten minutes, I called Bart. I knew the crew members were probably holding their breath. "Nav to pilot."

"I hope this is good news," Bart said with a laugh.

"One hour to go. Can you keep this heap flying that long?"

"Sure as shit stinks."

The mountains were now falling behind us and I gave Bart permission to descend to 16,000 feet and asked him to alter course to fly the most direrct route to our destination at Kwanghan. The real break was the weather. If we had had strong turbulence we wouldn't have had a chance. The weather was CAVU all the way. We were not out of the woods yet, but things did look a lot better. The two remaining engines purred. It was like music in our ears. Time passed slowly, but I knew we were going to make it. I made another observation and was happy to report the Chengtu Valley was dead ahead at twenty-five miles.

We prepared for landing. Jim called the tower and told them

to have the fire and crash equipment ready, then requested landing instructions.

"Chengtu approach, this is Rover 481, twenty miles southwest, with two caged engines, request landing instructions, over."

"Roger, Rover 481, we have you in sight. Cleared to a straight in landing on runway 38, emergency vehicles standing by, over, and good luck."

The landing was accomplished with expertise. Bart had to be the best pilot in the entire USAAF. I had said it before and I said it again. We taxied in with the red and yellow vehicles following, a mother hen being escorted by her chicks. Finally we reached our revetment, shut down, and climbed to the ground saying a little prayer of thanks to God for bringing us through. It felt good to plant our feet on mother earth once again. The thought went through my mind, we could have been strewn over the Himalayas freezing to death or worse. We assembled in front of the aircraft before we climbed on the waiting truck. Some took a look at the two dead engines first. Comments made about the loss of the two engines were not too complimentary. Looking at it another way, the other two got us here and that was the bottom line.

As our truck pulled away from the plane and headed for base ops, Bart shouted over the noise of the Army truck, "After chow I'm inviting you all to the officers' tent for a bit of cheer. I'll be opening a couple of bottles and we're all going to celebrate our deliverance and get a little drunk. We'll have at least three days to sober up before we leave."

"Yeah," approved one of the enlisted men.

When the truck came to a jerky stop in front of base operations, Bart, Jim and I jumped off the rear and went in. The others were driven on to their quarters. We completed our reports and headed for our quarters to unwind.

"Hey, you guys, wait up," came a voice from a jeep. It was one of our old buddies who was on rotation here. "I just heard about your hairy ride over the Hump. Let me take you to your quarters. I have a bottle of VO to drink to your luck. You are lucky bastards to have escaped with two engines out," he said as we drove off.

After chow, the enlisted troops made their way to officers country and we broke open a bottle of CC. "We would have knocked if you had a door," said Walt with a smile on his face. Walt was not a heavy drinker, but he did enjoy a good bourbon and we had one of the best. We introduced Whitey Jensen to the others and the twelve of us passed the two bottles around without benefit of glasses. Roy West had scrounged some beer for a chaser. Bart wanted to say a few words before we were all out of it. "Today you once again made me proud to be the aircraft commander of this crew. You all reacted to the emergency as professionals, but there is one guy who works all the time and gets little credit. I would like to propose a toast to our navigator, Johnny Lea. He is one cool customer," he said as he raised the bottle of Canadian Club.

I felt odd, getting this recognition from my peers, but I was delighted. "Thank you one and all, but I deserve no more credit than the rest of you. We are a team and only a team can survive in this environment." I thought to myself, he says I'm one cool customer, yet I'd felt the fear as I'm sure the others had.

Again Bart rose, "It's a damn shame we have to haul this trash up here instead of bombing the fucking gooks. We have no choice, but maybe the damn ATC will get their shit together one of these days and then we'll only fly the Hump on our way to Japan. That monster mountain is going to claim more B-29's in the future. Let's hope we're not one of them. Now let's get to the serious drinking."

"Just think, we have to go through all that shit to get here just to cool off. But what the hell, soon the monsoon will hit India and we can watch the mud blow instead of the dust," said Rich with a slur. Then he said, "Let's have that bottle of CC. I need a drink."

It was most uncharacteristic of Rich to get loaded but he too had to unwind.

Jim broke his silence with, "I sure will welcome the rain. It should break the heat and clean the air."

The guys started to feel the effects of the booze. Tongues were getting thicker by the minute. Some were giggling and stumbling and others passed out on our cots. The booze had succeeded in relieving the tension. It was also an opportunity for some who did not easily express themselves to talk, and to congratulate ourselves on being the best crew in the Twentieth Air Force.

15.

Two relaxing days passed before the two engines were changed, and it took all of two days to get us back on our feet. Operations requested a test flight on a short local before releasing the plane for the return flight across the Hump. We were to be on the flight line at 0900 hours the next day.

We arrived early with bags packed and ready to go but found we were going to be delayed for a last minute runup of the engines. This gave us a chance to visit with some of our old buddies on temporary duty there. The line chief, Master Sergeant Henry Dugan, told us the story of how A-3 was built.

"It was really crazy up here. The Chinks were building this runway from scratch. We wanted runways at least 8,500 feet long and 19 inches thick. Of course we thought cement would be used, wrong! They used rounded rocks and gravel covered by native concrete consisting of crushed rock, sand, clay, and water. Over 3,000 Chinese worked on it, and all by hand. It was an engineering miracle considering the construction factors and the primitive tools used. They hand broke and hand set the rocks. The ten-ton roller was drawn by hundreds of ragged Chinese and the endless tasks of watering, hole filling and tamping was unbelievable. This accomplishment left us with great respect for the humble Chinese coolie. Work on the airfield was still in progress when the first airplane came over the Hump. The majority of the coolies had never seen an airplane and a jeep had to be dispatched to chase them off the runway so the plane could land. After the first hundred or so aircraft had landed here they finally realized the big bird's right-of-way wasn't to be disputed without harmful physical consequences. Some still persisted in exposing themselves to the on-rushing giants in the belief that their close proximity to the viciously spinning props would remove their evil dragons, with the result that both coolies and dragons were unavoidably dispatched."

The story was interesting. I had heard that great numbers of coolies had actually been killed by aircraft when the fields had been constructed. And now I knew the how and why.

We got the call to report to our plane for the thirty minute test flight. We made our normal preflight inspections, everything was in order and ready for take off. There was nothing else to do but climb aboard and get the bird into the air. We found all systems to be operating properly and landed. By then it was noon and it was decided we would depart the following day. Since we had recovered our health there was time for a little sight seeing and we made the short trip to the town of Kwanghan. The most impressive thing in the village was the huge gate which guarded against intruders. Like many other Chinese cities it had a fort as protection. The people were very friendly and smiled no matter how desperate their situation seemed to be. We saw enough of the town in a few hours, no reason to return in the future. We strolled back to the field and spent the rest of the day lying around and getting ready to return to Dudkhundi. We were anxious to get back in the swing of things. Somehow we'd overlooked the most important holiday in America, July 4th. We were ashamed of ourselves. We'd slept most of the day and it had been like any other day to us. We made a pledge not to forget Independence Day next year, that is, if we were still around. It was the way of things here in "nowhere"; days ran together and it was difficult to distinguish one from the other.

The next morning we were up early. A light rain had fallen throughout the night and off and on during the daylight hours. The dampness was of no concern to us. After a short delay we were ready to return to Dudkhundi. We were airborne and climbed at a fairly fast rate. The aircraft was comparatively light and easy to handle. We continued our climb to make the initial altitude of 20,000 feet. We leveled off for a period of time and then climbed again. Step climbing helped to keep the engines from overheating. The flight was what we wanted, uneventful. After clearing the last high terrain we were letting down into the flat lands around Calcutta. We entered the traffic pattern and landed at Dudkhundi where we observed much preparation for the up and coming mission. At operations we found the next mission was indeed to Japan. Sasebo was selected as the target and staging would be through our forward bases in the Chengtu Valley. It would be a long mission, more than 3100 miles over hostile territory. The mission was small, only twenty-four wing aircraft were assigned; the 444th was assigned six. The frag order indicated a two-ton load for each bird for the target, a naval facility. The reason for sending such a small number of B-29's was obvious; we did not have enough war-ready supplies in China. Too bad! It was a shame our last effort had gone for naught.

We were not assigned to fly the mission. At this point in time there were more crews than aircraft. We were happy to wave them off and stay home. We all had letters to write and maybe we could stir up a little recreation, maybe volleyball.

The Sasebo mission, as the two before, was not without its problems. It was to be expected of a new command and plane. We were still learning and experience was the best teacher. Of the twenty-four planes assigned the mission, eighteen made it to Japan, twelve hit the primary and the others bombed targets of opportunity. The problem was again radar. Some had mechanical difficulty and others had operator problems. There was not much resistance from enemy aircraft and flak was light. However, on the return trip across China the Japanese Air Force attacked with eight fighters and a running battle ensued. During the firefight one B-29 was hit and one Japanese plane was shot down. Apparently the bombers were too well defended. The attack was called off and the bomber force continued to the Chengtu Valley without further incident. Results of the mission were classified as good: forty 500 pound GP's and 40 photo-flash bombs were dropped on the primary target.

The Sasebo mission was further evidence that we needed a great deal more training. There was also a step up in supply missions to China. We could never really hurt the enemy until we sent larger formations over the targets. I considered the extra trips ferrying supplies over the Hump worse than bombing missions.

Our crew was well into lead crew training and for that reason had not made a Hump mission since we dumped the cargo; however, the routine was broken when we were called on to make our first tanker mission which turned out to be a piece-of-cake. We had absolutely no trouble either coming or going. It was a nice feeling.

One day in the last week of July we were informed of a large scale mission. One hundred planes were scheduled to hit a coke plant at Anshan, Manchuria. The frag order received from the

147

XX Bomber Command had specified this mission a maximum effort, all aircraft of every organization in flying condition for combat would be committed. It was exciting to see the activity at our base, all organizations were combining their skills to prepare the armada for the strike against a formidable target.

The aircraft began leaving for the forward bases on 25 July. We led off at dawn carrying maximum fuel and a bomb load of HE bombs. We had to face turbulence and icing over the Himalayas. Again, weather was still our greatest foe. However, we made the passage with minimum discomfort and landed at A-3 minutes before the next plane of our group arrived. Safely on the ground, we knew we had one of the toughest parts of the mission completed. All we had to do next was to go against a predictably heavily defended target far to the north across China.

We were supplied with details of the mission which allowed us to get to work on flight plans. Manchuria was an unknown quantity. We had little intelligence to go by. We would at least surprise them, hopefully. Surprise was something you hoped for but seldom achieved. This was a daylight high altitude mission. The target was 1,300 miles away. Many speculated on chances of survival in this vast unknown arena. So little was known of the enemy strength because the Japanese had never been challenged in Manchuria. We were pioneers in not only a new aircraft, but in an environment unknown to combat airmen.

Four groups of the 58th Bomb Wing would be leaving from their respective bases at the crack of dawn. I was sure I hadn't slept at all when the alert came the morning of the mission. After all the last minute necessities had been accomplished we found ourselves in our aircraft ready for the big raid. With a thunderous roar the engines of the 444th's B-29's came alive on the signal received from the tower. All the groups of the wing had taxied out and started their departures, but before our scheduled takeoff our group was innundated with an exceptionally heavy thunder shower. The 72 B-29's of the of other three groups headed toward the target and we were ordered to return to the ramp and shut down our engines. We had missed the great show. Plans were immediately formulated to strike a target nearer as soon as weather permitted. Five hours after the mission had headed for Manchuria our group took off for a new target at Taku, China near Tientsin. Our mission was to bomb shipping in the port. Fifteen planes took off for the mission. We encountered little opposition. We clobbered the target and returned with the loss of one aircraft. We had dropped 114 500-pound GP's and the results were rated good. We were jubilant and felt we were finally becoming an effective fighting force. As for the mission of the other three groups, soon after takeoff the 40th lost one B-29 with eight men dead and three surviving. Subsequently four other B-29's aborted due to mechanical difficulties. Sixty bombers hit the primary target and bombing was improved due to a new diamond formation of four aircraft elements. The formation also improved defense. Seven of the aircraft hit targets of opportunity and one of the seven was hit by flak and set upon by enemy fighters. The B-29 escaped but with extreme damage and later the crew had to abandon the aircraft and bail out over occupied China. Eventually eight of the crew of eleven returned to the Chengtu Valley aided by natives in the area. Another plane was lost to unknown causes. The losses for the entire mission totalled three including one which went down over the Himalayas on the return to India.

As July came to a close we got the good news that all tactical B-29's were being withdrawn from Hump missions. The tanker runs to resupply the forward bases with aircraft fuel would continue, they had been stripped and were not considered tactical aircraft. We were happy to let the ATC planes take over the trash missions which was their primary concern, we would have our hands full with the real war. The saying going around the field was since ATC flew cargo planes let them take the trash. Bart had said many times in the past, "They were trained to fly cargo and we were trained to fly combat and anyway the acronym ATC meant, "allergic to combat."

The month of July ended with 237 sorties being flown to China which consisted of 753 tons of aircraft gas and 1,083 tons of cargo. The ATC aircraft had flown 419 sorties carrying 1,162 tons of cargo in their C-46's. We knew we would be called on from time to time to fly tanker missions, which we could accept.

16.

It was a day in early August when a drama unfolded which ranks with the most terrifying of my experiences. It was a lazy wet Sunday morning with the monsoon in full swing. The rain seemed to come down in buckets and it was difficult to see across the dirt road in front of our hut.

I had just slid out of bed and was stretching the kinks from my back after suffering through another night on the GI cot when Joe Diehl, a fellow navigator who with his crew occupied the hut next to ours, came crashing into our hut half dressed. He was as white as a sheet, almost speechless and wet to the bone. I looked surprised and amazed, "What the hell is wrong, Joe?" I asked.

"My God we need help. Bill Cummings woke up a few minutes ago and found a snake in bed with him. I think it's a cobra! What the hell can we do?" he said with a tone of defeat.

"Settle down! We'll be right there! While I'm trying to help, run to a phone and get the medics over here right now!" I said as I hurriedly pulled on my pants and shoes.

"What the hell is all the excitement?" asked Bart as he and the others sat up in bed.

"Christ almighty! Bill next door is in bed with a cobra. I'm going over to see what I can do."

"Wait, I'll go with you," said Bart as he jumped out of his bunk and in the same motion pulled on his pants.

We rushed in as quietly as possible followed by Jim, Rich, and a still half asleep Roundy.

"Roundy, you and Rich grab the operations jeep in back and go for Colonel Mitchell and make sure the medics have been called," ordered Bart.

They ran out to the rear. It was now raining harder, if that was possible. We looked across the room where Bill Cummings was lying on his back. He was as white as a ghost. I silently prayed he wouldn't have a heart attack. The remaining officers of his

150

crew were trying to keep him calm. Bill had discovered the snake when he started to roll out of bed and he had pulled the blanket back and looked into its black beady eyes. To Asian experts this might not be considered a large snake, but to Bill it was big enough to swallow him alive. Actually, the damn thing was five feet long and to all of us it was five feet of deadly fangs.

Bill had been prudent enough to lay the blanket back down as carefully as he could. The room was cool and we figured the damn cobra had slid under the covers for warmth. It had coiled between Bill's thighs and a false move might be Bill's last. If the cobra struck it could hit an artery and Bill would be dead in seconds. At all costs we had to keep Bill quiet and calm. I felt sure the snake could sense panic. From what I've learned in my few months in India, the cobra is fast, deadly and unpredictable. This kept racing through my mind. I think we all were as frightened as poor Bill. I told him help was on the way and soon we'd have him out of this predicament. I wasn't sure he really believed me, but he did manage a sickly grin. He could not hold out much longer before he did something that would cause the snake to react.

Within minutes Lieutenant Colonel Bob Mitchell entered the room half dressed and wet to the skin. Behind him, and pushing their way to the front, came a group of four medics and the flight surgeon. They went into action immediately. They set up a table close to the bed and on the table they placed a variety of medicines, alcohol, and syringes. Next to enter the room was an old Indian with a close cropped beard and piercing eyes, wearing a tightly bound turban. He was followed by a huge sergeant I had seen at the motor pool. The sergeant had hands which resembled hams and his arms were as big around as a woman's waist. The old man opened a cloth bag and pulled out a musette-like horn used by snake charmers and started to play his weird melody. The big sergeant lifted the blanket from Bill ever so carefully, I was surprised at how gentle this mass of muscle was. Those of us who had no part to play backed away silently praying for a miracle. Some had grave doubts about the outcome.

One of the medics gave Bill a shot in the arm. Almost immediately he settled back and his muscles relaxed. The old Indian continued to play while we watched for the response of the huge snake coiled between Bill's thighs. I bit my lip at the reptile's proximity to Bill's family jewels and all I could think of was the fright Bill must be feeling. Luckily he had always been level headed and a cool customer which no doubt saved his life. A less disciplined man might have reacted violently and help would have arrived too late.

Time seemed to stand still as the old man played on and the sergeant stood close by. There could be no false moves. Cobras were well known for their speed and deadly poison. Every year in this country many people were bitten and died. The consensus among us standing nearby was that if the snake struck it would probably hit in a vital area and Bill's life would slip away before anything could be done. However, the medics were confident they could give Bill the antivenom in time to save his life.

All at once, as the snake charmer played his haunting melody, the snake started to stir. The sergeant moved slowly and deliberately to the rear of the snake and kept out of sight. The tantalizing music continued without interruption. Some of the spectators slipped from the room, others looked helplessly on. After what seemed to be an eternity the big snake lifted from the sheet and its famous hood was fully extended. It rose slowly and seemed to keep time to the music with a slight sway to and fro. The moment of truth was at hand. I wasn't sure what the sergeant's part was in this drama, but we soon learned. When the snake's head cleared Bill's flanks with a flash the sergeant's right hand shot forward and grabbed it just below the head. The muscles of the sergeant's arms bulged as the snake fought viciously to get free, but he held on. He slid his left hand down the body until he had a tight grip on the tail too. Then he calmly walked out the door. As soon as he was clear of any obstructions he used all his reserve strength to extend the snake to arms length. With a flash he released the head and in the same motion cracked the snake as you would a whip. The snake's head parted from his long body and the sergeant merely dropped the still squirming body to the ground and went back into the hut.

We spontaneously started to applaud and the sergeant's face reddened in a blush. He had become an instant hero and was to be rewarded for his bravery with a medal and a promotion. The sergeant turned to face his admirers and said in a drawl, "Shucks, it twert nothin', I cracked the whip on critters bigger than that 'un back home."

Everyone was still in a state of shock when the sergeant and the old snake charmer left. The snake charmer had not uttered one word the whole time. They merely stopped as they reached the door and smiled. The native had teeth so white they looked like pearls in a dark pool. He too was to be rewarded not only by the squadron, but also by the men from Bill's crew.

It was chilly in the hut even though we were wet from perspiration. The medics helped Bill to a waiting litter. He had gone through a terrible ordeal and was still colorless. However, he sat up and asked for a shot of whiskey. Little time was wasted handing him one. After a long pull on the bottle he lay back and shut his eyes, completely spent. The medics carried him to the waiting ambulance and whisked him away to the hospital.

It was still early in the morning but all of us still standing in the hut had to have a shot of Bill's booze, too. It had been a strain on everyone's nervous system. We heard a lot of noise outside and were surprised to see a large throng had gathered and was cheering the sergeant and the old Indian standing in the downpour.

Bill remained in the hospital for a week. There were those among us who thought he would never return to the unit, but he did come back, although a bit more nervous than before. He stood down from flying for over a month before he was cleared to return to duty.

Colonel Mitchell had followed the sergeant outside and told him he would like to see him in his office later that morning. Then Bob returned to share the whiskey and told us he was giving the sergeant a medal and a promotion, also a choice of assignments within the squadron. Later we found the sergeant requested a transfer to an air crew. He would be instructed in the art of aerial gunnery and would be assigned to a crew when qualified.

"Colonel, I think that sergeant is one hell of a man. I, for one, am glad he's to be rewarded," said Bart. He spoke for all of us.

The snake episode forever changed our casual way of jumping into bed and opening doors. From that day on everyone, before retiring pulled the bedclothes back and made a search around the area as well as pulling the mosquito netting tight around the bed. Heavy rains had obviously driven the snake indoors for a warm spot to sleep. We were sure we hadn't seen the last of the cobra, so caution was the byword.

As time passed, the cobra story got better and better. The old rumor mill had blown it out of proportion until the drama we had witnessed was not recognizable.

17.

The snake incident finally slipped from vogue. It was back to reality and the damn war. The field order sent down to the groups was unique in that it called for two separate missions to be flown by the wing to two widely scattered targets. One was against a Japanese home island and the other to the southeast Asia area. It was hard to believe the first target, Nagasaki, Japan was 500 miles closer than the mission to Palembang, Sumatra. Both missions would be flown at night due to the extremely bad weather during daylight hours at this time of the year.

The targets were widely separated but were of strategic importance. The Japan mission would stage out of China and the Sumatra mission would stage out of China Bay, Ceylon. Our crew was selected to fly the Palembang mission. The trip was a long one, the target 3,600 miles away. Pladjoe refinery was reported to be producing 20 percent of Japan's fuel oil and as much as 75 percent of their aviation fuel. The Nagasaki target was naval and military installations in that immediate area.

We departed Dudkhundi for China Bay on 9 August. There was a total of 56 B-29's on our mission. We were briefed the morning of 10 August for takeoff starting at 1645 hours the same afternoon. It was to be the longest bombing mission of World War II. The 462nd Group was selected to send eight aircraft to a location north of Pladjoe on the Moesi River to lay mines. Their target was 4,030 miles away. This then became the longest mission ever recorded. It would take over seventeen hours to complete.

After the briefings were completed there was time to make last minute repairs if required. I was prepared to make this long and arduous trip but I knew I'd be a basket case when it was completed. The first aircraft broke ground at 1645 as planned and was closely followed by fifty-three more. Eight had aborted for a variety of reasons. After eight uneventful hours the target loomed dead ahead. We were amazed to see the target lit up like Broadway. The glow from the lights through the overcast was an eerie sight. The Japanese clearly had not expected any company. I doubt they realized we could make it this far. The first of our aircraft found the target nearly clear and were able to bomb visually. After that the weather closed in rapidly and necessitated the use of radar for bombing. The plan was for each aircraft to bomb in trail, which had its dangers, for all planes were in a blackout condition using no navigational lights and this required extra vigilance on the part of the crews. Our bombing altitudes varied from 10,000 to 17,000 feet. The advantage of bombing at lower altitudes was only the conservation of fuel. The disadvantage was that the enemy could bring more guns to bear. The smaller calibre automatic weapons fired tracers resembling fireworks. The red balls floated past and exploded impairing our night vision. It was terrifying because we were aware any one of the streaks could mean the end. They were not fireworks.

Thirty-nine B-29's hit the primary target with good results. Three hit targets of opportunity and twelve aircraft had aborted enroute. We had encountered antiaircraft fire, ground to air rockets and enemy fighters, but our Superforts sustained no damage and made no claims. The Japanese fighter planes were very cautious, they apparently knew of our computerized gunnery system and wanted no part of it. Time would tell how the enemy might react on future raids.

On the return trip one of the 444th's aircraft ran out of fuel and ditched ninety miles short of China Bay. The crew, less one member killed in the ditching, were picked up by a British ship twenty-four hours later.

The other mission sent thirty-three planes to the forward bases. One was lost enroute. Of these twenty-nine B-29's were sent against Nagasaki. Each aircraft carried three tons of incendiary and fragmentation bombs. Two aircraft aborted and three bombed targets of opportunity. Nagasaki was bombed by 24 B-29's with moderate damage resulting. Japanese fighters made no claims and the flak was light. The mission was to enter the record books because one 444th tailgunner shot down an enemy fighter at 600 yards with his 20mm cannon. For the Twentieth Air Force this was the first confirmed air victory.

The XX Bomber Command had planned a second mission to Yawata, Japan at night. The earlier success of the day attack on Anshan led to a change of plan. The Yawata mission would be a daylight affair and would be a command maximum effort. Every combat-ready plane would take part. Five-hundred pound general purpose bombs would be the load and each plane would carry six.

* * *

"It looks like another balls out mission," said Bart as we left the briefing room and headed for the club for a drink and some food.

"It also appears they are applying pressure on the Japs since we have taken Saipan, Tinian and Guam. Things are looking better and we're now on the offensive. It looks as if we're winning the Pacific war," said Jim with hope in his voice.

"I heard by way of rumor the 73rd Bomb Wing will be leaving Kansas as soon as they complete the airfields on Saipan. It will be good to share some of this war with them. I'm not selfish," I said jokingly as we opened the door to the club.

"As far as I'm concerned, I'd rather be out there flying from one of those islands rather than having to fly that bitchin' Hump," chimed in Rich.

As we approached the bar we were invited into the poker game, but declined. If we got involved in a game we'd not only miss dinner, but a lot of good sleep which we all needed. We were most interested in hearing what the rumor mill was cranking out and the bar was always the best place to get the good poop. There was an unusally large turnout at the bar and the subjects so many and varied it was difficult to keep up with each group. At least we were out of the weather and could enjoy a good drink and relax. Most of the talk centered around the up and coming mission to Yawata. No one would deny this was going to be a damn tough mission. We knew from intelligence reports that the enemy had good defenses there and a day mission would allow the enemy fighters to concentrate on each formation. There would be flak to avoid as well. On top of it all we'd have to fly the damn Hump twice. Most of us had a philosophical attitude. The wheels had to plan the missions and we had to fly them so what's the difference? Why worry? When your time comes, it comes.

After dinner we returned to the bar. The people who were already there made room for new faces. The subject under discussion was trying to determine who and how many of the guys who had come over with the original deployment were no longer around.

I didn't want to think about it. Those who have never been in a combat outfit can't imagine the terrible burden it is to pack a buddy's belongings to ship home and to find words to fit the letters to loved ones. It was impossible to justfy the loss. These are the small factors you never anticipate when you go to war.

I was in favor of moving away from that conversation and of starting a new one. When you spoke of home you forgot other troubles and just got homesick. The usual argument about which part of the U.S.A. was best seemed to be one never settled. Most of our crew knew where God's country was and we were glad he had made it California.

The next day dawned with torrential rain and howling wind. The rain made the whole area a quagmire. Transportation had difficulty getting crews to briefing and later to the aircraft. Every one was drenched and we had to wait for the downpour to let up to start engines and depart. We had learned to cope by keeping extra flying suits in our kits and changing immediately after we climbed aboard the plane.

In all, the wing got 98 B-29's airborne that day. As we left the area the ground appeared to be a great muddy lake. The only mishap occurred over the Hump when the 40th lost one plane on the way to their forward operating base in China. Early the following morning all planes had been refueled and were ready to depart from the forward bases for the long and dangerous mission. The 40th, 444th, and 468th Bomb Groups had little trouble getting airborne. However, the 462nd did. After launching seven of their B-29's the eighth crashed on the runway and blocked any further immediate use. After a few hours the 462 finally got eight more planes in the air and were joined by five from other groups who had not met the earlier takeoff time. The thirteen had been delayed so long their mission to Yawata became a night mission. The main target was the Imperial Iron and Steel Works, once again. The "V" formations were very effective over the target, however. As predicted, we were met by swarms of enemy fighters and very heavy and effective flak. The bombing formations varied in altitude from 20,000 to 26,000 feet. We fought our way in to the target area. The only relief came when the flak over the target drove the enemy fighters off. They hit us again when the flak ceased for at least thirty minutes after "bombs away."

Our position was on the right wing of group lead. We had kept a loose formation across China to conserve fuel and cut down on fatigue, but as we approached the Japanese coast the formation tightened up in diamond four ship elements which made up the separate formation for each group.

Japanese antiaircraft fire was intense and accurate as we neared the Japanese coast. It was so heavy it appeared as if one could walk on the black bursts and enemy fighter attacks began well in advance of the target area. We knew two things: we were in for one hell of a fight, and the enemy didn't want this target destroyed no matter what it cost them.

Our line of flight across the East China Sea was in a northerly direction. We wanted to stay over water as long as possible. We made a sweeping turn north of the target to hit it as we flew south; then we broke toward the sea to the west to minimize time over flak areas. Yawata was a naval installation and the Imperial Japanese navy was known to have very accurate antiaircraft batteries.

The enemy fighters seemed to be confused and disorganized as we started our turn to the primary target. They apparently did not anticipate the turn toward Yawata. All at once they got the message and made effective formation attacks mostly from twelve o'clock. Bombers were being hit during the fighter attacks. Mutual and concentrated fire power saved the day. The familiar "bombs away" was the signal to escape the area.

Flak over the target became even more intense, but in a way it was a relief. I could never figure out which was worse: enemy fighter attacks, or heavy flak. Neither made for a healthy future.

The 468th was ahead of us and lower. As we watched we saw one of their planes take a direct flak burst. It was a devastating sight. Then a twin engine Japanese "Nick" came in at twelve o'clock level and rammed the 468th lead ship's left wing. The enemy fighter's propeller cut deep into the wing, fuel gushed out, and both planes burst into flames. Debris from the crash as the planes disintegrated fell into the path of the slot plane flying in the number four position. The pilot swung up in an attempt to avoid the wreckage, but his vertical stabilizer was sheered off and the B-29 went down in a tailspin. The ramming was a well planned maneuver, not an accident. Suicide tactics were to increase as the war progressed.

Being in front of a formation provided a not always pleasant view of what was happening ahead and below. It was very difficult to erase the ghastly sight we had just witnessed. Three great silver birds dropped from the sky without a chance of survival. It was later reported, only one man of the three crews of eleven men each survived. The noise of battle is unsettling even in an aircraft which resists outside noises. The spent cartridges and the metal clips which held the machine gun ammo slid down a metal chute and caught in the bottom of the turret. This noise is especially loud for the navigator. The upper turret with four fifties firing makes for a lot of spent brass. Continued firing, however, was reassuring.

"Okay gang, settle down, the show is not over. Here comes three boggies at twelve o'clock level. Be sharp and shoot straight," called Bart from his vantage point.

He no sooner finished his call when Rich opened fire with the six fifties of the two forward turrets. The intense fire forced the enemy fighters to break down and away. Rich had hit at least one as they came through the formation.

"Nice shooting, Rich. Keep your heads out and stay calm: we'll make it," added Bart.

Things had happened so fast that before we knew it we were out over the East China Sea. Enemy fighters still came at us, but we knew they had to be running short of ammunition and would have to break off. None too soon for us; we'd had enough action for one day.

The night mission hit Yawata after dark and of the thirteen, ten hit the primary and all made it home. We were convinced night missions were definitely the way to go, but the brass didn't always see it that way.

It was reported that during the attack on Yawata the enemy had employed a new tactic: bombing from above the B-29 formations with air to air bombs. There were four separate attacks and one had been successful. The B-29 crew had stayed with their aircraft until it reached a lower altitude and then bailed out. They were probably among the first B-29 crewmen imprisoned by the Japanese.

The Yawata mission proved to be the most disastrous mission flown from the CBI to date and left the B-29 command in a state of shock. We lost fourteen planes plus one which had flown to Russian territory. To prevent the plane falling into Russian hands, the crew bailed out east of Khabarosk. Our group was credited with five enemy planes and the wing's overall score was impressive: seventeen confirmed kills, fourteen probables, and twelve damaged. We gave them a hell of a fight. Seventy-one B-29's hit the primary target and six bombed targets of opportunity. In all, 111 tons were dropped on the primary and the results were rated good. Our luck had held. Although we had sustained minor flak hits, none were in vital areas.

We crossed the great expanse of China, refueled, and returned to India. We had survived the great Yawata raid. We had one more mission toward eventual rotation; that is, if someone would make a decision on how many missions constituted a combat tour.

Strong rumors had been circulating about a new commanding general of the XX Bomber Command. The rumors proved to be true when General Curtis Lemay arrived from the European Command where he was known as an iron ass. Maybe it was what we needed!

From the beginning of General Lemay's assignment in late August it was clear things were going to be different. He had very astute ideas of how to conduct the air war against Japan. He revised tactical doctrine and instituted a heavy training schedule. Part of the new doctrine included flying twelve ship formations which proved to be effective. The doctrine also made daylight precision raids the order of the day. The general showed the men of the command that he was unafraid. He went as an observer on the very next mission. The next mission turned out to be the one we'd first been scheduled for and couldn't complete. The target was the Showa Steel Works at Anshan, Manchuria, the biggest mission yet for the 58th Bomb Wing. Our plane developed engine problems when we taxied out to the takeoff position and we had to return for maintenance. As it turned out we were luckier than some. Lieutenant Rodgers and his crew crashed nearby and Captain Mattingly and his crew crash-landed in China on their return from the bombing mission. However, Mattingly and his men eventually walked out with the loss of only one.

The mission proved very successful: ninety planes hit the primary and eleven bombed other targets. The weather was clear and 206 tons of bombs rained down on the target. They knocked out several coke ovens and inflicted other damage. Flak was light; however, fifty enemy fighters rose for the attack. They lost eight fighters, nine probables and ten damaged. Four of our planes sustained minor damage only.

Bomber Command laid on a third mission to Anshan for 26 September to wipe out the steel production from the area. Our aircraft position was lead of the second element. The target area was completely overcast which required the employment of radar. Radar results had generally been poor on precision targets. We flew the old four ship diamond formation and encountered a strong enemy fighter force of seventy-five planes to our seventy-three B-29's. As we bore into the target attacks were coming from all directions. Right at "bombs away" our tail gunner hit a Tony which burst into flames and disintegrated some 100 yards behind. Two other fighters were damaged by our gunners. We had a field day. A very happy event for our crew. Wing claimed eleven shot down, nine probables and thirty-one damaged. Our aircraft all returned safely. Bombing results were rated fair; there was little new damage.

When we returned to home station I found a number of letters from my family and one each from my cadet buddy's, Dave Lewis and Hal Landis. In the ten months since we parted company we'd written an average of one letter per month and I'd written just prior to the mission. Dave had put in for B-29's and had been notified his B-29 replacement combat training was to begin after the next navigator cadet class graduated. This meant he would be entering training right after the first of the year. It sure would be great if he were assigned to our group, but that would be too much to hope for. Hal was "somewhere in the Pacific," which meant little. However, I knew his unit designation and learned he was down around New Guinea hauling supplies, carrying troops and dropping paratroops. Those missions would not suit me even if it was a hell of a lot safer than our business. News from home was so welcome and it never failed to make me homesick and nostalgic. I frequently dreamed about home and the family. I received a package from my mother. She never forgot. Everything was rationed at home, but there was no use trying to stop her. Anyway, I really appreciated her packages. She is the greatest mother in all the world. The packages looked like a tank had driven over them, but I managed to salvage most of the goodies. Family letters included news of my two brothers. The oldest was in the Navy and the younger had enlisted in the USAAF for cadet training. Maybe the war would end before either went into combat. My folks had enough worry with me. They always admonished me to be careful. Skill, cunning and downright luck was what my future was based on.

18.

October was certain to bring increased combat operations, or as Bart put it, "We are in for a ball buster," and he was right. We had trash hauls as well as fuel and on top of that, combat.

Bart returned from a meeting called by the wing commander where matters of policy were announced. The one which concerned the combat crews was the new policy of getting mission credit for flying the Hump both ways "We've won one battle. We get credit for all Hump missions flown in the past and the future," said Bart.

"That's great, but I'd just as soon get my mission credit flying combat missions," said Jim seriously.

"I don't agree. We haven't been shot at on the Hump missions and that goes a long way toward peace of mind," I added.

"Engineering has been working hard to solve the engine overheat problem, and they've made good strides in improving the cooling system. Maybe we'll have less trouble flying the Hump in the future," Bart said with a sigh.

"The whole mess gets complicated, Bomber Command is concerned about getting material into China, yet they think the Japs may launch an attack on our forward bases at any time. Good news, however, weather over the Himalayas has improved and we won't have to RON at A-3 provided we have no mechanical problems on the trash missions. There's one other thing that came up during the meeting which was important, the invasion of the Philippines will soon take place under General MacArthur. It means we'll be staging out of A-3 to attack targets in Formosa to keep the Japs from interfering with the invasion."

"Our asses are going to drag, looks like things are going to get hot and heavy around here," said Jim.

"I sure feel like a good poker game, I feel lucky," I said changing the subject.

"Not a bad idea, Johnny, I'm running low on cash," said Bart.

"How about letting Jim and I in on the investment this time," asked Rich.

"How much do we need for a grub stake, Johnny?" asked Jim.

"About $500!"

"If you all want in, fork out a hundred a piece and we'll have a partnership," said Bart as he reached for his wallet and pulled out a crisp $100 bill. "I've been saving this for a rainy day and it's raining like a tall cow pissing on a flat rock."

We put our money on the table and Bart and scooped it up and handed it to me. "You guys know this is a gamble and if you want to pull out it's okay. I can't give you any assurances," I said.

"We've seen you play and we know you're a tiger when you gamble," said Rich with a big grin on his face. "I'll give it my best shot."

"We're glad to get to invest," said Rich.

"Let's get going, I'm thirsty," said Bart.

We arrived at the dining hall at 1800 and we sat at a table in the corner where we mapped our strategy and had dinner. Then we headed for the club hoping to find a seat in the regular game. I never drank much when gambling, usually just enough to keep loose. The game found me before we had finished our dinner. The regulars liked to play with seven, but could only get six. They accepted only good poker players, as they put it, thus the invitation. Most of the regulars had jobs that did not require flying. I was the only lieutenant at the table but rank made little difference at poker, money talked.

The game progressed without much in the way of spectacular hands, I was sure of one thing, there were three or four damn good players seated at the table and the others would be well advised to find less expensive amusement. I hung in there without much in the way of cards. I played into a couple of nice hands and all at once was ahead about $400. Being ahead made it easier to maneuver and having good cards made it esier to bluff. Then I ran into a little trouble with good cards that were second best. I weathered the storm and was still $100 ahead after two hours of play. I was getting a little tired and had decided to quit soon. Then came the hand of the night. It seems when one person has a good hand, it's not uncommon for others in the game to hold good cards too. So it was with this hand. The man to my left dealt five card draw and we all made an ante of a dollar. I kiddingly said, "Let's have a barn burner!" I had thrown in five or six hands

163

in a row. The cards had deserted me. Seven dollars sat in the middle of the table as the ante. We were dealt five cards. I slowly uncovered one card after another and found I had three queens.

"I'll open for the size of the pot," said the first man.

The next player said eagerly, "I'll make it $14."

"My bet is $28," said the next player.

I was amazed, two raises after the first four players had declared. I waited to see what the major who was seated to my right was going to do.

"What's in the pot?"

$84 was now laying in the heap. The major calmly counted out $84 and threw it on top.

I tried to sort out what the hell was happening. Apparently this was one of those pots which sometimes come during a game when all the players are dealt a good hand. I was holding three queens and never had a chance to raise. I hesitated for a few seconds, then counted out $168. The dealer had indeed dealt a barn burner. It was the pot of the night and I had a good hand, but figured I needed to improve my hand to win.

The dealer turned to me and said, "You asked for a barn burner and it looks like we've one in the making," then he said, "I'll call."

The man who had opened the pot was visibly shaken. "I don't know what the hell you all are so proud of, but I have to call."

The next player had been losing all night and finally had a enough. He pushed his chair back, rose, slammed his cards down on the table and said, "That's enough for me." When he raised his cards to slam them down, he flashed his hand and those across from him saw the three tens.

I thought he was better off out of the game. In his frame of mind he would be better off as a spectator. I concentrated as the players requested their draw cards. The first two players drew one card, followed by a two card draw. I decided not to keep the ace kicker and drew two. The dealer was last and he drew three cards, every one in the game was dumbfounded. He was holding a pair, it sure seemed. There were always clues in a game for those astute enought to recognize them. I always looked for an edge and seeing three tens and the other two discards gave me that edge. I'd caught sight of a king, also. I picked up my two cards and to my delight I'd had drawn the fourth queen. I knew the game was mine. Only two hands could possibly beat me, a straight flush or four aces. The damn dealer bothered me with his three card draw. I'd always been against using the joker and now I wished it wasn't in this game.

The first bet was made, a "C" note. The next two players also called without hesitation. I wasn't worried about them, I knew I had them beat.

The major to my right looked at the pot and said with bravado, "Let's kick it another hundred."

The pot was now in excess of $1000, and I decided it was now or never. I picked up my stack of money and counted as I put it in the pot. "My bet is $675 and I'm all in," I said waiting for a reaction, my heart was pounding.

The game had drawn a crowd intrigued by a game of this caliber. The crowd buzzed louder as the players examined their hands. The dealer picked up his money and counted it aloud, $210. "I'm all in for the $210." He separated all the money over $210 and it became the side pot.

I was amazed! what the hell had he drawn? I asked myself. All the players called except one who declared it too rich for his blood. There was now two pots, one $2025 and the other $1340. If I had the best hand it was all mine. If I was beat by the dealer, but beat the others, I'd collect the second pot.

The hands were turned over in order and I'd beat all up to the dealer. With a flash of showmanship he flipped over three aces and the joker. He had caught the last two aces and beat me. I collected the second pot. I said nothing although I was suspicious. I had not detected any misconduct, but I was positive he had "cold decked" us. I thanked everyone for a fine game and walked toward the bar, followed by my four partners.

"What the hell happened? asked Bart.

"I had a once in a lifetime hand and got beat, but what bothers me is that I'm sure the dealer cheated. Good card cheats are almost impossible to catch. Here, take the money and split it up. I'm sorry I didn't win the whole thing, there was another $2,000 in the main pot," I said as I waved for the bartender.

"Hell this is not bad for a couple hours of work," said Jim. "Maybe not, but I still feel keyed up," I said as I ordered the drinks.

"If you think that son-of-a-bitch cheated you we ought to kick his ass around the block," said Bart.

"Here's to Johnny, one hell of a poker player," said Jim raising his beer glass.

"You don't know what I felt like when that bastard turned over four aces, you could have knocked me over with a feather. We were lucky in one way, he didn't have enough to cover my bet or we'd have nothing to count," I said.

"If that bastard did cheat he was slick as snot," added Bart.

"What made me suspicious was the way he dealt the cards, just like a pro," I said in disgust. "It's all water under the bridge, at least we escaped with a profit, I'd have hated to lose all your money."

"The one thing that bothered me was how conservative that guy played until the last hand. Makes you wonder, huh?" said Rich.

"Hell's fire, let's forget the damn game and get a little drunk," said Bart.

We finished out the evening with a nice little crew party. A little after midnight we called it quits and passed by operations to see if we were on the board for anything before we hit the sack.

We were never to know whether or not the dealer had cheated, for in two weeks he and his entire crew were lost on the first mission to Formosa.

October was upon us. Fall brought better weather to the subcontinent from the standpoint of flying the Hump. Although we still had the Monsoon rains we preferred that to the oppressive heat of summer. The cooler weather helped us because we were among the first to be assigned to fly cargo into China. The big push was on. Munitions and fuel had to be flown to the Chengtu valley to be stockpiled for our attacks on Formosa. It was necessary to coordinate Formosan attacks with the invasion of the Philippines led by General Douglas MacArthur's forces. It would be the biggest show to date in the long road back across the Pacific.

United States forces had secured Guam, Saipan and Tinian. The Marianas now were ours. The 73rd Bomb Wing was programmed to fly out of Saipan and we prayed for their early arrival. We could certainly use the help.

Tokyo Rose kept us well informed. She let us know that the Imperial Japanese Forces would soon drive us from all of China. There would be no further inhuman attacks upon the innocent people from the land of the rising sun, the most sacred land of lotus and cherry blossoms and Samurais. The Divine Wind would blow. We were unsure of what that meant. However, in the months ahead it was clear the Divine Wind was also known as "Kamikaze."

For the most part Tokyo Rose had the best music program throughout the CBI and Pacific areas. Her propoganda was amusing and humorous. She generally had pretty accurate information, but where she got it was a mystery. It behooved us to listen up and filter out the garbage from the good poop. For instance, if our losses had been as she reported, the whole XX Bomber Command would have been out of business. We did have losses and no loss was really acceptable, but in war it was inevitable. You can't play in the mud without getting dirty. So-called experts had projected our losses to be less, but we had actually lost thirty-seven B-29's to all causes, from 5 June through 26 September 1944. Considering the length of our missions in new and untried bombers which still had bugs, we were doing well, working out and operating under the most deplorable conditions ever known to a military flying unit. However, the B-29 was a fantastic flying machine. It had a stable bombing platform the best gunnery system, was capable of carrying more bombs than any other bomber and was fully pressurized. On top of that it was also the fastest bomber flying, comfortable for the crew and a good airplane to navigate. We thought of the B-29 as the queen of the air.

The 444th Bomb Group had finally installed a new plotting and progress board to keep track of mission advances, and a better communications system was being employed which permitted communication with headquarters from a much greater distance. We could pass weather information as well as emergency messages.

We were scheduled for our first Hump flight on 2 October at 0600 hours. We had to drop off the cargo and return without refueling. It would be a very long day.

The flight went like clockwork from the beginning. Even breakfast was above average. We had a heavy load of bombs. Ten tons of HE and Frags, even though not fused, was cargo to be treated with great respect.

We lifted into the air at 0602. It was cool due to a heavy downpour late the night before.

We climbed slowly to 30,000 feet. Most of the crew were asleep before we got to our assigned altitude, but there wasn't any rest for the men who had to guide and steer the sleek machine. Jim was at the controls, Walt at the engineers panel and I at the

167

navigator's table. Sometimes on long trips I'd be the only one awake. When a heading change was required I'd go to the pilots console and made the correction in the autopilot myself without waking anyone. However, over the mountainous terrain, there had to be someone awake up forward. Even with the radar and absolute altimeter, I needed a little help. I kept busy, especially when everyone else was asleep. It made the time pass faster. Usually the only sound would be the dull roar of the four 2200 horsepower engines.

The view from the top of the world was spectacular. The peaks were covered with snow and the countless valleys and trails could be seen clearly in the distance. We came pretty close to some of the peaks. As we flew I thought of the construction of the Burma and Ledo roads across this vast and forbidding land. The small trails which could be seen were only used by caravans; no help to the war effort. The Himalayas were amazing in that they stretched for 1,500 miles with an average height of over 20,000 feet at the crest lines. It was no wonder all our supplies had to be airlifted into China!

We transited the highest part of our trip and soon the Hump was behind us. We started a slow descent and before long were in sight of the Chengtu valley. Our base at Kwanghan was directly ahead. Most of the crew awakened as we prepared to touch down. We landed and parked. Unloading started immediately. Then we headed for the chow tent by means of the ramp tramp, our old standby the 6X6 truck. After lunch the crew split up to do their part in assisting with the off load. Bart, Jim and I headed for operations to file our flight plan, get a weather briefing and any other pertinent info. The most significant was the intelligence reports of increased Japanese fighter activity over the Hump. We'd have to be more vigilant.

In less than an hour we were unloaded and ready for takeoff to Dudkhundi. Once airborne we climbed like an unburdened eagle and met no enemy aircraft. The trip had been perfect and made us feel more secure.

The next day we were informed we were scheduled to fly three practice missions to get our certification as a "lead crew." From what I'd seen, the lead is as good a place to be as any. Most enemy fighter attacks took place from the nose, but at least you could see them coming. Some said the fighters aim at the lead and hit behind. There was some truth in that, but everyone was vulnerable under attack.

We were fully certified by 10 October and were assigned to lead the first mission to Formosa on 14 October, the day of the Philippine invasion. Our mission was designed to draw off as many Jap aircraft as possible while destroying assigned military targets. I was walking on air when I thought of my new responsibilities as lead navigator of the 444th Bomb Group. It was quite an honor!

Each group received field orders. It was to be a wing max effort, the second largest mission ever flown by the XX Bomber Command. One hundred and thirty planes were launched from the Indian bases to forward bases in China. Of the 130, 103 reached targets in Formosa and dropped over 650 tons of bombs on primary targets. Both HE and incendiaries were employed with excellent results. We'd caught the Japanese defenders completely off guard. Therefore, little fighter opposition rose to challenge us. However, the Japanese flak batteries were fairly accurate and their fire was heavy. There were no enemy fighters claimed, but two B-29's were lost, one to enemy action and the other to operational difficulties. Our first lead mission was good; we'd proved ourselves capable.

The second Formosa mission was a turnaround using the same crews and aircraft and would be flown a day later from the China bases. Such a short rest period had taken its toll on not only the aircraft, but the crews as well. On this mission we lost no aircraft and claimed three destroyed, three probables and nine damaged. We had demolished the airfield at Olayama along with sixty-five of eighty buildings. The best news was that we'd destroyed or severely damaged a total of 116 aircraft on the ground. The Formosa missions were successful for two reasons: Formosa was comparatively close and Japanese defenses were not as formidable as in their home islands. Another plus was that the shorter distance allowed us to carry less fuel and greater bomb loads.

After completing two missions we returned to India. We were burned out and needed a rest. Bart requested and received permission for our crew to stand down and we were given a three day pass to start on the 18th. We could rest up a day before we decided where and what we'd do with the time off.

"We've got three days off, what do you all want to do?" asked Bart.

"Is there enough time to get to California?" Jim said with a big smile.

"I wish to shit there was, but you'll have to settle for something a bit closer," answered Bart.

"As for me, I'm going to catch up on my sleep," announced Roundy drowsily as he stretched his arms.

"So what else is new?" I added, putting in my two cents.

"Not funny," Roundy grumbled.

"I plan to visit an old buddy of mine in the 40th, so I won't be with the rest of you," announced Rich.

"That leaves the three of us. How about a few days in Calcutta?" asked Bart, then he added, "we can get a good hotel and live in style, what do you day?"

"Yeah, we can really live it up," said Jim.

"Count me in. It sounds great," I said.

"Then it's settled. I'll call the Great Eastern Hotel and make reservations for three gentlemen and get transportation while I'm at it. I hear the Great Eastern is the best hotel in the whole city, nothing's too good for us weary warriors!" said Bart as he snatched up his cap and headed for the door.

"Hold it Bart, we'll go with you."

We found a phone and Bart made the necessary arrangements. We'd leave the morning of the 18th. It'd be great to have a break.

"Let's go back and celebrate our good fortune by breaking open a bottle of Canadian Club," suggested Bart.

"Twist our arms," answered Jim.

"Boy, we can really impress the ladies of Calcutta," said Jim as we walked.

"What a dreamer. I haven't seen a woman except the old farm ladies since we arrived in India, at least none I'd drop into bed with," I answered.

"Any port in a storm!" said Bart musically.

"We shall see what we shall see," said Jim.

"We'll have a ball, ladies or no. I hear the food is pretty good at the Chinese and Indian restaurants. Let's face it, it won't have to be much to beat the shit we've been fed since we got over here," I said.

"Just to get away from here'll be heaven, the flying and combat is getting to me," said Jim.

"Come on Jim, next thing you'll be telling us is that you have battle fatigue or some shit like that!" teased Bart. He went on to say, "Here's to our vacation," while opening the bottle of CC.

The morning of the 18th arrived, we were packed and ready to go. Transportation was scheduled to pick us up at 0800, but as it always seems to go when you deal with the natives, the transportation didn't show up until nearly noon. We were frustrated as hell but there was nothing we could do about it.

"Do you think we ought to call the hotel and let them know we'll be a bit late?" I asked.

"Naw, let's just get going. They'll hold our reservation," said Bart confidently.

We left for Calcutta in the old worn out car we were lucky to find. Roads were dirt for the most part and lined with trees resembling parasols. The countryside was flat and dull, the farmer trying to scratch out a living from land that looked over-used and dead. Traffic was backed up and we moved at a snails pace behind ox carts and drivers who took most of the roadway and wouldn't move over no matter how long and hard our driver honked his horn. Cramped in the small car we tried to make the best of a long dirty trip. When we finally saw the outskirts of the city ahead our spirits rose. Calcutta was the biggest city in the province and we were eager to look it over.

We entered the city at 1500 hours and if we'd thought roads leading to Calcutta were jammed, we had another think coming. There were masses of humanity everywhere, civilians of every description as well as uniforms of a number of countries. The Indian people didn't look too clean except for workers in the restaurants and hotel employees. Women for the most part looked a bit tidier than the men and children. They wore their hair tightly combed and covered by a scarf or veil and dressed in soft multi-colored fabrics. The men wore turbans which were usually white, but occasionally you'd see one black or striped. Many men were heavily bearded and their clothing was loose and sloppy.

Calcutta was densely populated. India was one of the most populous countries in the world, and unfortunately, the people flocked to the cities. They came to find work and when it wasn't available, they'd beg for food and sleep in the streets.

Our car pulled up in front of the hotel and we started to unload our bags. The head porter intercepted us, "Sahib, I will tend to your bags and your every need. I am at your service day or night, nothing is beyond my reach," he said in a clear, unmistakably British accent. His laborers ran around jabbering in their native tongue which sounded like so much gibberish to us, but his commands were understood and the porters reacted as he barked them out. He led the way followed by we three and then the porters, what a parade!

"I'll go to the desk and get us registered," announced Bart. We watched as he approached the beautifully paneled reservation desk. The Hotel was obviously old, but first class, the floors were black and white marble in a checkerboard pattern, the walls were elegantly decorated with portraits of former British Viceroys and military leaders. The ceiling was very high, decorated in gold leaf with a cage in the center which turned out to be the "lift". The contrast to the establishments' surrounding area made this magnificent edifice even more impressive.

The hotel was apparently a favorite with the British military brass who sat in the lobby talking in low, subdued voices. They all looked prim and proper in their impeccable uniforms and eyed our entourage with disdain.

As we stood there we realized Bart was having some difficulty with the desk clerk. The commotion at the desk was getting louder so Jim and I walked over to see what the problem was.

"What do you mean we don't have a room? We sure as hell do, I made the reservation myself! Now get your ass in gear and figure out the problem, because we are here to stay?" said Bart with agitation.

"Sahib, the room you had reserved was released to three British officers when you did not arrive at the appointed time," said the desk clerk.

"Like hell! Get the goddamn manager right now before I lose my temper!" Bart barked.

"I am sorry. There is nothing I can do, but I will call the house manager, Sahib," answered the clerk.

I knew there was going to be a flap. Our leader was not one to give up. We were here and we were going to stay! If Bart lost his temper we'd most likely be at war with the British, right here and now. Jim and I tried in vain to cool him down, but it was impossible. Of course we'd back him up.

The manager arrived and took charge of the situation. He was obviously educated and had a flawless manner. "Sahib, we are terribly sorry for this mix up, but we have no available rooms at present. May I arrange accommodation at another establishment?" "No way. We made reservations here and it should be understood that we were late only because of the traffic on the

172

roadway. You people should've realized what we were up against since we're new to your country and had no way of anticipating the delays on the road," said Bart in a calm voice.

"Sahib, please understand, what can I do?"

"You can give me the key to our room and we'll work out the details with the present occupants," said Bart raising his voice.

The manager was in a quandary, he'd never before run into a Bart Ellis and I'm sure he hoped never to again. Reluctantly he handed Bart the key. Bart turned and the head porter sprang to life. He'd been waiting silently. A wave of his hand brought the lackeys to life, they picked up the bags and headed for the staircase as he led us to the lift.

The stuffed shirts stared as if we didn't belong. I was sure the British resented Americans in "their" India. What the hell did they think we were doing here, vacationing?

As we ascended Bart explained, "That son-of-a-bitch at the desk sold our room to three damn limey officers for a lousy pound note. I should've slapped the shit out of him. Well, we'll soon see what we're up against."

The lift jerked to a halt, the head porter slid back the two screen doors and waited for us to alight. In a few seconds the porters arrived and then we walked down the hall toward room number 313. At the door Bart stopped and said, "We're going to sleep in this room come hell or high water, but it may take a bit of persuasion, are you ready?"

"We're with you. Exactly what do you want us to do?" Jim asked.

"We may have to kick some ass, but limey bastards aren't going to steal our vacation. To hell with the god damn British Empire," said Bart as he slipped the key into the lock.

"All six of us looked on while he pushed the door open and entered, Jim and I on his heels. Behind me came the porter who dropped our suitcases and backed from the room. We knew we had a legitimate right to this room and the present occupants would have to go. Just before we entered the room we overheard one of the occupants say, "We did bloody all right getting this room from those bloody Yanks for only a quid, hey, mates?"

"This is bloody British land and we should have first picks," answered one of the others.

The three British officers were drinking from a bottle of scotch and had taken their shirts off. All three were wearing kilts. They froze at the sudden intrusion, "What in the bloody hell do you blokes think you're doing breaking into our room?" asked the big blonde officer.

"Let's get something straight right off, limey. This is our room and unless you feel fit, you'd better get your asses in gear and clear out," said Bart in a commanding voice and tossed a pound note to the leader.

"What do you mean, your room? We are here to stay and no bloody Yank bastard can move us."

"Bullshit! You have your money now get packed limey!" said Bart with a snarl in his voice.

"Look you bloody fucking Yank, don't be calling us limeys, ya hear?" The English officer took a step forward and added, "What the hell do you bloody colonials think you're doing breaking in here as if you own the place? Get out or we'll have to put you out straight away."

The fairhaired mustached officer was about six foot one and 200 pounds. He wasn't about to back off. Bart was his height though a bit lighter, but in his present frame of mind the match was close.

"Listen good, limey, we're here to stay. So get your ass in gear and get your shit out of our room." said Bart as he took another step foward, closely followed by Jim and I.

I knew things were about to happen when the other two squared away and looked over at Jim and me. They quickly sized us up. We were matched up pretty good. As we stood there I recalled an old saying, "The first blow is half of the battle." I looked at my adversary and remarked, "I've never hit a lady." This plus Bart addressing them as limeys got things started. With unexpected speed the three coordinated their attack in a practiced maneuver. The redhead I had just insulted came across the bed and hit me on the cheek, I ducked and fell backward over the bags directly behind me. I wasn't hurt except for my pride. I got to my feet and charged back at my opponent. Soon we were all in a tangled heap, but the battle ups and downs never produced any clear-cut advantage to either side. A real donnybrook, but what the hell, we were having fun, I guess! The struggle continued on the floor, standing, and on the beds. As if by some pre-arranged signal we got to our feet without a word being said, and looked at each other. "I have an idea any minute the military police will be paying us a visit and we'll all spend the night in the hoosegow instead of this damn room." Then we all started to laugh.

"You guys look like hell," said Bart smiling.

"You should see yourselves, mate," said the big blonde, then "How 'bout a spot of gin or whiskey?"

"Sounds like a great idea to me," said Jim as he brushed himself off.

"Canadian Club?" asked Bart as he zipped open his B-4, and offered a full bottle.

"My name is Sean, Lieutenant of the His Majesty's Royal Highland Infantry, my home is near London. This is Michael, he's an Irishman from the north and this David, he's a real Highlander and one of the best with the pipes."

"Glad to make your acquaintance, I'm Bart," he extended his hand as he continued with the introductions. This is Jim and the guy with the blood coming from his nose is Johnny. We're all colonials from Southern California, we fly from a base not too far from here by way of the crow, but by road one hell of a long way. Sorry I came on so strong, but we'd been waiting for this leave for awhile and got worked up when we found you had our room. The damn clerk down stairs was the real problem, but what the hell, we can work something out."

"Blimey, mate, as big as your bloody country is and you're all from Hollywood!" said Sean.

"Not exactly, Southern California is a big place. Johnny here, lives near Hollywood, but Jim and I live 60 to 70 miles from there," Bart tried to explain.

All six of us, slightly battered and bruised, sat around and drank and started to talk of home and family. Little was said of the war. It didn't matter what country a man came from, home is home and nothing can change how he feels about it. We found many things in common including the fact that we were all lieutenants fighting for our countries. Our differences were in our backgrounds, but we had no trouble understanding, except for the accents. Michael had lived in the a house near Belfast which had been occupied by at least five generations of his family. He had coal black hair and a heavy mustache which made him look a bit older than he was, he had deep blue eyes and fair skin and stood about six feet. My worthy adversary was from Edinburgh. He was average height, had flaming red hair and a mustache to match. His acccent was pleasing to my ears and when he laughed it came from his boot straps up, it was very contagious. He told us he was

175

a piper as was his father and his father's father, etc. However, unlike his father, David didn't pipe officially. His father had been killed during World War I leading a slow charge across no-man's land. He'd been awarded the Victoria Cross posthumously. David told us he wouldn't go anywhere without his pipes.

"Tell me, mate, all about the cinema stars. You must see them often," said David with great interest.

"Not really, I don't have any great interest in them," I answered.

"You must be joking, everyone wants to see the beauties," said David with a big grin.

I was on the spot and not wanting to disappoint our new friends, I told a few white lies about some of the movie idols. This satisfied them and we were able to pass on to another subject. Bart and Jim were aware of my false tales and merely listened and smiled.

More drinks were poured and then we decided it was time to hear the pipes. Soon we were marching around the not too large room in single file behind David and the pipes. I loved the haunting sound. To me the pipes symbolized the fighting ability of the 'Ladies from Hell,' better known as the Highlanders. The Scots were known for their ferociousness in hand to hand combat and since he had been my opponent in our short battle, I was convinced. The music went on and we became more inebriated. Finally we decided we had to quit drinking before we were unable to go out on the town. David was in better shape than the rest because he'd been playing, but he didn't miss too much.

Some kind of sleeping arrangements were called for, there were six of us and beds for three. After careful deliberation management solved the problem. They brought up two cots and a mattress and we drew lots and a rotation roster to preclude anyone getting stuck with a bad bed for three nights. It was wall to wall beds and we had to climb over them to get to the bathroom. We didn't care, we were having fun and didn't plan to spend that much time in the sack anyway.

"Johnny, you shouldn't have called me a lady," said David seriously as he put his bag pipes in the case.

"Ah, hell David, I meant no harm. Anyone can see you're not a lady, you just dress like one." Before David could misunderstand, I added hastily, "You know I'm only kidding you, don't you? Anyway, my apologies, I was only reacting to a situation. Bart and Sean should take the blame, they started it, and oh yes, we don't much care to be referred to as bloody fucking colonials, either."

We had a good laugh then moved to get started in the bathroom or we'd be here all night getting ready instead of seeing the night life of Calcutta.

When we were done we took the lift to the lobby and headed for the rotating doors. Just as we reached the doors the skies opened up and the rain came down in sheets, one couldn't see across the street. We did a 180 degree turn for the hotel restaurant. As we walked together all the old Englishmen seated around the room stared in amazement.

The dining room was as ornate as the rest of the hotel, it was fairly clean and really quite elegant. We found a table which would accommodate six battered roughnecks. The table was laid with silver and linen, crystal, and china plates, old and beautiful. We were impressed at not only the table setting, but the service, it was excellent. The food was nicely prepared and tasty if not identifiable. We weren't too hungry so a lot of the food went back, I was sure it didn't go to waste in that land of starvation. We were having a fine time swapping yarns about our military and civilian lives. Sean told us his regiment was leaving soon for Burma and this short holiday was their first and probably their last in India. As we sipped our wine we were getting a little more loaded. No one in the restaurant complained, but we were getting loud and boisterous. We'd decided to liven up the hotel bar and we were sure the old fuddy-duddies would be relieved to see us leave.

We felt we were the ones fighting this war and might die doing it, so we wanted to live it up and have a little fun because all too soon we'd be back to the business of killing. We talked as if we'd been friends for a long time instead of a few hours, especially after the way we met. We learned we were much the same and enjoyed each others company. The teasing about colonials and how the great British Empire was beaten by a handful of raggedy-ass militiamen was the main topic, but never were the words "bloody yank" or "limey" repeated again.

The three days raced by and we were happy we'd found new friends. We knew our friendship wouldn't diminish even if we were from different parts of the world, it would make us richer. Our British friends departed first and there were tears in six pairs of eyes as we shook hands and embraced wishing each other the best of luck on our way to victory. The vacation had ended, it was time to get back to the war.

Darkness was setting in as we entered the gates of Dudkhundi, I had mixed emotions about our leave. It'd been great to be free and meet new friends but the memory of the starving beggars of the streets stayed with me. I suppose it will never change in cities like Calcutta. I have a difficult time understanding people dying by the millions each year while the sacred bovines wander the streets making a mess and a nuisance of themselves.

Rich and Roundy were waiting at the hut, the reunion was like coming home. They wanted to hear of our vacation and both admitted the error of not going with us.

"We have news, orders have been issued awarding the whole crew the Air Medal," said Rich with a big smile.

The award had come as a surprise, we'd given little thought to decorations, but it was nice to know we'd been recognized for a dangerous and tough assignment. Nice to wear something on your uniform besides a set of silver wings. The Air Medal announced you were not a rear echelon troop. Roundy then told us we were scheduled to fly a lead crew training mission in the local area the next day to train new crews. The new crews were to get an orientation to the groups' proceedures.

"I wonder what they expect of us? I hate flying those damn practice missions, we get enough flying in doing the real thing," griped Bart as he threw his B-4 bag on the bed.

"I really can't say, the orders were on the bulletin board at operations, I thought you'd be happy to get back in the cockpit after debauchery for three days," kidded Rich.

"I'm glad we're getting some replacement crews and we all know the training in the states doesn't prepare you for what the real world is all about, but I wish they'd waited a day or so," I said pulling clothing from my bag.

"Not a lot we can do about it, we're a lead crew and it's part of the job," added Jim philosophically.

"Every time we get a new commander we start a new training program, it gets a little boring," said Bart.

"I'm hungry, anyone want to join me?" asked Rich.

"Sure, why not, after all we have to get our stomachs accustomed to the shit we eat here," answered Bart.

"We haven't eaten since this morning, I'm hungry," I said as I followed them out the door.

"How were the girls?" asked Rich as we walked toward the

mess.

"Not worth the chase. We'll give you a run-down after we eat," said Bart.

"Is that a shiner you're wearing?" asked Roundy.

"Could be, we had a bit of a donnybrook our first day," answered Bart.

"I can't wait to hear all the sordid details," said Rich.

We finished dinner and headed for operations to check the board once more. Sure enough we were on as lead, but happily the schedule had been changed and we were to fly the following day. We then headed for the officers club to have a beer and tell the guys about our adventure in Calcutta. We made each event sound as though we had spent our time in heaven. We'd loosened up since we found that we didn't have to fly the next day. It would give us a chance to rest, catch up on a letter or two and get our laundry done.

The next week was spent on training flights helping the replacement crews get ready for combat. It wasn't easy, but very necessary.

We received the word General Lemay had laid on a big training mission to a combat target, a new approach about which we were dubious, but he was the boss. This one was aimed at Rangoon, Burma, a shake down to put together the replacements' training plus new tactics and formation flying for the experienced crews. The mission was scheduled for 3 November, 1944.

The idea of bombing targets 1,500 miles away for practice was ludicrous. How they could call it a training mission with the damn Nip's shooting at us while we're bombing them was a mystery to me. But, as Kipling put it, 'Ours is not to reason why, ours is but to do and die', very apropos I thought.

However, the results were excellent. 4,000 tons of practice bombs rained down on the enemy from 22,000 feet. Only one of 50 aircraft was lost. Now we could get back to the real war.

Briefing for a very important mission took place the next day at 0900 hours. When it was concluded we realized we were to be involved in a very controversial mission. The target was the *King George V* floating dry dock. It had taken the British two years to tow the dry dock to Singapore from Liverpool and set it up. When the Japanese took Singapore they found the dry dock intact. The British still carried it as a ship of the line, though it was in enemy hands, and refused to scuttle it because it had taken them so much effort to get it there. It made no sense, but they had obstinately opposed all plans by the Americans to destroy the dock. The American argument was sound. The Japanese used the dry dock to repair ships to attack the allied forces. The American command had decided to go ahead with the mission and face the wrath of the British later. We of the 58th Bomb Wing had every intention of putting the huge dry dock on the bottom mud of Singapore harbor. It would be like shooting fish in a barrel. The mission was 3,800 miles long and Singapore was well defended by fighters and antiaircraft guns. It took over 8½ hours to get to the target and approximately the same to return, if all went well. Previous experience taught us that many B-29's would be forced to make unscheduled stops on the return for a variety of reasons. Takeoff time was scheduled for 0600 hours which meant we had to get out of the sack around 0300. It was difficult to sleep before any mission, but one with such an early go was a back breaker.

For some unexplained reason I had a bad feeling about that mission. I was very uneasy. Maybe others had similar feelings, but if so, it was not openly expressed.

My uneasiness disappeared as we lifted into the sky and headed for the southeast rendezvous point. Each group had committed 15 aircraft to this raid. When we reached the assigned altitude at the rendezvous only 12 of our planes had made it, about what was expected. We were leading the 444th formation and looking good when we left the rendezvous on the long trip to Singapore. We flew a loose formation sending out signals at predetermined times so followers could home in on us. It was an effective way to keep the group together. We flew at 15,000 feet, climbed to 22,000 feet for the drop some 15 minutes prior to IP. Heavy flak was expected at the IP followed by concentrated fighter attacks all the way to the target, and probably for some time after the drop. After 8 hours we were getting close to our goal. Our formation was tight and ready for the final run. The radar picture was excellent making navigation much easier. We had been flying for some time between Sumatra and Malaya along the length of the Straights of Malacca. Our line of flight had given the enemy early warning. They controlled that entire area; though perhaps not sure of our exact target, they still knew the general area of our intended drop. Our 12 planes were gathered in close, as was the rest of the wing. Five minutes away we turned toward the target. Pops in the tail turret reported the formation was excellent at that point. This was when we were the most vulnerable; evasive action could not be taken until bombs away. Thus far there had been little effective flak. We observed radio silence and therefore were unable to determine how those to the rear were doing except by visual sighting from the tail. Fighter attacks increased and kept Pops too busy to report. We reached the target and the flak became more intense as the fighters waited. The huge bombs could be seen as they hit and sunk the dry dock, we'd done our job. As our bomb bay doors closed there was an explosion and we heard the tear of metal. We had taken a heavy hit on the port side aft of the wing and forward of the tail. Another burst spun me around and wrenched off my flak helmet, warm ooze flowed over my face and neck. Was I dying? It didn't hurt too much, I felt faint but didn't lose consciousness. There was a lot of commotion in the cockpit as I drifted off. Someone asked me to lie down, not to try to stand. I relaxed and felt oddly peaceful. After a few minutes I was cleaned up and a compress bandage applied to my wound. A piece of flak had sliced or burned the skin at the hairline. Blood had flowed over my face and blurred my vision. Blood was everywhere; my charts, instruments, and the entire area were splattered. I had a terrible headache that pulsated and burned, but I was okay and mighty lucky. I wasn't the only casualty, both Bart and Ron Ellis, our left scanner had been hit.

After the flak had hit the plane air leaked making pressurization nerly impossible. Those on the crew who were free stuffed wet paper and rags in the holes. The flak had made a cut on the side of the aircraft as if a king size can opener had been used.

We were fortunate in one way, we were still flying, there had been no great structural damage and none of the three casualties had lethal wounds. Ron had been hit in the upper leg; we were told by members of the crew that the wound appeared to be like an incision made by a surgeon and a tourniquet was applied to keep him from bleeding to death; we hoped fragments had not hit the bone. Bart had sustained a wound in the thigh and lost a lot of blood, a tourniquet was applied along with a pressure bandage. He said he wasn't in much pain and like me refused morphine. Ron, however, was hurting and was given a syringe of the pain killer. My wound looked the worst initially due to the excessive amount of blood around my crew area, but I only felt throbbing in my head and was assured by my nurse, Walt, that I had no permanent damage.

I felt weak and not up to the rigors of the responsibility of getting us home, with reluctance I summoned Roundy forward to take over for me. He was a trained navigator but hadn't worked at it for some months. I was there to assist if he got into trouble and Rich was also there to help. Bart and I laid in the tunnel, with Ron on a cot in the rear. Jim had assumed command of the plane and we returned to Dudkhundi without further mishap. Bart had slipped into the right seat to assist with the checklist, gear and flaps. An ambulance met the plane and we were loaded and whisked away to the hospital.

I was released from the hospital five days later and placed on limited duty. The flight surgeon wanted my eyes checked and warned me about infection. Bart and Ron remained in the hospital. We were lucky, neither had any bone damage. I looked like one of the turbanned locals with my white bandaged head. When I looked back on the feelings I'd had before that mission I wondered about clairvoyance. Was it possible to sense disaster before it struck? Three Purple Hearts and no one crippled was okay by me. We had survived a number of missions, in fact, we were right on top of the missions accomplished board.

The whole crew visited our two hospitalized buddies a day or two after my release from the hospital. Neither had required surgery and were soon released.

The piece of flak which had hit me was found on the floor of the plane; it had also done a job on my instrument panel it was a mess. I still have the jagged piece of metal as a good luck charm.

Our plane and crew was removed from the active mission roster and assigned to ground duties. When the three wounded were together it looked like we'd gone through the civil war. The flight surgeon had grounded us indefinitely. Caution had to be observed in that climate because infection was a real hazard and prevention the best cure.

The wounded had to find things to do to keep busy. In a few days we'd written more letters than in all the time we had been overseas and were in constant search of reading material. Rich and Roundy were called on to work at group headquarters and Jim went to squadron operations. After laying around for the better part of a week I asked the squadron commander for a temporary job and was put in the operations section doing mission planning and helping with photo interpretation of radar scope pictures. I enjoyed the work but missed flying. Once a day I had to report to the medics for a check of my head wound, they redressed it each time. When there was not enough work around operations I went to squadron headquarters and helped to censor mail.

I assisted in planning the next mission which was going to Omura, Japan departing the following day. The field order called for twenty-five aircraft from each of the four groups, the 678th Bomb Squadron input 9 birds and the two other squadrons added 8 apiece. Our group would be dropping incendiary and general purpose bombs from 23,000 feet. The bomb loads would be mixed within each aircraft; the fire bombs did the damage and the general purpose bombs discouraged fire fighting.

A typhoon passed through Japan prior to the arrival of our planes leaving very bad weather conditions over the target area. When informed by radio of the problem, formations were told to bomb secondary targets located at Nanking, China. Unfortunately some of the aircraft did not receive the word and continued to Omura. Of the 96 aircraft on the mission, 29 bombed Omura and the rest hit the Chinese target. The Omura mission was accomplished by the use of radar and results were unobserved. The Omura planes were hit by 65 enemy fighters which pressed their attacks from 100 to 250 yards, 100 attacks within 100 yards. Only two Superforts reported damage. The B-29's claimed 2 fighters destroyed, 2 probables and 12 damaged. One B-29 was downed by flak, four more were lost to other causes. Winds over the target were in excess of 150 MPH. One loss was from the 468th Group, an aircraft which headed for the nearest friendly field rather than crash land in occupied China. They made it to Vladivostok on the Russian coast. Plane and crew were immediately interned, but the crew was released and allowed to escape into Iran some three months later. The Ruskies had what they'd wanted for a long time, a B-29. The name of the plane was General H.H. Arnold Special.

The Reds wasted no time in making copies of the truly fine design. They duplicated every system and called theirs the TU-4, it was a carbon copy of the B-29.

We started planning for the second mission to Omura because no damage estimates had been received from the first. In the nine days we had to get the planes ready much had to be done because the aircraft had been too busy lately for more than minimum maintenance. The mission was to be a maximum effort. I was notified to report to group headquarters to assist the group navigator in planning the mission. Each group was asked to have 29 planes ready to go to the forward bases at least one day before takeoff on 21 November.

All aircraft were airborne in the early morning. It was another daylight raid with the 444th bombing from 23,000 feet using the same type bombs as in the last. The 468th lost one plane on takeoff, killing all but the tail gunner. The 462nd ditched one plane just off the Japanese coast. The Japanese were ready when the bombers reached the Japanese homeland. This mission was attacked by the largest number of enemy fighters to date, things had warmed up. Many of the over 300 attacks were coordinated attacks, some with as many as nine enemy fighters attacking a single bomber. Phosphorus air-to-air bombs were dropped from above the B-29 formations. Forty-six bombings by the Japs were attempted.

The enemy fighter attacks were analyzed later and it was learned a total of 301 individual attacks were made against the B-29's, 33 percent or 100 attacks were from the nose; 27 percent or 80 attacks from the left quarter; 17 percent or 52 attacks from the right quarter and 23 percent or 69 attacks from the tail. It was plain the enemy preferred attacks from the nose due to the great rate of closure. Also the enemy attacks were designed to spread the formation by flying through. On more than one occasion there were head on collisions.

The bombers hit their targets in spite of the fierce defense and 61 bombers dropped 199 tons of bombs on the primary target with good results. For 6 B-29's the enemy paid dearly with 27 fighters lost, 19 damaged and another 24 probables. A second B-29 was flown to Russia on this mission, the odd thing was that it was from the same squadron as the first which had gone to Vladivostok ten days earlier. That squadron had earned a reputation and it wasn't good. All commands were briefed, a crew compelled to fly to Russia in the future was to destroy their aircraft before it was taken by the Russians. All diplomatic pressure for the return of the two B-29's had fallen on deaf ears in the Kremlin. The same old story. In addition to losing their aircraft the crews were treated as prisoners of war. After four months of negotiations the Reds reluctantly released the second crew and they crossed the Iranian frontier. It was February 1945 before the first crew made it to Iran. It was said the Russians were worried about Japan being unhappy with them for cooperating with the United States, things haven't changed too much since then. Most people who flew B-29's agreed we were fighting two enemies in Asia.

19.

Mail call brought good news. Dave Lewis was at Lincoln AAF, Nebraska waiting for crew assignment to a B-29 overseas training unit. His letter was mailed the day he arrived from San Marcos and he was to ship out to Pyote, Texas, better known as "Rattlesnake Bomber Base," in the very near future.

Believe me, Rattlesnake Bomber Base was in the middle of Nowhere, West Texas and was named appropriately. How the Army found these out of the way places to train people has never ceased to amaze me. I suppose the land was much cheaper.

Dave was so happy to have escaped from the training command into B-29's that location made little difference to him. He was like a caged tiger. I looked forward to seeing my rebel buddy again someday. I'd never been closer to any man except my younger brother. Dave and I thought the same thoughts and had figured we could win the damn war if we were together. I remembered when Dave, Hal and I were in the cadet program. We had worked hard to stay together, and ever since we parted there'd been a void in my life. I wondered where Hal was, probably in on the Philippine invasion. Had I not been assigned to a crew of great guys, my life would have been lonely.

I calculated how long it would take Dave to get overseas using the new crews' experience as a gauge. He should leave Pyote at the end of February or the beginning of March. I sure wished he was coming over now, we were due some more replacement crews and aircraft. We never seemed to be able to stay even. With Dave making it into the B-29 program, that made two out of three; not too bad. There have been times since I arrived in India when I questioned the wisdom of wanting this program. The disenchantment was not flying the B-29, but the conditions under which we had to exist to fly it.

We got the word, Lord Louis Mountbatten, British theater commander was most unhappy about our recent sinking of the *King*

George V dry dock at Singapore. He apparently expressed the opinion that the USAAF had sunk a ship of the British Navy, an act he considered a grave error. Rumor had it the British figured to recapture the dry dock some day, but the Japanese would never have allowed it to fall into allied hands intact. We had saved the enemy the trouble. In the three years the Japanese had used the dry dock they repaired hundreds, if not thousands, of war ships for the Imperial Japanese Navy as well as for their Merchant Marine. We realized many American ships had been sunk because that fine repair facility had made it possible for their ships to return to action in a short period of time.

* * *

* * *

"Have you heard the latest news, Johnny? The Brits are now going to award a citation for our heroic sinking of their *King George V* floating dry dock," announced Bart as he hobbled in on his crutches.

"Oh yes, one more bit of information. You, Ron and I are going to get the hero treatment."

"What the hell are you talking about now?"

"Maybe we are not real heroes, but this Saturday we are going to receive two decorations."

"For what?"

"They are going to pin the Purple Heart and Air Medal on our big chests."

* * *

* * *

Saturday morning was beautiful. No rain had fallen all night and the sky was clear and blue for the review. We stood before the group commander as the adjutant read the orders and we were bemedaled. I was thrilled and proud to be recognized by the greatest military force known to man, the United States Army Air Force.

20.

December brought cooler weather, making life more comfortable. It also ushered our crew back to flying status, minus Ron Ellis who had not responded to treatment as well as hoped. He would be out at least two more weeks. Being able to fly was better news than the cooler weather. Nothing is worse than a combat crew being grounded.

A number of gunners were available who for varied reasons were not presently on an established crew. From this pool we had assigned to our crew a staff sergeant from Phoenix, Arizona by the name of John Wright. Sergeant Wright was one of the three survivors of a crash landing a month earlier. He had been thrown clear of the burning B-29 and had landed in a soft muddy field escaping injury. He'd flown two missions since the accident and was eager to be assigned to a crew as a regular member. We, on the other hand, were most happy to have him. He had a fine reputation as a top gunner and armorer. John was our first replacement; we hoped he would be the last. Command tried to keep integral crews. They found this to be more satisfactory. However, we were standardized to the point that flying with a different crew was not difficult.

Our first mission after our layoff was to Mukden, Manchuria on the anniversary of Pearl Harbor. The target was the Manchurian Aircraft Manufacturing Company. A month had passed since our last combat mission and we'd missed four. We were ready to get back into the swing of things and December 7th sounded like a good day to start. We staged out of the forward bases in China. We were to drop HE and incendiary bombs from 22,000 feet in a daylight raid, another ball buster across some of the worst territory in Asia. Most was uncharted and hostile.

We were assigned the group lead which turned out to be the wing lead since our group was designated as first in.

"Johnny, you're going to have your hands full leading the whole

187

wing. If we can get everyone there and back with good bombing results it'll be a hell of a way to celebrate Pearl Harbor Day," said Bart as we left the general briefing.

"We'll give it the old country try," I answered.

"That's about thirteen hours flight time, not including flying the hump going and coming, isn't that right, Johnny?" asked Jim.

"It sure as hell is. Give me a few more minutes to finish my flight plan and I can give you a better guesstimate," I answered as we walked in to mission planning.

"We'll help you if you need it and then go down to the line and check out the bird," said Bart.

"Good show. I can always use the help, but there isn't that much to do. After we get to A-3 tomorrow I can recalculate the winds for the final ETA over target," I said opening my navigator's briefcase and taking out the instruments of the trade. Within a few minutes I found Jim's estimates were very close.

"Let's get a ride to the flight line. The rest of the guys are waiting at the plane," said Bart.

Jim hailed a truck and we threw our stuff aboard and headed for the plane.

"I'm happy we aren't going back to Singapore. That was one long son of a bitch," said Jim in an uncustomary use of swear words.

"I don't expect this one to be a breeze, even though it is a 1,000 miles less to fly," I said.

"The crew should have most of the pre-flight done by the time we get there. Let's get it done ASAP so we can leap off and get up to Kwanghan early," said Bart as we climbed off the tailgate of the truck.

"Let's hope in the next war they have better crew transportation," said Jim.

"What next war? Haven't you heard this is the one to end all wars," I said laughingly.

"That may be true, but I doubt it. The way most people around here talk you'd think we might have to kick the hell out of the Soviets after we take care of Japan," Jim answerd seriously.

"I'd hate to think of a new war before we had a chance to go home for a while," I answered.

"Christ, let's win this one first, you two," said Bart leading the way to the cockpit.

Fifteen minutes later we were ready to leave. "Dudkhundi tower, this is 542 on hardstand seventeen. Request engine start and taxi instructions, over," called Jim from his co-pilot's seat.

"Roger 542. You are cleared to start engines. Call back when ready to taxi, over."

We started engines and were cleared to the runup spot. Check-lists were completed and we again called the tower. "Tower 542 ready for the active, over."

"Roger 542, you are cleared to the active and expedite; we have incoming traffic ten miles. After takeoff turn left at the airport boundary to your initial heading. Happy hunting."

"Thanks for your help, and we'll see you in a couple days," answered Jim as he changed frequencies on the radio.

We made an easy turn at the boundary and started the long climb to clear the peaks of the Himalayas. Things became routine as each crew member completed his after-takeoff check. My work was really just starting. I couldn't relax as most of the others could. As we climbed slowly the conversation on the interphone was loose and easy. I called Bart and asked, "Have you heard the latest from the intel boys?"

"No, what's up?"

"The 73rd on Saipan flew their first mission the end of October down to Truk. The big news, however, was that they hit Tokyo four times in a row up to a couple days ago. They lost ten or eleven B-29's on four missions and got about twenty Nip fighters."

"That's great, how much did they drop?" he asked.

"I don't know, but they had a total of 300 planes on the four missions."

"I'm glad those "Johnny come lately's" are finally helping with this shitty ass war," said Bart in his familiar tone.

"They ran six missions to Truk and Iwo Jima and got full credit for combat missions. Christ, we fly every damn place and we get operational time." I said.

"I hear we may not be going to Japan any longer since it's so much easier for the 73rd. I think they are going to let us take all of southeast Asia as well as China and Manchuria," said Jim.

"Only until they need a balls out mission to Japan. Then we'll be going back; you can bet on it," said Bart.

"No doubt he's right," said Rich as he entered the conversation.

"I thought you were asleep, by now," I said.

"Not funny. I'm not Roundy," answered Rich.

"I heard that. I'm not always asleep," interrupted Roundy.

"I knew you weren't because you're still tuning up the radar. It hasn't been too good as yet," I said.

"I'll have her percolating good real soon," answered Roundy.

"I hope so. We're getting near the big ones and we need all the help we can get," I said.

"Before all you troops bed down back there I have something I'd like to know. What do you want to name this plane, since it's been assigned to us permanently?"

"Most of the permanent planes around the group are getting nice paint jobs. Especially, the naked gals painted on the nose," chimed in the tail gunner Carl in his deep southern drawl.

"The only thing painted on this airplane is the wing, squadron patches and the numbers," added someone else.

"Don't forget the bombs and camels painted on the nose," added Jim.

"True, but we have to settle on a name. I'll put up a bottle of booze for the best name. I have no preference. The things I would like to see painted on the nose is those Jap flags for shooting down a fighter," said Bart.

"Don't forget we have two to put on there now, skipper," said Roy West.

Soon the conversation came to an end and the plane was very quiet except for an occasional radio call. Most of the guys thought this trip fairly routine, but as far as I was concerned it was never routine. The lack of navigational aids and the strong winds as well as the up and down drafts kept me on my toes.

The quiet was broken by a call from Roy. "Hey skipper, I almost forgot our newest member is the artist everyone is getting to paint those great naked gals on their airplanes. We should get priority now."

"Sounds good to me."

"I would be most happy to oblige, sir," answered the new gunner.

In a few minutes it was quiet again and the flight went smoothly on, with only an occasional bump.

"Pilot from nav, over."

"Go, Johnny."

"You can start your descent to 20,000 and come right three

190

degrees to a heading of 037. We're an hour out."

"Good show. Let's get everyone up and alert. I can use all the eyes we have to make sure we don't get in trouble. There are a hell of a lot of planes up here."

We turned on final approach and touched down as predicted. The flight had gone without a hitch. We taxied off the active runway and were guided to our parking spot not far from operations. I was hungry and tired. A bit of food and a bed would suit me fine.

When the aircraft exits were opened we were met by a blast of cold air, which nearly took your breath away. Winter was setting into China. I knew temperatures over Manchuria the following day would be close to 60 degrees below zero.

"I'm going to check things out at ops. Jim, you and John come along. The rest of you get your hut assignments and we'll see you all soon," said Bart.

"I'd like to get as much poop for tomorrow as possible," I answered as I got to the ground. The wind chilled my face and made it tingle.

We stood in front of our plane waiting for transportation and could see a number of planes coming in. It never failed to impress me as I watched the planes in the clear blue skies over Kwanghan.

"Sergeant Smith, be sure the maintenance people take care of the two minor squawks we wrote up in the forms. We want to be 100 percent for tomorrow morning takeoff. We are leading the wing and I'd hate to abort for some grounding item," said Bart to the flight engineer.

"I'll take care of everything. Not to worry, sir."

After we finished at operations and ate dinner we went to our room and found arctic sleeping bags. At least we knew we'd sleep warm that night. The rooms weren't heated and the temperature sometimes dropped below freezing. In what seemed to be a very short time, we were alerted and climbed out of our warm beds into the frigid morning air.

"Christ, I'm so cold I think my balls have retracted like a landing gear," said Bart as he pulled on his flying suit.

"You're not alone. My butt feels like it got the deep freeze the second I got out of the old fart sack," agreed Jim.

None of the rest of us got into the conversation; we were too cold. I had pulled my clothes into the bag and tried to dress that way, no easy chore. "This is nothing like home," I said as I pulled on my boots.

"I'm so cold I think my body could use some anti-freeze," said Rich.

"Don't worry, you'll have all the antifreeze you need in a few minutes when we drink that GI coffee at the mess hall," said Bart as he pulled on his heavy winter flying jacket.

"I'm not sure I'm hungry, but the mess hall is the warmest building around," said Jim.

After a meager breakfast and about a gallon of coffee each, we went for final briefing. The display board in front of the briefing room had a large map showing our intended route to the target far to the north. There was a great deal of information on the big board, radio frequencies, target information, aircraft position assignments, and a host of other bits of pertinent data, much of which was covered orally by the briefing officer. We all copied the information from the board. We wanted no errors on this important mission. The information most significant to me was the number of flak batteries and where they were concentrated. A lot of work had been done by the intelligence and operations people to insure accurate information. We relied on their expertise in utilizing the data from debriefing, crew reports, and photo missions. I knew there was no way to get to the target without flying over the heaviest flak concentrations. The Japs knew where we'd bomb and what route we'd follow to get there. Another item of considerable attention was the number of enemy fighters available. We realized we were in for one hell of a fight. The final briefing item was the weather; it was going to be cold and clear the entire flight. The big show was on.

"It looks like we'll have over a hundred planes on this mission. I'm happy we'll be the first to go in. What surprise there is will be ours," said Bart.

"The most important thing is we'll be bombing visually and maybe the Nips won't have a chance to light their smudge pots before we get there. The planes behind will have to fight the damn thermals," said Jim.

He was right; more than once we had trouble trying to get to the center of a target after the incendiaries started burning. The thermals could reach thousands of feet into the air and toss a B-29 on its back. Not the best way to fly a B-29. Orders to hit the center of burning targets seemed foolish. Bombing the fringes would do more harm, but we didn't call the shots.

192

"I feel like I am briefed out, sometimes I think they have too much info to pass out. I guess they know what they're doing," said Bart as he got up to leave the building.

"I'm just now starting to get thawed out enough to climb into our silver overcast and go to Manchuria," said Jim.

"Silver overcast! Where did you come up with that?" I asked.

"When you fly something as big as a '29, it covers the sky," answered Jim. He had coined a phrase which was to be used often in the future to describe a B-29.

The truck to haul us to our aircraft pulled up. We threw our bags on, climbed up the tailgate and huddled together for warmth. We arrived at our "silver overcast," unloaded our gear and started our final pre-flight inspection followed by the aircraft commander's inspection. Finally, we pulled the props through twenty blades; that is the crew formed a line and each man kept the prop moving as he pushed against the blade. Then the next man in line did the same. A necessary chore prior to each flight to make sure the engine was ready to go.

"I expect the Japs will throw everything they have at us today since it is the anniversary of Pearl Harbor. I am determined to teach them a lesson. Just make sure you keep your eyes open and your heads out of your ass. Be sure to stay as calm as possible when the fighters come in. Now, let's saddle up and go get 'em. Good luck to you all," said Bart and everyone broke for his aircraft entrance point.

We made an interphone check while waiting for the flare signalling the group to start engines.

"There it goes, green. Start number one," ordered Bart and the flight engineer engaged the starter. The noise was deafening as twenty-nine engines barked to life at the same time. One by one each plane got all four props turning.

"Kwanghan tower, this is Pioneer Leader ready for taxi. Over," called Jim.

"Roger Pioneer Leader, stand by."

The dark sky lit up with arching amber flares as each B-29 of the 444th started for the taxi way carefully entering at the proper time to take the right formation spot. It was a beautiful sight to see all the props turning as the aircraft taxied, and thrilling when each aircraft in the long line got to the runup spot and turned 45 degrees to keep from spraying the plane behind with debris as the engines were runup to full power. After a short runup each of the planes in turn taxied on to the active runway and waited for the command to roll. The flare went into the sky and we increased our power to maximum and then released the brakes. The big plane lurched forward picking up speed as it progressed down the runway and lifted gracefully into the sky. All the planes at A-3 were airborne in a short time. We turned toward the north and started our climb. We flew a loose formation to conserve fuel.

"Tail gunner from pilot. Over."

"Go ahead, sir," he responded with his customary drawl.

"How does everything look back there? Can you give me a count?"

"Yes sir, just one moment." There was a short pause as Pops counted the aircraft trailing behind. "Sir, I make 28, over."

"Okay, let me know if anything changes, over."

"I have a feeling the Japs are waiting for us up there." said Jim.

No one answered. I had the same feeling, but didn't have time to worry about it. I had to keep the formation as close to track as possible so that we wouldn't waste time getting to the target thereby conserving fuel. It was no easy task with the lousy maps we had to use; we were trying our best to remap China with the photo recon planes as well as our individual reports. I worked with a chart which had nothing but coordinates and lines to indicate where I wanted to go. We were quite used to this type of chart by now. The only other things on my chart were reporting points and where the IFF changes were to be made. It was my responsibility to get us over the target and Rich's to put the bombs on it. I felt confident that both of us would make out just fine.

"How are we doing?" called Bart after we'd been airborne a few hours.

"Not bad. I just sent our position and progress report by CW to the head shed. It was received and recorded. They wished us luck."

"It will take more than that," he responded.

"Pilot from nav, do you see a tall peak at 2 o'clock about twenty-five miles away?"

"I sure do, Johnny."

"Great, I guess I'm not lost. I figured we'd be abeam of that mountain at 0400Z and twenty miles to the west. In one more hour we'll be passing over Peiping. Radar should be a big help because we'll be close enough to the ocean for good maping. The enemy should have plenty of warning about where we're heading. The only thing of surprise will be which target we have chosen and even that shouldn't be too hard to figure."

"It looks like we're right on course and as far as the Nips are concerned all we can do is our best. Tail gunner remember when we turn to come over the IP report how the formation looks and if there are any stragglers, any questions?" asked Bart.

"Got ya, sir. I'll stay right on top of it."

I was not sure I liked the idea of leading the whole wing. So much responsibility! However I was confident all would go okay, at least up to this point we'd had no problems.

"How's it going Johnny?" asked Bart.

"I'm up to my ass in alligators, but don't worry we're doing just fine. We're ahead of flight plan about ten minutes and we're about two hours from the target. The weather looks damn good. I hope it goes well. I'd hate to waste all this effort!"

The next two hours seemed to fly by. It always did when you were busy. We were now at 22,000 feet and long con-trails were stringing out behind each airplane. It looked like arrows pointing right at us. As we arrived over the IP the formation closed in and we were now a closeknit unit ready for battle. I turned the formation to the proper heading, speed, and altitude. Now all I could do was monitor our track by use of the camera. Rich took over with the bomb sight. It was his ball game now. When the pilot set the plane up on the autopilot then he too could only sit and watch as the bombardier guided it to the drop point using the Norden bombsight. As we progressed toward the target some fifteen miles ahead the formation became very tight. It was our best defense against fighter attacks, but I was never convinced it was best against flak attacks.

"Pilot to crew, there's a large formation of enemy fighters at 12 o'clock high coming in. Get ready."

My heart started to beat faster as the first of the enemy fighters came in firing at us from the nose. It must have been hard for Rich to keep his eye glued to the bomb sight with all the noise and excitement, but he did. I felt the plane lurch as we were hit somewhere behind me, probably 20mm cannon shells, but we seemed to be okay. The CFC gunner controlled the guns with his switching arrangement and he was firing all six .50 caliber machine guns directly ahead. All the other aircraft up front were doing the same. Up to this point we were being attacked only from the front, so the other gunners were just waiting for attacks from another quadrant.

"I got him. I got the son of a bitch. Did you see him come apart?" cried Roy from his upper CFC position.

"Hold it down. Keep calm. It looks like the Japs are lining up for a chow line, so hold your fire until they are in range and good shooting, Roy," said Bart in a very calm voice.

The chow line that he spoke of was a line of fighters on each side of the formation. They'd pull ahead just a little then turn in toward the lead plane simultaneously from each side. The enemy fighters flew just outside of range at the same speed and altitude; then they'd peel into the formation and try to rake the bombers as they came in. They generally broke underneath the bomber formation after they had no further targets. The maneuver was known as a "pursuit curve" in the USAAF and had its dangers for the aggressor. When in the pursuit curve the enemy fighters were exposed to our fire and it was our best chance to bring them down. The fighters pressed their attacks as we continued toward the target. One B-29 was reported spinning toward earth and many fighters were also going down. The fighting was fierce. The enemy fighters abandoned their chow line and were now attacking from all directions. When this happened it was most hectic, but we pressed on toward the target. All of a sudden as if by some unheard order the fighters quit their attacks. We knew all too well what that meant. The flak bursts started to find our altitude and speed.

"Bomb bay doors coming open," announced Rich as we neared the point of release. The plane was flying toward the target, straight and level. This was the most critical time. The flak came at us with determined fury. We were in the midst of the black bursts, which looked harmless enough, but we knew differently. The shock waves of exploding heavy shells rocked our B-29, but she flew on. At times you could even hear the expended fragments falling from bursts high above. It rattled down like pebbles striking metal. The noise from the two forward turrets located just to my right made my ears ring even with my head set on. The spent cartridges as well as the metal links which held the cartridges together were sliding down the metal chutes into the holding box within the turret. It made me think of the first time I'd heard that noise while back in Kansas during training. That seemed like eons ago, but the noise never failed to get my attention.

"Bombs away. Bomb bay doors coming closed," called Rich. This was the signal for the pilots to once again take control of the aircraft. It was always a welcomed call. Now we could get the hell away from the target.

As the call of bombs away was made I took the last of the series of 35mm camera shots using the radar scope. These pictures were of great assistance in determining how effective our bombs were. The flak continued to pelt the formation. Another B-29 fell from the sky. It was sickening. As we turned slowly to the south and away from the target the flak decreased, we knew it was time for the enemy fighters to make their last passes. We knew they'd be running short of ammo and would have to break off, unless they had launched additional fighters to intercept us as we came off the target. We always knew the most determined attacks occurred before bombs away, but nevertheless it was no time to let down your guard.

The flak ceased and as predicted the fighters were at us again. We waited for the tail gunner to give us an accounting, but he still had his hands full.

"I got one, I got one," called our newest gunner John Wright. He had hit a twin engine fighter known as a Nick as he came in from the high position and was trying to split the formation. John had hit the enemy at a range of less than 100 yards and the fighter had disintegrated before his eyes. We had now accounted for two positive kills to our credit. Not bad for one mission.

We turned away from the target and from all accounts things had gone well. We could see flames and smoke rising from the target area. The enemy had also tried to obscure the target by smoke prior to our drops.

"Tail gunner to pilot, over."

"Go Pops, what's up?"

"Sir, I finally got a pretty good count. It looks like all the 444th planes are still with us; can't see the others, but sir, I saw at least three of our planes go down. One other thing, sir. It looks like we kicked their asses down there. Everything is burning."

"I sure hope so. I don't want to go back there again," said Bart without too much emotion.

On the return trip to Kwanghan we were much more relaxed. We landed and refueled and were on our way back to India. After landing at Dudkhundi each crew was ushered into the debriefing room and interrogated by the operation and intelligence people.

When the entire crew reported what they had seen, the picture was complete and we were dismissed. We headed for the tent outside which contained the booze. We were ready, willing and able. Each of us was handed a large shot glass of Four Roses. Some drank slowly and others let it go down in one or two gulps. As for me, I could never drink my whiskey at a gulp. My stomach received the warm fluid and my whole body reacted. I put my glass down on the table and without asking the medic refilled it to the brim. I didn't argue. I just sipped at it and felt my head become light and my tongue get thick. All I needed was a few ounces of whiskey being as tired as I was and I'd be on my ass.

Our report to the debriefers had been very accurate. We had given enemy aircraft markings: how they attacked; where they attacked; what color the flak was; as well as how much and how accurate. We also got confirmation of our two enemy fighters shot down. Occasionally, more than one gunner would claim the same fighter as a kill. This made confirmation difficult and then the kill was divided. In the case of the two that we'd got they were confirmed kills by our gunners and we received full credit. Now we would be able to paint four Japanese flags on our new plane.

Another round of drinks was poured to those who could hold it. I wasn't one of them. I'd had it. All I wanted to do was to get to my sack and lay on it for a couple days.

21.

Twelve hours of sleep was what it took to get me back to the real world. I pulled the mosquito netting back and put my feet on the floor. I was the first to wake, but I figured if I'd had enough sleep, so had the others. I made no attempt to be quiet as I prepared to head for the showers. Soon the other four were awake and not all of them happy about it.

"I'm as hungry as a Bengal tiger! Get your asses in gear and lets get to chow," I said as I walked from the hut not letting any of them have a crack at me.

As I shaved they came into the shower room. Only Jim was fully awake. The others looked as though twelve hours asleep wasn't enough.

"Why so happy? I'm still half asleep," said Bart as he yawned and placed his shaving kit next to mine.

"Christ, what you guys need is a good shower and a couple drinks to put you back on your feet," I answered.

"Maybe you're right. I never sleep that long, but for some reason I've been tired lately," said Bart.

"That was one hell of a mission! After all we were gone for three days and we didn't get that much rest," said Rich as he lathered up.

"I'm kind of anxious to talk to some of the other guys and see how they made out," said Bart.

The meal was pretty good for a change, even though it was lamb. I was getting to hate lamb with a passion, but you had to eat. I was sure if it weren't for the jars of peanut butter my mother kept sending I would turn into a lamb.

After dinner we headed for the operations building to see the results of the mission. A lot of people were milling around looking at the strike photos and going over the results. The overall results were rated as good. Our group's results were rated excellent. We hit the Mukden Airplane Manufacturing Company and the adjacent arsenal with twenty-one planes, dropping ninety-eight incendiary and 194 500 pound GP's on target. For the entire wing the final results had 108 B-29's dropping in excess of 300 tons. We had lost 7 B-29's, two to ramming and four others to ordinary action. The seventh plane hit a mountain while returning. We had shot down a total of twenty enemy fighters with ten probables and thirty damaged. The enemy had used eighty-five fighter interceptors and had flown 185 coordinated attacks. One other B-29 had survived a ramming and had returned to its forward base in China without further problems. One of the rammings had occurred when a twin engine Nick was hit by fire as he approached the tail of a B-29. The Jap went out of control and sheared off the tail of another B-29 as he tried to recover. The Nick broke up in mid-air and the B-29 went out of control and fell to earth. Another ramming occurred as a Tony attacked head-on from the front of a B-29 and was hit by the bomber's guns and again went out of control and rammed the B-29 in the nose destroying both aircraft. A third ramming happened as a Zeke attacked a formation from the two o'clock position and was hit by the forward guns of the B-29 at 300 yards, the enemy pilot bailed out and his plane was chewed up by the B-29's props, it fell in pieces, but the B-29 escaped undamaged.

The B-29 that hit the mountain was from the 468th Group and all aboard perished. Another of the 468th's aircraft had crash landed at Pengshan, China.

The loss of a plane and crew due to navigation error bothered me, even though we'd lost none from our group. I prayed I'd never hear of another plane hitting a mountain, especially if I were the lead navigator.

We were fortunate, but more than that we had a damn good formation and a good smooth lead. It was the reason we returned without a loss, the seven losses were all from the other three groups. The crew was real up-beat with two confirmed victories. Our ace gunners had come through. We expected Roy West to get his share, but our newest gunner getting a kill was a big plus. We invited all the enlisted crew members and our two newly assigned ground crew members to a small celebration at our quarters. Master Sergeant Ben Duncan, crew chief and Staff Sergeant Robert Miller his assistant made our family fourteen since we still considered our wounded gunner as part of the crew. We all had a good time; a couple of the guys got a little drunk. We'd been a close knit crew from the start. During the party we decided to pick a name for our airplane. It had to be done before the heavy drinking started. A lot of names were proposed. Some were too long and others didn't fit. There was one name I liked best, not because I'd thought of it, but because it fit. I had asked Pops to submit the name since he didn't have an idea of his own. I didn't want to be the winner; it would be best for one of the enlisted guys to win. The name did win, our new B-29 was officially christened *Lucky Lady*.

Lucky Lady had been a good airplane to us. We had flown her on the last four or five missions and felt she was lucky. We felt comfortable flying her. When we had been designated a lead crew and had the choice of other planes we felt so good about *Lucky Lady* we kept her even though newer aircraft had been assigned the squadron.

The wheels were set in motion, we all planned to watch the artist do his work on our "silver overcast." He had one day to complete his task, we'd been scheduled for another combat mission. John was under the gun and he knew it. It made him nervous, but he was determined to get the job done, at least most of it before the Bangkok mission.

We were one of eleven planes from the 444th Group to be scheduled, but because of scheduling problems we were cancelled. I was disappointed for one reason. I considered Bangkok one of our easiest missions. It was designated as a training mission and for four new crews it would be their first. It brought memories back of how I felt on my first mission. Anticipation, excitement, fright and eagerness could best describe the feeling.

The Bangkok mission produced good results. General purpose bombs were dropped from 20,000 feet. You generally think of a training mission as one which could be accomplished without losses; however, this mission produced one of the most devastating losses our wing had suffered. The 40th Bomb Group arrived in the target area and found the target completely covered by clouds. The decision was made to hit the secondary, Rangoon, which was reported as clear. Tragedy struck during the bomb run to the target. One plane in the center of the formation was carrying a mixed load of GP and incendiary bombs and without warning exploded. It disintegrated and the explosion took with it three more B-29's flying close by. In addition to the four planes lost they sustained damage to seven more. There was no plausible reason for the accident, yet it happened. Of the thirteen planes the 40th had on the mission only two managed to return to home station, the others were scattered along the route at emergency landing fields. It was a terrible blow to the 40th and a very sad day for all of the 58th Bomb Wing. Losing planes was a fact of life. At times you controlled your destiny, but in most cases fate dealt the cards. The loss of the four planes just prior to bombs away meant all those good men died in vain.

Between 18 and 21 December the XX Bomber Command had ordered three widely separated missions. They were Hankow, China on the 18th; Omura, Japan on the 19th; and Mukden, Manchuria on the 21st. The missions were bunched up so one could only speculate that there'd be a stand down for Christmas.

We flipped a coin with Pappy Karns and his crew to determine who'd fly which mission as lead. We were the only lead crews and we had to fly three missions. One of us would have to fly two. It was decided the loser of the toss would fly the first mission and the last. The winner would fly the second. We won the toss and elected to fly the second mission to Omura. The catch would be if they ran into trouble and could not fly one or both missions; then an alternate plan would have to be devised.

"We won the toss gang," reported Bart to the rest of the crew as he returned from base operations. "If some unforseen event screws up our plan we'll have to drop back ten yards and punt."

"Not a bad deal. The last Mukden mission was a piss cutter," said Jim as he sat up on his bunk.

"As far as I'm concerned it's better that they're flying two missions. They need it more because they're behind us in mission accomplishment," I said.

"I nearly froze my buns off on our last trip to China and those poor bastards are going to have to stage out of there to meet the mission requirements, that's a shitty deal!" said Bart.

"Yeah, they got screwed, but better them than us. Five days in the frozen Chengtu valley would be too much," said Rich.

"One of these days command is going to make a firm policy of how many missions it takes to complete a tour. Then we'll be sorry we didn't fly these two. We've already missed a month of flying because of our wounded," added Roundy.

"That's easy for you to say, you can sleep most of the time, put something in the pot then make comments. We've never refused to fly, all we try to do is not volunteer," I said.

"That's bullshit. Who are you trying to kid? I know you better than that. If they needed a navigator for a special mission, you'd volunteer," said Bart.

"Why don't we forget about the whole thing for now and go up to the club and sip a brew. Any volunteers?" asked Jim.

It was raining cats and dogs. Raincoats were in order. We all got to our feet, put on our raincoats and ran for the jeep. We were happy with the prospect of a couple days off. Letter writing, laundry, reading and getting *Lucky Lady*'s paint job finished could be accomplished.

"Our squadron insignia is the best I've ever seen. It's so descriptive. I wonder who did the original art work?" asked Jim as we drank our first beer.

The squadron insignia of the 678th Bombardment Squadron was unique. There was a round field of blue with a cobra spitting a bomb superimposed over a black ace of spades. Our other two squadrons were equally proud of their insignias, but we were sure ours was best.

We decided since we hadn't made one of the Omura missions of the past it'd be a good idea to sit down with the intelligence people to get as much advanced information as possible. We figured it to be a tough mission and a long one. We were to lead and it was important for us to be briefed on all facets even before the general briefing. There were mosaic maps as well as reconnaissance photos. I liked the photos. They were actual pictures taken of the target area. The study included routes in and out as well as known flak batteries and airdromes.

The Hankow mission departed early the next morning for the forward base. Our planes were to arrive in China after the Hankow planes were airborne. I hoped the timing would be good otherwise it would really be a mess at A-3. The Hankow mission didn't figure to be a tough one. It was a mission that included the forces of the Fourteenth Air Force. It was the first mission planned with outside air units and the last in China. They were to attack the dock area to destroy the facilities as well as any enemy ships in the harbor.

Our mission with thirty-nine B-29's left A-3 for Omura. However, because of poor weather conditions over the target, thirteen bombers went to the secondary target of Shanghai harbor. The main force dropped by radar through the overcast and results were unobserved. I knew we were right on target from the position of the formation. We lost two Superforts to operational accidents, none due to combat. Our forces claimed five enemy fighters destroyed, four probables and twelve damaged.

The last mission of the year was the Mukden mission. We knew from experience it was going to be rough.

"I hope all goes well for Pappy Karns and his crew. Somehow, I feel a little guilty," I said as we rose on the morning of the 21st.

"If you had your way we would be flying the mission instead of them. They're off and running now; let's go up to group and see what news there is. Hankow was a milk run," said Bart as he stretched and sat up.

"I guess you're right. We both had the same odds and like you say they'll get two missions out of the way. It's just that we know how that damn Manchuria is: guns freezing up and a shitpot of fighters and flak," I said as I got out of bed.

The sun was shining after a day and night of heavy rain. It looked like it was going to be one of those rare beautiful days we'd seen so few of since our arrival. We headed for the bath house to clean up and when we returned the other three were still in the sack. We gave them a piss call and left for chow.

"One of these days they're going to take this jeep away from us. Up to now no one has bothered to check on it. I guess the motorpool officer thinks we're still authorized transportation. I'm not going to tell him otherwise," said Bart as he climbed behind the wheel.

"It's one of the few pluses that happens rarely in the military. So relax and enjoy it," I said.

The beautiful weather of thirty minutes before turned threatening and it started to rain as we drove to the dining hall. "Maybe we had better go back and get the others. They'll really be pissed off if we make them walk to chow," said Bart as he turned the jeep around and headed back to the hut.

"Lot of good it did for you to pick us up. We're all getting wet in this damn jeep," announced Roundy.

"You would bitch if you were hung with a new rope. We came back for you so you wouldn't have to walk," said Bart as he struggled to see through the windshield.

"Let's make a run for it," said Jim the minute the jeep stopped.

We got inside and it was warm and dry and we were all hungry. "Oh, my favorite: shit on a shingle," said Roundy.

"There's no accounting for taste. It looks like dog food to me," barked Bart.

We had no choice, it was SOS or nothing. We sat down and washed it down with hot coffee. "Is everyone finished or would you like seconds, fat boy?" asked Bart sarcastically.

"We were finished before we walked into this kennel," said Jim as he feigned nausea.

The rain abated and we decided to make a run for the jeep. Then we drove the short distance to the Group Operations Center.

"What's the big rush?" asked the duty officer.

"We didn't need another bath, major," answered Bart.

"What's on your mind?" asked the major.

"Well, sir, we'd like to see what's happening on the Mukden raid," answered Bart.

"Let's go into the comm center and see what they can tell us. The main force is about fifteen minutes from the target right now. We should have more information within the hour," said Major Barnes. "You can hang around here if you like or call me in an hour," he added.

"We'll wait. Let's go down the hall and get a cup of coffee," Bart said as he waved his arm at us.

"Fine, if you don't mind having the enamel on your teeth peel off," said the major with a smile.

"I think I'll walk over to the club; anyone want to go with me?" asked Rich.

"Yeah, I'll come," answered Roundy.

They walked toward the door and as Rich reached the door he turned and said, "If you get any word before we get back, call us, okay?"

"No sweat, as soon as we get the poop from the group we'll give you a call," answered Bart.

The hour ran to two; finally the major walked into the coffee room and said, "The mission is complete. Forty-nine B-29's took part in the mission, but because of the bad weather only nineteen hit the primary and results would have to be assessed later. We had a total of ten birds from the 444th."

"What about losses?" asked Bart.

"Don't know. We may not get that information until they get back. The planes were so scattered around they had trouble counting noses," said the major.

"We understand. Thanks for your trouble, sir," said Bart.

We all agreed it was easier to fly the missions than to sweat out the results. We climbed into the jeep and drove to the club. We found Rich and Roundy and gave what information we had, and decided to wash the taste out of our mouths caused by the battery acid they called coffee at group.

"We still don't know about Karns, do we?" asked Rich.

"Why don't we quit worrying about Karns. We all take our

chances. After all we didn't sentence him to death, you know!"
said Bart in a disgusted voice.

Christmas morning 1944 was unlike most days of late. The sun
was out and it wasn't raining. Today we'd have the traditional
Christmas meal of turkey with all the trimmings. As our table
guests we had Pappy Karns and his officers. We'd decided there
would be no talk of the mission before or during the meal. We
wanted nothing to spoil it.

"It was a disaster, as far as I was concerned. We lost two planes,
one to ramming and another to aerial bombing. As for our crew,
we had one casualty. One of our gunners was mortally wounded.
He was hit by fragments from either flak or aerial bombs. However, the mission to Hankow was a piece of cake, so everything
works out. Now we have two more missions behind us, that much
closer to getting out of here, but we'll have to get a new gunner,"
said Pappy.

We had a lot to be thankful for; we'd survived the first year
with only a few scars. It'd been tough at times, but we gained
experience and it had made us a better crew. It gave us the feeling
of confidence for what lay ahead. There have been so many replacements since we left Kansas it was hard to count who from
the original crews were left. We decided not to pursue those
thoughts; better to think of pleasant things.

Late that evening we left for our hut. The sky was clear and
a million stars shined from above. I felt very close to my loved
ones. I was sure the others did, too. No one talked of home for
fear of making their homesickness worse.

Training continued until the new year. If we hadn't been able
to fly we would've gone stir crazy. There was a bunch of new
replacements that had to be trained to combat standards. No book
could teach them the ways of the real war.

The month of December saw an end to the bombing of targets
in China and Manchuria. The Omura mission of 19 December
proved to be the next to the last mission the XX Bomber Command
would fly against targets in Japan proper.

"Good news!" said Bart as he returned from a staff meeting at
group headquarters. "Henceforth, we'll only fly the Hump to stage
for missions to Formosa. The new straegy is the 73rd Wing on
Saipan and the 313th Wing newly located on Tinian will concentrate on bombing Japan and the 58th Wing will take care of all
of southeast Asia as well as Formosa. This calls for a drink," he
said as he threw his hat on his bunk and reached for the bottle

of "CC" on the shelf.

"Is that all the poop from group?" asked Jim.

"Yup. Maybe we can get this war over some day soon," said Bart.

"That reminds me of what that lying recruiter told me when I joined the Army to win the war. He said 'sign here and you should be happy to get in now, because the war is going to end in less than 18 months.' That son-of-a-bitch is probably still a recruiter in Los Angeles and I'm here in the anus of the world," I said as I rose to help Bart drink some whiskey.

"Christ, what brought that on?" asked Bart.

"I was just thinking about him when you said we will get the war over some day. I should sue the bastard for passing false information or something," I said.

"Forget it, if we knew then what we know now half of the guys in this outfit would be draft dodgers or over the hill," said Bart.

"I sure am tired of 1944. Maybe 1945 will be better. At least it can't be any worse. It seems like we've been in too many SNAFU situations since we got here," said Jim as he picked up his cup to have a drink.

"The war seems to be going our way. I wouldn't be surprised if we ended it in a year or two," said Rich.

"Let's hope it doesn't go two more years, we've been at it for three now. The Japs are far from being beaten, even if the war is going better. They'll make us pay in blood for every inch they give up, and if we have to invade Japan, it's claimed we could sustain a million casualties," said Bart seriously.

"I agree. They are tough customers and we know they don't give up easily. We'll have to annihilate them, I fear," I said.

"Let's talk about something more pleasant. What's up for the big New Year's party?" asked Jim.

"All I know is the party will be at the club and there'll be a hell of a lot of drinking and a hell of a lot of headaches to start 1945," said Bart as he drank from his cup.

"Do we have any New Year's resolutions to make?" I asked.

"Not as far as I'm concerned. I hate to break them so why make them?" said Bart.

"Well, it may sound corny, but my resolution is for all of us here to survive. Whether the war ends next year or not we should complete our tour in the not too distant future. Wouldn't it be great for us all to return to the States together?" I said as I raised my drink to a toast.

207

22.

1945 arrived. How time flies when you're having fun! World War II was entering its final stages from all indications. The air war in Europe had been won and the land war was now in its final stages. The Battle of the Bulge had slowed momentum, but not for long. The Pacific war had established a true offensive nature. Our forces were on the move everywhere, no more defensive battles, we were carrying the war to the enemy. The move toward Japan from island to island was going well and covering hundreds of miles with each leap. Japan on the other hand had lost the initiative and was now on the defensive which meant we had brought the war to their sacred homeland. They would feel the sting of war just as those countries who had been overrun by the men of Nippon had.

Along the Soviet-Manchurian border a truce of convenience had been arranged between Moscow and Tokyo, but the Japanese did not trust the Soviets; therefore, they had to maintain a large force near the frontier. The allies had completed land communication between Burma and China. As for the 444th Bomb Group as well as the other groups of the 58th Bomb Wing, it was war as usual. We were told there would be a step up in operations. We could expect to fly more missions per crew. The first mission of 1945 was scheduled and we were notified to report for briefing on New Year's Day.

"We are lead on this mission," said Bart as he returned to his seat in the briefing room. He had checked the status board as the multitude of crew members were still entering the large room. We had arrived early and waited for the briefing to commence. There was considerable noise in the hall until the group commander and his staff entered.

"Attenshun!" called someone from the front of the room. Colonel Baker and his staff found seats in the front row.

"Seats gentlemen," said the colonel as he walked to the podium.

208

"I've a few words to pass on before you start your briefing. First, I want to wish all of you a happy and victorious New Year. Word has been received through channels from XX Bomber Command indicating we won't be involved with the air war of Japan, China, or Manchuria any longer. We have plenty of work to take care of in this theater. The XXI Bomber Command will handle Japan. I'm sure you've already heard this news through the rumor mill, but it's official now. I want to leave you men with this thought. You have pioneered the combat testing of the B-29. It was done with skill and distinction. The B-29 has been successfully flown and maintained in the maximum extremes of operating temperatures. Operations have truly been global in scope from Singapore to the frozen reaches of Manchuria and distant Japan. I'm proud you made me part of it. Thank you and God bless you," the colonel turned and walked from the stage to his seat. The briefing officer took his long pointer and walked to the first of the large displays on the huge board.

"Gentlemen, as you can see, these photos show your target and the surrounding area. We'll be going in at 20,000 feet and this mosaic was taken from that altitude. The primary target tomorrow will be the train marshalling yards." He pointed to a spot on the map, "We feel if this mission is successful we'll not have to return to Bangkok for a while, at least not until the Nips rebuild, and I'm sure they will. We'll carry 1,000 pound bombs and will be the second group of the wing to cross the target. The 40th will be just ahead with the 462nd and 468th following closely. Time over target will be 1300 hours. Colonel Baker will be the command pilot and will be with Lieutenant Ellis. The lead navigator is Lieutenant Lea. He has requested all navigators report to the plotting room immediately after this briefing concludes. Now, I'll turn the briefing over to the intel officer. Good hunting and good luck."

The briefing continued with information on the defenses, escape and evasion and all other matters concerning the mission. Finally, the main briefing ended and all the navigators headed for the plotting room. I was especially interested in the new men and what we could do to help them.

"These 2,300 hundred mile missions seem to be short because they only take ten or eleven hours. It just goes to show you how we can get brainwashed. In Europe four or five hour missions are considered long," I said as I stuffed my briefing material into the briefcase.

"I'll take all the Bangkok and Rangoon missions they hand out," said Jim.

"We'll have to give the old man a good show since I don't think he's been to Bangkok," said Bart as we left the room.

"Do you guys want to wait for me? I have a little pitch to make to the navigators. Why don't you go over to the PX and then come back. Pick up some razor blades too, please."

"Okay, we'll be back in about fifteen minutes," said Bart.

* * *

"Hi guys, why don't we all gather around this map on the wall and I'll show you a couple details I picked up. Then if you've any more work to do on your logs and charts you can take care of it after. Remember we are scheduled for a 0700 takeoff with time over the target of 1300. Any questions?" I asked.

I checked all the flight plans to be sure there were no discrepancies and ended the short session.

"I'll see you all at 0500 for the final weather briefing and if the weather changes significantly we'll have time to adjust our flight plan. See you then," I said as I gathered up my maps and charts and stuffed them into my navigator's briefcase.

Just as I got to the door, Bart pulled up in the jeep, but before we could leave, a sergeant intercepted us, saluted Bart and said, "Sir, the squadron commander would like to see you right away." He saluted, turned and without waiting for an answer departed.

"What the hell's that all about?" I asked.

"Beats the shit out of me. He's probably going to take our wheels away from us. Well, it was good while it lasted," Bart said as he put the jeep in gear. Jim and I hung on to keep from being thrown out. "Maybe I had better take you two back to the hut, then go see Mitchell," said Bart.

"I'll go with you for moral support," said Jim.

"Okay, if you like. Bob is okay, he won't eat my ass out too bad. We'll be back ASAP."

"Okay, good luck," I said as I climbed out of the jeep and headed for the hut.

"Hey, Johnny, when we get back let's go down to the line and see how the *Lady* looks and do a little cleaning up. After we see

210

the boss I'll go by and tell the enlisted troops, see ya," said Bart as the dust blew up behind the jeep.

Fifteen minutes later they were back. I heard the screech of the jeep's tires as it skidded to a stop in front of the hut. Bart and Jim came in with big grins on their faces.

"What's up? You two look like the cat that ate the canary," I said as I met them at the door.

"You're never going to believe this!" said Bart.

"Damn it to hell, what the hell's going on?" I asked anxiously.

"Hold your pants on and give me a chance. Jim and I went to see Colonel Mitchell thinking we were going to lose the jeep, but it wasn't the jeep he wanted. In fact nothing was said about the jeep. The news is we're going on R & R. And believe it or not we're heading for Australia on the first of February for two weeks. Now, how's that for news?" asked Bart.

"The only better news I could imagine would be the news that the war was over and we're going home," said Rich as he jumped off his bunk.

"Hot damn, I've always wanted to go down under. And you say nothing was said about the jeep?" I asked.

"It beats the hell out of me how we've gotten away with it, but let's just enjoy it," said Bart.

"The damn motorpool has so many vehicles they probably don't know where half of them are," said Jim.

"Tell us more about the details of the rest leave. It's really hard to believe, but those guys in the 8th Air Force in Europe get R & R's before they have been in combat eight months, so why not us?" said Rich. "I know because my brother is in the 8th Air Force."

The only one that wasn't jumping for joy was Roundy. He was still lying on his sack as if he were more interested in sack time than Australia.

Bart explained the details, "Apparently we've a house in Sydney leased for our squadron and two crews will rotate through each two weeks. In fact they've got two houses one for us and one for the enlisted troops, not bad huh?"

"It'll be great to see real people instead of these blasted Indians. I hear the Aussies are like Americans or at least as friendly. The maintenance guys who stopped in Australia before they got here said the gals are hungry for Americans. And, I hear their beer is damn good," said Jim.

"I hope nothing goes wrong," said Roundy as he finally raised up on his elbow.

"I'm surprised to see that you would be more interested in R & R than lying on your ass all day," Bart said sarcastically.

"The seasons down there are just opposite from the northern hemisphere; it'll be August for us. It's about the same latitude as Los Angeles. It should be great beach weather for us Californians," I said.

For some reason my remarks got Roundy a bit upset. "You guys are always giving me a bad time about not being a Californian. Shit, I'm glad I'm from Illinois," Roundy said in a hurt voice.

"Relax, we'll take you along anyway," said Bart with a smile.

"I'll bet a guy could get in nice trouble in Australia with all those unattended women there," said Jim with relish.

"I hear they're all looking for American husbands," I added.

"Just be hard to get. I hear the beaches are like southern California. Maybe even better. Sorry Roundy," said Jim.

"Everyone knows they have no beaches in southern Illinois," said Bart waiting to see if Roundy would rise to the bait. Instead he lay back down and sulked.

"I can hardly wait. Christ, it's a whole month away," I said.

"Roundy get your ass out of the sack, we're all going down to the line and work on the bird. I'll give you ten minutes to get ready and then we're going to get some chow," said Bart.

We ate then found the plane was being washed. We decided to go back to the hut and wait an hour before returning. I got off a letter or two while we were waiting. As I wrote my folks I thought of how ridiculous it was to put "somewhere in India" on my letter as a location. I was sure my father knew approximately where we were. Even the papers at home used a date line of Calcutta. Oh well, what's the difference? We all had to pull the mail censoring detail and knew how some of the guys wrote. Many told of classified events and put down their exact location, contrary to orders. Their letters looked like paper doll cut outs after we censored them. Some of the letters had torrid details of events or illusions from some fantasy love affair. It made me blush at times. Those letters were personal and were not to be discussed with anyone. Everyone to their own taste, I guess.

The next morning was dry and cool. The group had twelve planes airborne at the appointed time. The mission thus far had gone well. After we leveled at our enroute altitude Bart allowed Colonel Baker to ride in the pilot's seat. The colonel was a fine pilot, but had little time to fly. I understood he was in aviation most of his life and was somewhat of a pioneer. Jim kept a close eye on him to be sure he followed all procedures. When we were well away from any populated areas the gunners were allowed to test their guns, which was a necessary precaution prior to entering a combat area. I always made a practice of sitting on my flak suit instead of trying to work with the armor hanging from my shoulders. I'd wear my flak helmet, however. I felt the family jewels had to be protected, but the armor wouldn't stop all the flak.

The formation directly ahead could be seen as we turned from the IP toward the target. Flak was puffing about, especially in front of us. As the 40th dropped their bombs smoke rose rapidly and I was sure the two groups right behind us would find part of the target obscured. We had a tight formation as we neared our release point. Pops reported as we turned from the target that huge fires were burning and we had clobbererd the marshalling yards and surrounding buildings. Each airplane had dropped eight 1,000 pound bombs. The entire wing with forty-nine planes had put 179 tons on the primary target. No B-29's were lost and ineffective enemy fighter attacks produced only one probable and one damaged enemy fighter. It was a good feeling to get everyone home without a loss. The mission was rated as excellent. The target was completely destroyed.

The next mission was to be the last flown to Japan by the XX Bomber Command. We were not scheduled; we'd lost an engine on the last mission when only thirty minutes from Dudkhundi. At first it appeared the engine could be changed prior to the mission to Japan, but that was not the case. The engine which we had to shut down was a high time engine and would have had to be replaced soon in any event.

We were scheduled in advance to lead the mission to Formosa set for 9 January. We decided to see if we could help our ground crew with the engine change. We had little to do and it would keep us busy. We knew they'd appreciate the help. After the engine was changed we took *Lucky Lady* for a test hop and all was in order. We still had a few days before we were to head for A-3.

Since we had so much time we all went to group intelligence and decided to do some homework on the target. As Jim and Bart were talking to the intel officer I saw a folder lying on one of the desks. The papers indicated it was a report for the group commander and his staff. The first thing that caught my eye was the column labeled 58th Bomb Wing losses as of 31 December 1944. As I read Bart came over to where I was standing and said, "What is so interesting?"

I pointed to the sheet of paper and hoped Jim would keep the intel officer busy for a minute or two. The rough draft listed losses of B-29's to combat related incidents as follows:

June thru September, 1944, 37 lost on 9 missions. October thru December, 1944, 35 lost on 14 missions. Totals 72, B-29's lost flying 23 missions.

I could not see the total losses for cargo and training missions, but it listed the different targets and a figure of 4577 tons of bombs on primary targets. Another statistic from the sheet which interested me was the accounting of enemy aircraft lost. They were listed as confirmed; probables; and damaged. The figures listed were 139/92/214.

"Gentlemen, those are classified papers," the lieutenant said as he came over and closed the folder.

"We have security clearances and we were part of those figures so what's the big deal?" asked Bart.

"Well, I was told they were for the old man's eyes only. A need to know was stipulated."

"We have a need to know. After all, we are a lead crew and it's important to know intelligence, or we wouldn't be here now," explained Bart.

"I'm sorry. If group wants you to know, they can tell you," said the intel officer.

"Come on guys, we have no more business here," said Bart as he headed for the door.

"What the hell were you guys looking at?" asked Jim as we walked to the jeep.

"They're making a report to group about aircraft losses both enemy and friendly and we saw most of it before he caught us," explained Bart.

"Kind of scares you, doesn't it," I said.

"Compared to what? Who knows what's good or bad when we are doing something that was supposed to be impossible. What pisses me off is some shave-tail telling us we have no business looking at those figures. It's us who break our asses on these missions not him, that's the bottom line," said Bart.

"You know the one item that caught my eye indicated our group apparently has the best overall record of sorties vs losses. We're also right up on top with the total tonnage and enemy aircraft destroyed. The figures I couldn't see was how many men were listed killed, missing and wounded. Whatever it was it was listed on the next sheet. I was just about to turn to it when donkey dick caught us," I said.

"It doesn't change a thing; we do our best and that's all that can be expected. Survival is the name of the game," said Bart as we pulled up in front of the hut.

"The thing that'd help and was not on his report was total tonnage on secondary targets and another thing, they need to have an estimate of how much damage was done to each target by percentage," said Jim.

"Maybe that was still to come," I said.

"If I was making the report I'd also include how many aircraft were employed by each group; total flying time on each type of target, priority targets, miles flown, and then the report would be of some use," added Jim.

"Maybe they don't want us to see the big picture. Those assholes in intelligence think they are overworked. They sure as hell don't turn down the battle stars we earn for them, do they? They should have to fly a few missions and see how long they could go without pissing their pants when the flak and fighters are as thick as flies," said Bart as he dropped on his bunk.

"Maybe we're not being fair. Hell, everyone can't fly. Actually, they do a good job. Just plotting flak batteries and other information they gather from the combat crews is very helpful in escaping a lot of flak over the targets. Remember on our last mission to Singapore, how we escaped a lot of flak by using the information they provided. Anyway, we'd all go bananas if we couldn't fly and had to do their job," I said philosophically.

"Aren't we going down to the *Lady* to work, Bart?" asked Jim changing the subject.

"Sure, right after we have noon chow. The enlisted troops will be there too," Bart rolled over and then said, "call me in a half hour, I need some sleep."

We spent the rest of the day cleaning and checking out the plane. When we were finally finished we headed back for evening chow, a couple drinks and some friendly cards.

Briefing was held the following morning for the Formosa mission. It would be a daylight mission dropping GP's and incendiary bombs. The group aircraft left that afternoon for A-3 to spend the night in the deep freeze of the Chengtu valley. We were scheduled for an early go the next morning.

The new year saw some operational changes. During 1944 all missions were conducted by the whole wing; however, 1945 was to see some missions flown by one or more groups on certain targets depending on priority. The Formosa trip would be a wing effort due to its priority. The mission had few problems and was very successful without the loss of a B-29. Though we did have some planes return to base with mechanical difficulties, the mission was classified as excellent.

We finished out the month with two more missions. The first was against Formosa with excellent results and, once again, no losses. The second mission was a first in many ways. We flew to Singapore on our first mining mission and had excellent results with no losses. It was one of the toughest targets we had been on. We dropped the mines from 4,000 to 5,000 feet. We had attacked with only two groups for the first time. The 444th and the 462nd Groups in one formation. This mission had earned us a commendation from Lord Louis Mountbatten, Supreme Allied Commander of the theater. I guess we were back in the good graces of the British High Command.

We'd ended our flying for the month of January and all we could think of was our R & R in Australia. We were scheduled to leave the afternoon of 31 January. We were ready!

23.

Sydney via Perth was our routing. We were to follow the same route as if we were heading for Palembang, Sumatra. However, we'd fly a little further south to escape enemy interception. The trip was to be a long one. Fortunately we were flying one of the stripped down B-29's. It was normally used as a tanker. The reduced weight gave us greater range and speed. All aboard were happy. The length of the trip didn't dampen our enthusiasm.

It was like a dream actually heading for Australia. The stories of the beautiful sex-starved women stirred our imaginations. The beaches of Australia were of the best in the world and Aussie beer was second to none.

We made an uneventful landing at Perth, located on the west coast of Australia on the Indian Ocean, and rapidly took care of our fuel problems as well as filing a new flight plan for the trip across the great continent. We were anxious to be off and on our way. We received permission and soon were on the runway and into the air once more. Our route of flight would take us over the vast deserts of the west, the great Australian Blight, the name for the large body of water on the south coast. Then to New South Wales and finally landing just outside of Sydney.

"This trip is a lot like flying across the United States distance wise, but it sure is different as far as the scenery is concerned," I said trying to strike up a conversation.

"I wish it were the USA!" said Ray Siversen from the radio compartment sadly. "You could always let me off in Omaha."

"Dream on," chimed in Pops from the rear.

The cross country trip was passing rapidly. On radar we picked up the ocean and within minutes a visual siting was made of the blue Pacific. The RAAF base was located north of the city. Radio contact was established and we landed at Richmond. We were met by a large contingent of Aussie airman happy to see us arrive. After the baggage was unloaded a vehicle drove us to operations.

Just after our arrival at ops the crew who was taking the plane back to Dudkhundi walked in.

"How was it, Dutch?" asked Bart of his pal, Lou Van Dorn.

"Great, Bart, you'll find out!"

"You guys look like you need to rest up before you head back," said Bart. They looked well tanned and happy, maybe a bit tuckered out, but smiling. They went on to tell us of how things were done in Sydney especially in and around King's Cross. If what they told us was true we were in for a hell of a time.

Our bus pulled up in front of the building and we began loading our bags. "Have a good flight home. The bird is in good shape," said Bart to his counterpart.

After a half-hour ride we pulled up in front of a nicely kept two-story house. The house had been leased for our crews while on leave in Sydney. The enlisted men had a similar house nearby. It was located within walking distance of Kings Cross. We carried our bags in and were met by a matronly lady who kept the place up and was in charge of assigning rooms and such. The house looked very comfortable, almost like home. It was hard to imagine this place after dusty and hot India. We had all agreed not to mention India while in Australia.

We were assigned two to a room and after a shower donned clean uniforms and set out to see what the area had to offer. Both Roundy and Rich had decided not to go along. Bart, Jim and I took a cab to see what the night life was like. As we drove, one thing was very apparent: there were few Australian men to be seen except for old fellows. It appeared there was no scarcity of girls. Abundance would better describe the situation. All sizes, shapes and hair colors were visible.

"Let's find a pub and have a beer," suggested Jim.

We asked the cab driver to take us to a popular spot. He pulled to the curb in front of a pub called Rory's. It looked fine to us. We walked in and found ten or fifteen men either seated at tables drinking or playing darts. We went to the bar and Jim ordered three beers. All conversation stopped. I was afraid we might not be welcomed. Had some GI screwed up here and made them resent an American uniform?

"Hold on there, Yank!" a large gentlemen said as he lay his large stein of beer on the bar.

We turned expecting belligerence; instead all the men in the pub crowded toward us to greet the conquering heros. "No Yank buys beer here," another said. We looked at each other in amazement unsure of what we'd gotten into; then we understood. The large man had waved off the bartender from picking up the money Jim had laid on the bar.

"Sir, we have plenty of money; we can buy our own beer. In fact we'd like to buy you gentlemen a round," said Bart.

"Your money's no good in this pub; you're our guests," the first man said. Soon the beer was coming and before we could drink it another pint was put before us. The beer was good and it had a high alcoholic content. The guys we'd talked to prior to arriving here had told us how good the beer was, but I'd heard little about its potency.

"Tell us, Yank, how's the bloody war going up north? We hear such little real news, except the campaign in New Guinea where a lot of our chaps are fighting the little yellow bastards."

"Well sir, we only know about what we're involved in, except for an occasional briefing on how the war is going in general," I explained.

"Oh, you're not fighting in New Guinea?" he said puzzled.

"No sir, we're flying the B-29's out of India," said Bart.

"Then you are bombing the Japanese!" another said.

"Yes sir, wherever it hurts them most is where we're sent. Our responsibility is all of southeast Asia, China and Japan. Recently, we were told we would only fly to southeast Asia and Formosa," Jim added as if he felt left out.

"Blimey, the bloody B-29! That's the machine that carries so many bombs. We have heard about you chaps," the bartender said.

"You chaps must be killing a lot of those little bastards," another man added.

"It's a little hard to count from where we are, but from all indications we are giving them hell," said Bart with a smile.

We'd rather have talked about women, but they were too happy with the subject at hand. No women were allowed in this pub, talk about segregation! The beer continued to flow and I was getting drunk. I was sure my pals must be feeling the effects, too. After an hour of steady drinking all I could think of was getting to bed.

"You certainly have a lot of unattended ladies in this city," said Bart trying to change the subject and not make our hosts unhappy at the same time.

"You chaps haven't been around ladies for awhile, I gather," said the bartender.

"No sir, we haven't. But we don't want to make anyone unhappy," I said.

"Not here in Sydney. The girls hereabouts are friendly and love to go out with you Yanks," the bartender explained.

It seemed as though we would never extricate ourselves from the pub, but finally we decided it was time to leave. We had to promise to return. The old men were fine people; it made us proud to have them as allies and friends. I knew they were sincere in their outward friendship and generosity. This was going to be a vacation to remember for some time to come, I was sure. My last recollection of the pub members was of them saying, "God bless you, Yanks, for keeping the Nips away from our door."

We staggered to the door. The fresh cool air hit me and I knew I was alive. "I'll call a cab," announced Bart. His efforts to hide his intoxication were useless.

A taxi pulled to the curb and we climbed in. The problem was trying to explain where we wanted to go. The driver became more confused by the second and we made matters worse by trying to help. Three passing young ladies entered into the conversation. I'm not sure where they came from, but any help would be appreciated. Before long some of the men from the pub also joined in to try and find where we were living. My last recollection of the evening was lying back and falling asleep.

I woke the next morning to the soft sound of voices and the smell of bacon cooking. I was very hungry. It'd been some time since I'd eaten. I was very confused as I rose to my elbows in an attempt to get my wits about me. I had one hell of a bad headache. Then I found I wasn't alone. Frightened, I slipped out from under the bedclothes for a look around. I was in a bedroom on the second floor and after surveying the area, trapped. My uniform was gone and there was no escape except out the door to the hall. Was I dreaming? I was near panic as I returned to the bed and gently shook the beautiful, bosomy young blonde. "Please, wake up," I whispererd in her ear.

She stirred and then rose to a sitting position. She had a beautiful smile, but I had a difficult time keeping my eyes just on her smile. She was a thing of beauty and I'd spent the night with her.

"Good morning, love," she said as she pushed her long hair back over her shoulders revealing her magnificent upper torso. I was

220

almost speechless. I was very inexperienced with affairs of this type. I considered the situation and was torn between desire and danger.

"Where are my clothes and where are we?" I asked almost afraid of what her answer might be.

"Love, we are at my home, and mother is cleaning your uniform. It was a mess," she explained.

"How do I get out of here?"

"Why? Do you want to leave?"

"With your parents downstairs, need you ask?"

"Easy love, they helped me put you to bed," she explained.

"Oh my God. I must be dreaming."

"Not at all, Yank. By the way, what's your name?" she asked.

"Johnny Lea. And Yours?"

"Kimberly, most people call me Kim and my surname is Clark."

"Kim, nice to meet you. I only wish it were under other circumstances and alone!"

"But, we are alone, love. Now, get back into bed and relax. In a bit mother will call us for breakfast."

I felt foolish standing before her in my birthday suit, so I climbed back into bed. She squirmed over to me and whispered into my ear. It sent a shock wave through my body, I thought I was going to explode. She smelled so sweet and her warm body was so alive and firm. My mind was off the danger just one floor below as I relaxed in her arms. One thing led to another and soon the world stopped as we made love. Kim was unconcerned about her family one flight below, but I still had to face them. I was in a fix, but I'd enjoyed the fruits of love and knew soon I would have to face the music. We lay in each others arms completely spent.

"Kim, what are we going to do?"

"We could stay in bed forever if you could live on love alone."

"I'll bet your father is down there with a shotgun and is going to kill me."

She laughed and then said, "Not to worry. I told you he helped me get you up here and into bed. He knows you're here and is not unhappy."

I was dumbfounded. How could this be? A lovely girl of eighteen, obviously not a whore, yet here we were. "I can't face your mother and father, especially without any clothes. Are you trying to tell me your family approves of us being in bed together?"

"Not with anyone, but with you it's alright."

"My God did we get married?" I asked as I looked at her ring finger to see before she answered if I'd done something foolish.

"No love, but it's a good idea."

"You don't even know me. You didn't even know my name, so how could it be okay?"

"Please don't feel uncomfortable. Mother will have your clothes here soon and then we can go down and see my family, I know they're dying to meet you."

"Like hell. I'm going to jump out the window."

"Don't be silly. You have no clothes and it's a long way to the ground. Anyway, don't worry. Everything will be just fine."

"You don't understand. I'm embarrassed. How can I look them in the eye knowing they know we slept together. Are you sure I can't slip by them and go out the back way?"

"There's no way out, silly! Anyway they trust me. They are very understanding parents."

"I hate to ask this next question, but have you done this before?"

"What?"

"Brought home a stranger and took him upstairs to bed?"

"Of course not!"

"Then why me?"

"You needed me and I could tell you were a nice chap."

"I hope you're more of an expert at judging character than I am. Every time I think I have it all figured out it backfires. I think you're the most beautiful girl I've ever taken out. Remind me to ask you later how I got here and maybe you can tell me what happened to my two friends."

The moment of truth was at hand. There was a soft knock on the bedroom door and I froze momentarily, then ran for the bathroom and closed the door. I waited for the axe to fall. Instead, Kim came into the bathroom and said, "Here are your things. Are you going to take a bath?"

"I might as well be clean for the slaughter," I said as I turned the water on in the large tub.

"Oh good, I'll join you."

"Do you think that's a good idea?"

"Why not. No use wasting water. Anyway, I can scrub your back and you mine."

"I'm afraid I'll not be able to keep my mind on just your back."

She pulled the cord on her robe and let it slip to the floor. She

222

stood before me naked. She had the body of Venus with arms. She had all the things in the right places and was well built from head to toe.

"I've never taken a bath with a man," she said as she advanced toward me.

"You're not alone. I've never been in a bath with a woman, but I guess there's a first time for everything."

I thought I could never repeat this story because no one would believe me. I'm not sure I believe it either. Needless to say, I did little serious washing. After all, how could any red blooded American under those circumstances?

All good things must come to an end. We dried each other and dressed. My uniform was pressed, with military creases, and my shoes were shined. I took a deep breath as I prepared to face the music. We left her bedroom and walked to the stairs and slowly descended. We stepped into the large old fashioned dining room and seated at the head of the table was Kim's father. I was happy to note there was no shotgun in his lap. At the other end of the table was a boy of ten years. I swallowed as I heard her father say, "Come in, come in. Did you have a nice rest, my boy?"

I cleared my throat and said, "Yes sir, it was very pleasant." How I wish I'd chosen my words with a little more care.

He smiled and said, "Sit here next to me."

He was a huge man of about fifty years, well over six feet and probably 250 pounds, none of which was fat. His hair was thinning and his teeth were not too good, but he was all man.

"Father, this is Lieutenant Johnny Lea. My father," she then turned to the other end of the table and introduced her younger brother. "Meet my little brother, Greg." Then she explained, "Lieutenant Lea is an American flier of the B-29."

"How-ja-do, sir," he said.

I waved to the boy and then turned to shake the hand of Mr. Clark. His hand was like a ham. I thought I had large hands until he wrapped his around mine. Just as I was being seated, Kim's mother entered through the swinging door which separated the huge kitchen from the dining room. She was carrying a platter of eggs and bacon. After introductions I felt more at home with these wonderful people. Kim's mother was ten years younger than her husband. She was a beautiful woman. She looked a great deal like her daughter. She had blonde hair graying at the tips.

I could see they felt good about having a man in uniform in

their home. I was beginning to feel the embarrassment start to ebb.

"Sir, are you to be stationed in Australia?" asked Greg.

"Please, call me Johnny. No, I'm only here for two weeks on rest leave."

He wanted to ask more questions, but his father interrupted and said, "After breakfast, son. Let the Lieutenant eat his meal while it's warm." His wife joined us and Mr. Clark said grace. The young boy never took his eyes off my uniform, especially the silver wings and campaign ribbons.

"Do you like them?" I asked Greg.

"Oh, yes sir."

"Johnny."

"They're beautiful. I would love to have a set of wings like yours."

"I'll send you a pair as soon as I return to India." The boy was overjoyed.

As breakfast progressed I think I found why I was so well received. I was the same age as their son who had fallen in the North African campaign a year before. Another reason was that the Australian people had few young men at home and we filled in for them. We were also considered by many as the saviours of Australia.

I knew these people were rationed everything, yet we had butter, eggs, potatoes and tea, as well as fresh fruit and juice. I'm sure those who didn't live on a farm fared much worse. They were using scarce items to make me feel at home and I appreciated it beyond words.

"Will you stay with us?" asked Mrs. Clark.

"I have to report to my quarters and let them know where I am in case of an emergency. You never know when your leave might be cut short. I'd love to stay with you for at least a short time but, I don't want to wear out my welcome."

"Son, we would be most happy to have you stay with us. It'd be like having our Tim with us again," said Mr. Clark with a tear in his eye.

I almost felt as though they were trying to adopt me and I wasn't sure I wanted to be tied down. I could get in over my head real fast and I didn't need any more responsibility at this time, yet I didn't want to leave either.

Breakfast ended. Mr. Clark, Sunday paper under arm, headed for the bathroom. Mrs. Clark cleared the dishes from the table and was soon lost in her kitchen. Young Greg didn't want to leave, but was told by his sister to go and play. He reluctantly strolled off. Greg said as he left the table, "I must go tell my friends of the Yank flier we now have!"

His choice of words made me uncomfortable for a few seconds. Kim took me by the hand and led me to the large living room where she said, "Here we can be alone and talk."

"Kim, you and your family are wonderful. But I can't stay here. I'm too uncomfortable sleeping with you with your folks just down the hall. It might be different if you had a guest room. Then it would look better and I wouldn't feel so guilty."

"Silly, we have Timmy's room. It hasn't been used since he left for the army. You can use it. It's right next to my room."

"I first have to return to my squadron's house. I have to tell them where they can find me. Now that we're alone can you tell me what happened to my two friends?"

"They're both fine. At least they were. The tall chap is with Judy. She lives about ten miles down the lane. She's a widow. The other chap is a short distance down the lane with Anne, my best friend."

"It sounds like we were taken care of nicely. I guess we were too drunk to know what was happening, at least I was."

"We can use Daddy's car later if you would like to visit with them. None of you were able to take care of yourselves when we found you. It just seemed right for us to take you home and take care of you. After all, I'm sure if the tables were turned your people would do the same."

I wasn't sure anyone would take care of us as these people had anywhere in the world. "It seems because we are Americans you people would do anything to make us happy. It really isn't necessary. We'd help you without all this care and attention," I explained.

"If we hadn't been sure of what and who you were, we wouldn't have taken you home. We knew you hadn't been whoring around," she said. She seldom beat around the bush.

"Let's get the car out and go visit your friends and then I'll take you to town and we'll be able to spend some time alone. How's that?" she asked.

"Sounds like a winner to me."

She rose and went into the kitchen. She returned a short time after and said, "Let's go Johnny. Would you like to take a dip after?"

225

"A dip!"

"Yes, my mother is packing a picnic basket right now. We have fine beaches here."

"I'm sure you do. We saw some of them as we flew in. We have nice beaches in California, too."

"I was wondering what part of the States you were from."

"I'm proud to say I'm from southern California like my two friends."

Kim smiled and said, "I'll go up and get my bathing suit and towels. Please, rest for a few minutes and I'll be right back."

My eyes were glued to her as she left the large room and ascended the stairs. She was like a vision. I was still unsure whether I was dreaming or it was really happening. As I waited I tried to gather my thoughts so that I might be able to see clearly what I was getting into. I heard her quietly descending the stairs and I rose to meet her. She was so lovely with her flowing blonde hair trailing behind as she swiftly closed the distance between us. She had her arms filled with suits, towels and a blanket. As she got to me, she dropped them at my feet and put her arms around my neck and pulled my head to hers. We kissed and a fire started deep inside me. "We had better leave or you might be in trouble," I said.

She laughed softly and smiled. Kim had nice, white, even, teeth, unlike all the stories of the women with teeth rotting that we'd been told.

The 1939 Ford sedan was like new. It had been used sparingly due to the shortage of fuel. The car was parked in a barn-like garage located behind the house. I pulled the two large doors open as she started and backed the car out. I then closed them and climbed in beside her. I felt more at ease as she drove down the lane past other houses similar to hers. In a matter of minutes we pulled into the yard of another old farmhouse. She slipped out the door and turned and said, "Come along, love."

I hesitated, and then said, 'I'll wait here. I feel much more at ease out in the open."

She turned and walked up the wooden steps and knocked on the door, then entered. I wondered how Jim had fared! Soon, she came out to the car as I enjoyed the warmth of the sun.

"They are having their breakfast and asked you to come in."

"Why not tell them we'll meet them at the squadron house when they finish; then we won't be delayed."

Without saying a word she turned and went back into the house and quickly returned. She slid behind the wheel and we were off in a cloud of dust. She asked where I was staying and I could only tell her the approximate location from my dim memory. I was sure if she got us in the neighborhood of the pub we were in last night I'd be able to find my way.

Without hesitation she drove toward the center of the city. In a matter of fifteen minutes we were in front of the pub. It sure looked different in the daylight. "I believe we came down that street." I pointed toward the east.

She drove slowly, as I tried to find a landmark. "There, the large building over there. I remember seeing it as we left for the pub last night. Turn here, it should only be one or two blocks." We drove slowly and soon I recognized the squadron house just as one of my friends opened the front door to come out, which confirmed we were at the right place.

"That wasn't too difficult," she said as she parked at the curb. "After all, I am a navigator!"

She laughed. "You weren't navigating too well last night!"

"You would have to bring that up. I was hoping you'd forget. Let me run in and see what's going on. I'll be right back." I entered the house, then came back out and said, "Come in Kim. I'll get a few things together and have a quick shave."

There were no rules concerning guests, either male or female. We found my room. It was empty except for our bags which were strewn out on the bed. "Maybe, we should have driven to where my other friend was staying. But, he's a big boy and I'm sure he'll be just fine," I added.

Bart and I shared the room. Jim's room was next door. Kim and I waited for Jim and his girl. It was thirty minutes before they walked in. It gave us a few minutes alone to discuss the next two weeks.

Introductions were made and I found that Jim's girl was a very handsome woman. It's true, I thought. This place is loaded with talent. "I have to go to my room and pack a couple things. Come along, Johnny, and help." said Jim. I knew he wanted to talk. We might not have an opportunity later. I followed him to his room. "My God, John, what the hell is happening? I woke up in bed this morning with Anne. I almost shit when I found out where I was."

"Sounds familiar. I was trapped in an upstairs room without a stitch of clothing. I was sure my number had come up when I heard the family downstairs and me naked as a Jaybird in bed with their daughter. I wouldn't believe anyone if they told me the story I just told you, but it's true."

"You think I don't know. It sounds like a replay of what happened to me. What the hell do we do?" he asked.

"Relax and enjoy, I guess. We're on R and R don't you remember?"

"Sure, but how in the hell can we keep this pace up for two weeks?" said Jim as he threw his towel and trunks into the small bag we shared.

"Let's play it by ear. We have two honeys here. I can see a hell of a lot of fun coming out of it," I said as we walked to the door.

"By the way, what about Bart? Do you know what's up with him?" I asked.

"Yeah, we called the place where he's at and told them we were going to the beach. He may join us later," explained Jim.

"Good enough. Now, let's get going. I'm anxious to hit the water."

It was decided since Kim's auto was a four-door sedan we'd all go together. Kim gave us a short tour of the city; then we headed for her special beach. It was breathtaking; the beach was beautiful. The sand was so white it made you squint. You needed sunglasses. The waves were enormous as they broke on the sand. We were lucky to have found two companions such as these, I thought; what a life!

The two girls headed toward the small enclosure to change into their suits and we went into the hut next to it. "Can you believe this, Johnny?" asked Jim.

"Man, let's live it up and get in the water. I've had visions of a beach like this. It's been a long time since I swam in the ocean," I said as we headed back to the blanket.

"Here come the gals," said Jim. "Man oh man, what a pair of dolls," he said as they swayed gently toward us.

"Do you like the water?" I asked.

"We are Australians. Does that answer your question?" said Anne.

"I guess so. How about it, are you ready?" I asked. Before I could get to my feet both girls took off running toward the mountains of water. Jim and I quickly followed. The water was cool, refreshing and rough. We body-surfed then swam out beyond the breakers. The water was clear. One had little trouble seeing far below.

"Some say swimming out here is dangerous," said Kim.

"Why? We're all pretty good swimmers," I said.

"What she means is there've been a few attacks by sharks around here," said Anne as she headed for the beach.

"Christ, sharks! I don't need to tangle with one of those big bastards," said Jim as he followed. As for me, I waited for Kim to start and we swam slowly side by side until we reached the crest of a large breaker and then rode it in.

"Are you two hungry?" asked Kim.

"Swimming always works up an appetite," I answered.

The two baskets contained enough food to feed a small army, but we didn't need a small army to make a big dent in the fried chicken and salad.

We lay in the sun and felt warm and happy. We talked of what we were going to do that evening. It was decided to have dinner at some small restaurant and take a moonlight drive after, in separate cars of course. The girls went to change as we did and it gave us a chance to discuss what to do about the remainder of the two weeks. "I hope we can walk away from this when we leave. These girls sure sound possessive. I'm not sure I want to be tied down the whole time. It's almost like being married," said Jim.

"I'm having the same problem. I want to be with Kim and I like her family, but hells fire, I sure don't want to get hitched! What bothers me is how do you turn it off? The family has a room which the son had before he was killed in North Africa and they want me to use it. I'm sure if I balked they'd let me stay in Kim's room."

"Crazy, huh!"

"I wonder how Bart is making out," I said.

"He's a confirmed bachelor, but the way these gals attack down here one never knows. I know a guy could do a lot worse than Kim."

"That's the way I feel, too. I wonder if all the girls in Australia are the same. They seem to be starving for a little attention."

"Let's find Bart and we can all go to dinner together."

"Sounds fine. We have two weeks with no schedules or formations to worry about. Let's get our crap together and go find him."

"Here come the gals now. It's a good thing we're leaving. I'm starting to burn. It's been a while since I lay out on the beach."

We all jumped in the car and headed for Judy's house in hopes of finding Bart there. We arrived at the small farm within thirty minutes and as we drove up we saw Bart and Judy returning from a walk. Bart was dressed in civilian clothes. It was odd

229

seeing him dressed in civies. We had no civilian clothes. It was against regulations to wear anything in public but a uniform, during WW II.

"Hey, mister, have you seen an ugly tall Yank flier around?"

"What a smartass! How the hell are you two?" asked Bart.

"Good as gold," answered Jim.

"What are you going to do, desert?" I asked.

"Not a bad idea. I like it here. The company is unsurpassed and she even has clothes that fit me."

It wasn't hard to see what he was talking about. Judy was a couple years older than her two friends, but she was a dark-haired beauty. It astounded me to think that three Americans visiting a place eight or nine thousand miles from home could find three such lovely women.

The girls went into the farmhouse and Bart, Jim and I had a chance to discuss future operations. It was mutually agreed we'd spend the first week with the girls, then we could have a week to look around and see the sites and relax. It was also decided we would all meet at the Clark's house before we went to dinner that evening. We still had to go after the other car we'd left at the squadron house.

Later that evening both the other couples arrived at the Clark's. Mr. Clark broke out the bottle of Canadian Club I had given him. We all had a pre-dinner drink. We left and found a nice small restaurant for dinner. Later we went to a club called the Trocadero, for dancing. The day had been from beginning to end a wonderful holiday. Not once had we thought of the brutal war we had to return to in a couple weeks.

* * *

The first week passed as if it were a runaway train. We all had found happiness and a deep affection for not only the girls but their families. When I informed the Clarks I had to return to the squadron quarters, they were visibly shaken. Mrs. Clark cried. I wasn't prepared for this show of emotion and reconsidered. "Maybe, I can make arrangements to stay a couple more days," I said.

Mrs. Clark threw her arms around my neck and hugged me. How could I leave these wonderful people? I almost wished I'd never met them. I knew now I'd have to hurt them, but it was not only them. I felt the pain, too. Our affair had turned serious,

230

something I tried in vain to avoid. It got out of hand from the very beginning and I wasn't sure, but I thought I was in love. I knew Kim was. If I had asked her to marry me she wouldn't have hesitated, but I didn't want to go back to combat and possibly leave her a widow.

The sad day finally arrived. I had to bid my new family good-bye. It was every bit as hard as when I left home and when I stood at the curb in San Antonio and watched my mother and father leave for home so long ago. I asked Kim to please not come to the airport. I'd rather say good-bye at the squadron house than at the airport and she reluctantly agreed.

"Will I ever see you again, Johnny?" she cried.

"I'll return. I'll miss you. This war can't last forever. I'll do my best to come back soon." The promise of corresponding with each other need not be said. I knew my dreams would be filled with but one subject. After a tear-filled farewell with Mr. and Mrs. Clark as well as young Greg, Kim and I had a few minutes alone to sort out our lives as she drove me to town.

* * *

After the plane became airborne I tried to reflect on my stay in Australia, but every thought kept bringing me back to the Clark's and especially Kimberly. My mind formed a vision of her and I knew she was the finest girl I'd ever met. Her maturity for her age was astounding to say nothing of how well she made love. She tried to please me in every way. God, did I miss her. Things would never be the same. I knew my chances of returning to Sydney were remote. What was I to do? Emotion was racking my body. I thought I was going to cry, but I held it under control. I wondered how Bart and Jim felt. I knew they, too, must be suffering. I was sure we'd be able to talk about it later.

* * *

Soon it'd be light and we'd nearly reached Dudkhundi. I'd counted every mile that separated Kim and I. Now we were worlds apart. The mouth of the Ganges passed under our left wing as we prepared for the landing. Back to reality it would be difficult. R & R's were supposed to give you a new vitality. It had done just the opposite for me.

24.

The day we reported back to duty was the same day the United States Marines went ashore on a small island which in the future would save hundreds of B-29's and their crews. Ours would be no exception. This tiny island, unheard of by most Americans, proved to be one of the bloodiest battles of World War II. It was called Iwo Jima.

It was very difficult to get Kim off my mind. I'd had a wonderful leave and returning here left me confused. I wanted desperately to finish my combat missions and return to the United States, but on the other hand I wanted desperately to be with Kim. In my mind I was still unsure whether I was in love or just infatuated. I wasn't sure what love was! If you feel bad about being away from a person, are you in love? I was sure of one fact: I was back in India and had a war to fight and it would take all my concentration and energy. I decided after considerable thought I'd have to write to Kim and ask her how she felt. As I wrote the letter I constantly looked at the 8 X 10 picture of her which she'd had taken just prior to our meeting. She had given it to me the last day we were together. She was a living doll; when she smiled she radiated beauty. At the bottom of the picture she wrote, "I love you. Please come back to me," signed "Your loving Kim."

Everyone we met wanted to know all about Australia. I told them nothing of my escapade. It was a secret I wanted to guard. Our dark tans gave evidence of outdoor living. It made almost everyone envious. They wanted details, but I avoided those of Kim and dwelled on how the other people, weather and beaches were. But word of the lovely women were what they wanted to hear. It was impossible to speak of Australia without nostalgia gripping me.

Time for play had ended and I had to get back to the work at hand. We were scheduled for a combat mission the following day. The odd part was that we'd follow the same route we'd taken on

232

our way to Australia. We were going to Kuala-Lampur, Malay States. There would be two of our four groups attacking. The mission would be a medium altitude raid dropping 1,000-pound bombs in daylight. None of the crews assigned this mission were happy about going in at 11,000 feet. At that altitude many more guns would be fired against us, especially the automatic weapons which were fired at an almost constant rate. Our complaint was that the B-29 was designed for high altitude, so why fly down low where you got the shit kicked out of you? Later in the year this tactic of flying missions at low altitudes would become commonplace, especially on night missions. The advantages of going in low were twofold: more bombs could be carried and less fuel burned.

All necessary preparations had been accomplished, and we were ready to go. But, my heart wasn't in it. It made little difference. Duty called and our crew reported to *Lucky Lady* for combat mission number 28. Almost nine months had passed since our first aerial adventure over an enemy target.

The 444th and the 462nd Bomb Groups combined launched over 60 B-29's for the long and hazardous mission. We arrived in the target area with fifty-nine planes. Ten bombed targets of opportunity and all others hit the primary target. Only one enemy fighter was shot down and seven were damaged. The results were classified as excellent. I was glad to get out of the target's area: the tracers were most unnerving as the shells arced from the ground up through the formation. We made the long trip back to our home bases without incident.

During our debriefing we heard a strong rumor that the 58th Bomb Wing would be leaving India soon. The rumor was considered logical, but when did logic ever make a difference? The Army in all its infinite wisdom seldom followed logic. In any event the rumor had us moving to the Marianas in the Western Pacific. It was unclear which of the islands we'd be going to. It mattered little to me; anywhere would be better than this dusty and overheated hell-hole.

Each passing day made the rumor of our departure more realistic, especially when Tokyo Rose's broadcast was picked up one night informing the men of the 58th Bomb Wing to get ready to leave for Tinian. It never ceased to amaze me how she got her information. Most of the time she was right about things of this nature, though of course she always got the Japanese propaganda into it.

Life went on for the men of the 444th Bomb Group, but something had changed; people started saying that Dudkhundi wasn't all that bad, at least compared to Charra. It took no genius to realize that. Charra was and always will be the worst place on God's green earth, except Charra was never green.

The group decided to take all the partial crews and reform them into new crews. After nine months of war we had many partial crews. Some co-pilots were being made aircraft commanders. Jim had been offered a command and declined. He wanted to stay with his original crew to finish his tour. It's at times like this you remember there were only a few of us that came overseas and were still together. We counted noses and were surprised to see we hadn't lost as many as we had first thought, but the list was long. It was best not to dwell on these statistics or morale would sink.

We received word that we'd lead our group on a maximum effort mission scheduled to strike Singapore. This proved to be the last maximum effort mission to be flown from India. When we received word the target was Singapore we knew we were going to the toughest target in all of Southeast Asia. We still remembered our last venture over the hellish target. It was a bit frightening. We were going to bomb from 23,000 feet using incendiary bombs on the oil supplies which provided a great deal of Japan's oil. The ungodly hour of 0400 was selected for takeoff which meant no matter how you tried, sleep would be nearly impossible. But, orders were orders. Everything was in readiness as we taxied on to the active runway with two minutes to spare for takeoff. The power was advanced and our plane started down the runway. Just as the throttles were advanced to maximum power, we heard a loud pop and oil pressure on number three started to drop to the danger zone. We quickly cut the engine and aborted the takeoff. Luckily it happened before we'd gone very far down the runway. We slowed and turned off at the runway intersection to get out of the way. We hadn't been eager to fly the Singapore mission, but it was a great disappointment after so much preparation. Our philosophy was simple, "Live today to fight another day." I considered myself almost free of superstition, but there was always the thought that luck had a lot to do with it. Most of the guys had some kind of lucky charm. Mine was a beat up red baseball cap I'd worn from the beginning of my B-29 days.

234

"Christ, I feel left out. Almost every plane in the squadron is on the mission and here we are with our fingers in our asses," said Bart disgustedly.

"What are we going to do for the next couple days?" asked Jim.

"We could always catch up on our sleep," answered Roundy.

"I swear you're going to sleep right through the damn war," snorted Bart as we arrived at the hut. The natives called our huts "basha." Somehow it made little difference to me what they called these sub-standard jail cells. Even though we gave Roundy a bad time about sleeping it only took a few minutes for all five of us to be in dreamland. After a few hours of sleep we were refreshed.

"In a way I'm glad we didn't go on that ballbuster to Singapore. The last time we went there the Japs treated us rudely," said Rich as he pulled on his boots.

"To say nothing of getting our asses shot off. But you know you can get your ass shot off on any mission if your number comes up!" I said.

We decided to organize a volleyball game to use up some of our energy. We played until we were pooped, dirty, and thirsty as bears. It was time to go down to the line and help the ground crew with the plane. We were informed that before maintenance could be performed we had to off load the bombs. Rich was our leader in this endeavor. The big problem with having incendiary bombs on the airplane is their volatility. Any disturbance could be catastrophic as we'd learned when the 40th lost the three airplanes before they dropped their bombs a few missions back. Sparks caused by maintenance or any enemy attack could make one hell of a mess.

After having what was laughingly called lunch the whole crew gathered in front of operations and waited for transportation to the plane. We all helped unload the bombs on to the waiting dollies and soon the armament section was there to take them back to the bomb dump. We had off-loaded the bombs as if they were cartons of eggs. There was no sense fooling around with jelled fire.

Our plane was fixed and had been tested. In fact they had hung new engines all around. We practically had a new aircraft. It was ready to go. On the 26th of February we were informed that we'd lead the group on the next mission to the Johore Straits, Malay States on a mining mission. This was to be the first time our crew had been called on to drop mines. It was also the first mission the

235

444th would fly as a separate group. The other three groups of the wing were assigned other targets. This would be the longest mission flown. We were going to lay mines from 4,000 feet at night. I preferred the night missions especially when we were down at 4,000 feet. The enemy fighters would have a hard time finding us and usually they didn't seem too interested in pressing attacks at night. The nice thing about this mission was we wouldn't have to get up at midnight. All briefings were completed and all was in readiness. There were twelve B-29's scheduled. Drop areas were assigned each plane. It would be impossible to accomplish the mission in formation. We had too much area to cover. We would fly down together and afterwards rendezvous for the return.

The mission went like clockwork from beginning to end. We had ten planes of the twelve over target dropping twenty-nine tons of mines. We had covered the area completely. I enjoyed the thought of unsuspecting Japanese ships hitting our mines and going to the bottom.

Seven weeks had passed since the new year and the statistics looked real good. We had flown 748 sorties; dropping over 3,400 tons on primary targets and had lost seven B-29's. By the end of March 1945, XX Bomber Command had flown another ten missions, five of which the 444th had participated in.

Our next mission was scheduled to Rangoon on 17 March. It was the of type mission I liked. It was half as far as Singapore and half as dangerous. We led the mission with twenty-one B-29's from the 444th and a total of seventy-seven from the wing. The formation came across the target at 30,000 feet. The flak was moderate and few enemy fighters rose to challenge. The mission had put 591 tons of incendiary bombs on the primary target and again the results were classified as excellent.

On 29 March a special officers call was scheduled and all officers were to attend. Bomber Command was to preside. The briefing was confidential and mandatory. We knew something big was in the wind and had a pretty good idea what it was. It turned out to be the worst kept secret of the war. Tokyo Rose had informed us long before. I hoped the rest of Tokyo Rose's predictions were incorrect. She had promised few of us would survive if we kept bombing Japan. She said we were barbaric to attack innocent people from a peace loving nation. What she forgot was that this war was not of our choosing. The war started with many innocent men being killed at Pearl Harbor during the sneak attack. So we figured all's fair in love and war and let the chips fall where they may. Japan was going to suffer for their infamy. It was the B-29's who were going to bring them to their knees.

The general started the briefing by saying, "Gentlemen, we have met the challenge of war and we have learned. Soon the XX Bomber Command will be history. Many of you've heard by way of the rumor mill that we're going to leave this part of the world, and for a change the rumors are true. The 58th Bomb Wing will be assigned to the XXI Bomber Command and will be stationed on the island of Tinian. B-29 wings are located on Guam, Saipan and Tinian at present. We will have our own field on one side of the island and the 313th Wing will be on the other side. At present the landing facilities and other necessary structures are being completed. Needless to say, you will all be residents of that small island in the very near future. There will be no further combat operations from India by B-29's. We will stand down all flying units as of now. All activity will be channeled toward getting every flying machine ready for the long trip to Tinian. All supporting units will be heavily engaged in the hard work of pulling up stakes and moving to a location that brings us within range of Japan without operating from forward bases in China. This move will allow us to finally use all our resources against the Japanese homeland. Gentlemen, I know this news will be impossible to harness, but keep this in mind from this day until we actually leave. We suggest each unit and crew double their vigilance over its own aircraft to prevent possible sabotage. Some of you in non-flying positions will start leaving soon. My best estimate for the complete transfer of personnel and equipment should be accomplished not later than mid-April. Remember, let's pull together and get ready as rapidly as possible. We want safety to be the key word. Thank you for your attention and good luck."

I felt he knew more than he was telling, but he was the boss and the confirmation of our departure was great news. After dismissal most of the officers headed for the club. This called for a celebration. It was finally official; we were going to leave India!

"Man, that is the greatest news we've had since we got to India! I'm really anxious to leave India and the Hump behind," I said.

"You're not alone. I never want to see this hellhole again," said Bart.

"I thought it was the anus of the world," said Jim with a big

237

smile.

"That too," answered Bart as we reached the club. "By the way, have you heard from your honey in Sydney, lately?" he asked.

"You bet! Haven't you?"

"Are you kidding, she writes every day. Next thing I know she'll pop the question."

"That serious, huh?" said Rich.

"Maybe for her, but not for me. She's a find that any man would be glad to have, but I'm not the marrying type," Bart explained.

"I get a lot more mail than I send and each letter gets more serious. I don't want to marry either; at least not now," I added.

"What the hell are we going to do until we leave?" asked Jim.

"Maybe we ought to study our navigation since Tokyo Rose thinks we'll get lost and fall in the ocean," said Bart as we got our first beer.

"Not funny! Christ, what the hell does she think we've been doing all this time, getting lost?" I said indignantly.

"Don't get pissed! I was only kidding. Anyway, if I didn't think you were the best I'd look for another navigator."

"Thanks a lot for the off-handed compliment."

"What do you say we organize a pool for the date and time we arrive on Tinian?" asked Bart.

"I would rather organize a volley ball tourney," I said.

"Sounds fine to me, how do we start?"

"Each squadron can enter as many teams as they like. Each team will put up say, 100 dollars for prize money. Play can start tomorrow. Winner take all. It will be good for us and a good way to spend the time. It beats the hell out of playing cards and drinking. If someone wanted to oraganize a horseshoe or softball tourney, they can do that too," I suggested.

Word came, we would start leaving on 9 April according to a flow plan from group. We had to push to finish the volley ball tournament. We had a meeting and voted the prize money of 1600 dollars to be spent on a party for the whole group. It was a unanimous vote except for the team that won. The base took on a new meaning. We had Dudkhundi ready to sell back to the British. They were getting the best of the deal! Dudkhundi wasn't much when we arrived. Now it had buildings, a much improved runway, and other facilities. We Americans were good at the game of improving facilities and then giving them back.

* * *

Our route of flight would take us over the Himalayas, but more southerly than our trips to A-3. We would pass over Burma, the southern part of China, pass north of the Philippines, and on to Tinian. It would be a long trip, but there'd be a fuel stop at Luliang, China. Any minor mechanical problems could be taken care of there. The advanced party of the 58th Bomb Wing was already on Tinian to supposedly set up the facilities for the main body. Judging from past experiences we were not expecting much, so we wouldn't be disappointed.

The big party was hosted by the winning volley ball team to the delight of all. We had two days left before we kissed this place good-bye. The group commander was feeling no pain and wanted to say a few words. I thought it would be impossible to calm and quiet this mob, but he got order of sorts. "I wouldn't interrupt this party if it were up to me, but the wing CO thought you all should know what heros you are. He has some figures he wanted me to pass on about what you've accomplished since we got into this shooting war. So here it is: Total combat sorties 3,058; dropped 11,477 tons, nearly three million pounds of bombs; 3,405 transport missions; lost eighty-two B-29's and shot down 400 enemy aircraft. I might add, a record per sortie no other command has achieved. Those are mighty impressive numbers, but it does not tell the whole story of the deplorable living and operating conditions we had to endure. Some of you older crews had an opportunity to enjoy an R & R which I'm sure helped keep you going. Ah hell, enough of this talk; let's have a ball. I intend to keep this place open as long as there is one officer still on his feet!"

25.

Getaway day arrived. It was 7 April and all was in readiness to pull the plug and escape to our new base far to the east. Everyone was excited about the prospect of leaving India. Not many would regret this day, I was sure.

Many men had been involved in planning this move at higher headquarters and moving a wing of 200 B-29's and other support aircraft, equipment and men without some problems was impossible. But, for all indications, they'd done their homework. Things were moving smoother than anybody anticipated. Schedules were posted with takeoff times and other information pertinent to the move was listed.

Our aircraft rose from the runway at Dudkhundi for the last time and no one would shed a tear. We remembered the promises of the past and knew there was no place in the world that would fit the description. We all knew the move had to be an improvement, but no rose garden. Our scheduled departure time was 1800 hours local time. That should get us to our destination in daylight. We'd lose four hours due to our passage east. We were hopeful of not losing any time due to maintenance. We didn't want to make our first landing at night.

Our plane carried a heavy load of equipment and personnel. We figured to cover the distance in approximately fifteen hours and as in most instances *Lucky Lady* responded with excellence. We would soon be assigned a new aircraft because of our lead crew status. We'd have to part with the *Lady* and it wasn't going to be easy. She climbed steadily into the northeast sky as we headed for the forbidding mountains we called the Hump. We had to detour at one point to avoid large concentrations of Japanese troops who were capable of firing antiaircraft weapons. We also detoured around the highest peaks to avoid climbing to high altitudes.

We flew steadily and the drone of our engines had a soothing effect. According to my log book this made my 29th crossing of the Himalayas. The fear I originally had of these wild snow covered peaks had faded. However, I'd never lost respect for them. I knew this would be my last crossing and for that I was grateful. There was a note of cheer among the members of the crew as well as our passengers. They acted as if we were going on holiday rather than a new place to fight from. No matter what the circumstances, we had a lot of enthusiasm and Esprit de Corps. We were proud of our outfit.

The flight progressed and everyone became more relaxed with the possible exception of myself. I couldn't afford the luxury. I had to stay on the ball and do a good job of making sure we were exactly where we were supposed to be at all times. To wander off course could be fatal. I especially wanted to prove that Tokyo Rose was full of shit. We transited Tibet and Northern Burma and were now over China. We determined that our fuel was adequate to continue without stopping at Luliang. We pressed on with vigor, as the saying goes. We left China behind and started across the South China Sea with a course that would take us just north of the Philippines, then over the Pacific Ocean and finally, Tinian.

* * *

Voice contact was made with Tinian for the first time. We would be landing within fifteen minutes at our new home. Excitement radiated throughout the plane. We entered the traffic pattern and looked down at the small island with anticipation. The two huge runways stuck out against the white coral that surrounded it. The glare of the coral was overpowering. One would have to wear dark sunglasses here. We could see the construction equipment still working on some of the taxiways. The Navy CeeBee's had been working around the clock to get the facilities ready before our arrival. It was figured close. We turned to final approach on one of the large runways which stretched over 8,000 feet. It was a luxury we hadn't experienced since we arrived overseas. We touched down on the runway and we could see the other planes of our squadron following us in.

The jeep ride from the cantonment area to the landing field gave us our first opportunity to see part of the island of Tinian. It was pleasant with a nice ocean breeze. The war seemed very far away as we drove down the coral road toward base operations.

We had to stop and ask directions from one of the passersby.

We arrived at base ops and could see B-29's parked in all directions. It was no wonder our squadron CO was concerned. Aircraft were being towed to individual revetments by the large cleat tracked vehicles to clear all the taxiways and to make sure they weren't bunched up. The enemy would have a field day if they caught all the aircraft gathered in one area.

Base operations was the type of GI building so common during the war years in that part of the world. The CeeBee's had erected quonset huts like mushrooms grow. We entered the building and were about to ask if they'd received any communications from the new B-29 due in when the radio came to life.

"West field tower, this is AAF 224, over."

"This is Tinian west, 224, read you five by five."

"Roger Tinian, we are fifteen miles out, request landing instructions, over."

"You are cleared for a straight in approach, 224, landing runway able, winds zero-niner-five at one zero, clear to land, over."

"Roger Tinian, runway able."

Then there was silence. We asked directions and were told to follow the "follow me" truck. We approached the end of the runway. "There she is about three miles out on a straight in approach. Do you see her?" asked Jim.

"I've got her. She looks nice and new with her black belly and shiny silver finish," responded Bart.

The new B-29's arriving had factory paint jobs with black bottoms; we were sure we knew the reason they'd been painted in that fashion; we'd be flying a lot of night missions.

We watched the big bird settle on to the runway with a screech of tires as they met the concrete surface. The landing was smooth. The "follow me" truck raced ahead to guide the new crew to a parking place along the coral taxiways. We followed off to one side to keep from being blasted by coral dust from the prop-wash. When they arrived at the designated spot a cleat-track was waiting. The driver of the yellow truck jumped out and guided the B-29 to a stop and gave the pilot the signal to cut engines. Soon the cleat-track moved into position and backed the aircraft in to its parking place.

The hatches opened and the crew disembarked. The first to

duck out of the wheel well was the aircraft commander. He walked toward us and saluted. "Sir, I'm Lieutenant Riley, the AC."

"Ellis here. This is Dawson and Lea. I guess you know you're a member of the 678th Bomb Squadron of the 444th Bomb Group."

"Yes, sir. We have our orders right here." He pulled the big manila envelope out as his co-pilot and bombardier approached. "This's Miller, co-pilot and Wright's our bombardier. The navigator will be down in a few seconds. He's always the last one off with all the crap he has to do. He's one damn good navigator, even if he is a rebel."

We continued to talk for a minute or two trying to explain what was going on even though we'd just arrived today ourselves. I was standing with my back to the plane when Riley said, "Here he comes, finally. I want you to meet Lewis, our Navigator."

I looked at Riley for a split second and then spun around and was shocked to see my friend, Dave. "My God, it can't be. . . . "

"The hell it isn't. Ya'all surprised to see me?"

"Surprised! I can't believe it even if you are standing in front of me!"

Dave moved rapidly toward me and he threw his arms around me in a friendly hug. I knew I had tears in my eyes, but didn't care. I was so delighted, I was at a loss for words. "This is one for the books. You know, the Army never lets these kind of things happen."

"Well, here I am in the flesh! I see they promoted you to first liuey."

"Yeah, they lost their heads. Tell me, when did you know you were coming to our outfit?"

"We knew it before we left the states at the Port of Embarkation. It was hard to believe. I could hardly wait to get here and see the look on your face."

"Now you've seen it. Was I as surprised as you thought I'd be?"

"More so. We were damn near sent to India, but at the last minute they changed our destination to Tinian. We departed from Mather AFB three days ago," explained Dave.

"Christ, I'm sorry. I haven't introduced my asshole buddy from cadets," I said as I discovered everyone watching quietly.

"No excuses needed. We got the picture from the way you two acted," said Bart with a smile.

"We've only been here a few hours ourselves so we don't know much about this place except it looks like heaven compared to the anus of the world, India. By the way, have you heard from Hal? I haven't heard from him for some time. I guess he's in the Philippines."

"Are you kidding! Just before I left Pyote, Texas I received a letter from him telling of his unit's transfer to Guam," explained Dave.

"You've got to be kidding! Guam is only a hundred miles from here! Maybe, we can get together soon. I was thinking of him as we passed over the Philippines and thought he was there. Damn, it's good to see you."

"We'd better get our butts in gear. Colonel Mitchell wants to greet you back in the squadron area and we have to get you guys set up before it gets dark," said Bart as he led the way to the big truck which had just arrived. Bart had a couple bags in each hand. We all lent a hand and soon we were off to our new home.

Dave and I talked all the way back. We hadn't seen each other for a year and a half. We had a lot of catching up to do.

"I'm sure lucky to get assigned to your squadron," said Dave.

"This is a damn good outfit. You'll like all the guys. They stick together," I said.

We arrived in front of the squadron headquarters, led the newcomers in and made the necessary introductions. Bob Mitchell made them feel as we did, part of the family. Then it was time to get them squared away. We put up their tent and as we were putting on the finishing touches, Riley said, "There isn't much here, is there?"

"It won't take the CeeBee's long to get more buildings up and then it should be pretty comfortable," said Bart as he inspected our work.

"You're right, it could be a lot worse. Thanks for taking care of us. Now all we have to do is unpack," said Riley.

"We'll let you get unpacked. Then if you want, we can show you around and introduce you to some of the guys," offered Bart.

We returned to our tent to find Roundy still in the sack. "It can't be true. The sack rat is still asleep. Christ, you would think he overworked himself. Let's give him a piss call," said Jim as we headed toward his cot.

"What the hell is going on?" asked Roundy as he lay on the floor looking up at us. We had rolled him out of his cot on to the floor. We all laughed.

"If we hadn't wakened you, all the food in the mess would be gone and then you'd starve to death," Bart said with a sneer on his face. "Anyway, we have to straighten out this rat's nest and get some clothes hung up, so get your ass in gear and lend a hand," ordered Bart.

"I sure am hungry," said Roundy as he struggled to his feet.

"You eat after. Get cleaned up, we're going over to supply and see if we can get a truck to go after lumber," said Bart

As Roundy dressed, we set out for the supply tent. "Sergeant, we need to borrow a six-by-six for a bit."

"Well, sir, we may need the trucks," the supply sergeant explained trying not to incur Bart's anger.

"I need a damn truck so let's not hassle about it. All the crews are in and we won't be too long. Maybe, I can return the favor in the future," said Bart in a forceful but calm manner.

"Okay sir, but please don't let it out of your sight. The CeeBee's will steal it in a second. I only have a weapons carrier right now. Will that be okay?" asked the sergeant.

"We'll make do, thanks."

We decided to leave Roundy and pointed the truck in the direction of the bomb dump. After directions by some fellows from the 313th Bomb Wing we found the gate to the bomb dump. It was located atop a hill overlooking the ocean to the east. There was no guard at the gate. We drove in and found what Jim was looking for, a stack of 2 X 12's and large wooden crates which had housed bombs. We backed the truck to the stack and helped ourselves. The truck was loaded to capacity when the armed guard found us.

"Sir, what are you officers doing?" asked the guard with a puzzled expression.

"We're picking up some old lumber for tent floors," answered Bart.

"They have officers on detail?" asked the guard unbelieving.

"They're shorthanded since we just got in this morning," explained Bart.

"I guess there's a first time for everything in this man's army," said the guard as he scratched his head and walked away muttering to himself.

"You sure shitted that poor corporal. I've never seen an expression like his in my life," I said as we finished loading.

"Get your ass behind the wheel and don't criticize my methods," said Bart with a smile.

We climbed aboard and headed out the gate and down the hill and back to the squadron area.

"We need more lumber," explained Jim.

"Okay, let's get our asses back and hit up the supply sergeant for a six-by-six and no excuses," said Bart as we departed.

"I'll need nails, hammer, and a saw to get started on our project," Jim said.

"Whatever you need we'll get. You're the carpenter," said Bart as we pulled up in front of our tent. "I'll leave Roundy here to guard our cache and I'll get a bottle of CC for bribing the sergeant," said Bart.

"Damn good idea, he looks like a drinker; it'll be worth it," said Jim.

We unloaded the truck rapidly and headed back to supply with the weapons carrier.

"With a bigger truck we'll have no problem," said Jim.

We drove the short distance to supply and drew a crowd. There seemed to be great excitement in the living area at the sight of the lumber and bomb crates. Many questions were asked. We knew if we didn't get back to the dump soon there'd be a stampede and a good thing would be over. There was plenty of unused lumber, enough for all we were sure if someone didn't screw it up.

"Sarge, can I speak with you outside for a second?" asked Bart.

"Sure thing, sir. What can I do for you?"

"We've a little something for you here." Bart handed the sergeant the bottle and then said, "We need a larger truck to haul some more lumber. How about it?"

The sergeant took the bottle with a grin which soon turned into a smile as wide as an alligator opening his jaws as he looked in the paper sack, then said, "The 6 X 6 is around back."

We climbed on the truck and were off in a cloud of dust in quest of our lumber. There was no time to waste. It was getting late. We knew our secret was out, but it would take others some time to get a truck and we knew exactly where to go. We got to the dump and the corporal scratched his head again as we drove past him at the gate. With this large truck we hauled enough lumber not only for ourselves but for our new neighbors.

We unloaded the lumber and Jim returned the truck and also got the necessary tools to construct our floor and furniture. The supply sergeant had become very cooperative. Soon the word got out on how to get a truck and there was a caravan of trucks headed for the bomb dump and one happy supply sergeant with his new found wealth.

The next day Jim started measuring and cutting the 2 X 12's to length and before our very eyes a floor was built and ready for the tent to be repitched. We all helped, including Dave and his bunch. By nightfall we were comfortably sitting in our new home. The following day we would build the floor for Dave's crew. In a matter of days construction was in different stages throughout the area.

Jim had built wardrobes from up-standing bomb crates and bed racks with the remainder of the 2 X 2's. Then he scrounged old aircraft inner tubes and cut them in strips and pulled them tightly across the rack and secured them. The beds were comfortable and unique. He was very inventive. We were happy he had all the understanding and experience of a builder. He was sought out by many to explain how to build different creature comforts.

I lay on my new bed and thought of this place and the war which seemed so distant. The feeling I had inside was one of relief. I knew the war over Japan would be more fierce than before. The enemy knew of our strength and would have to fight with more determination in an attempt to turn the tide. I didn't think it was possible to slow or stop us now. The Air force had never in its history been driven from attacking a target. It was a tradition which would be carried on against the Japanese homeland.

Okinawa had been invaded a week before by the massive force of American ground troops and they had made good progress. But, fighting had been violent. A new situation had developed called Kamikaze. The Kamikaze or Devine Wind as the Japanese called them was exacting a terrible toll of US ships. The Kamikaze pilots were flying planes with bombs attached. They were flown by half-trained pilots with a will to die for their emperor. Things would get worse rather than better. As many as 350 Jap suicide planes were attacking the American fleet at one time. Losses were staggering. The allied forces shot hundreds down, but couldn't stop them all. It was hell for the sailors aboard the ships.

In Europe the allies had knifed into Germany and the news of the concentration death camps was made public. Germany was through.

Iwo Jima had been secured at a terrible price in American lives.

The airfields were being repaired and new ones built. This gave us an emergency landing field half way to Japan, a good feeling.

The following morning we got up early and finished Riley's tent and after lunch an officers call was announced. After the how-goes-it meeting we were assigned the responsibility of training the new crew. I was delighted to know I'd be working with Dave.

26.

Tinian is one of fourteen islands forming the Marianas. The islands of the group are stretched over 380 miles in a generally north-south direction. The three principal islands are Guam, Saipan, and Tinian. Two of the nearby islands are also well-known. They are called Rota and Pegan. Both islands were occupied by the Japanese. US forces had neutralized and bypassed them. The Marianas are located 1,500 miles east of the Philippines and just north of the Tropic of Cancer. Tinian itself is six by three miles in size. Saipan, three miles to the north, is slightly larger and Guam is the largest island of the group.

Tinian had the largest concentration of aircraft in the world. In addition to the two B-29 wings, it served as the forward staging base for all fighters and light bombers. The Navy had patrol bombers as well as fighters and last came the 509th composite group of atomic fame with their B-29's. There were also countless support type aircraft stationed on the small island.

The climate was good. It rained often, but not the type of rain we struggled with in India. Here, most people continued with their duties when it rained. Only at night does one bother with rain gear. The rain on Tinian makes everything fresh and dissipates rapidly. The monsoon rains of India caused endless flooding and mud slides. The air was fresh and had the pleasant smell of the ocean.

We were happy to note we were indeed getting close to the magical number of thirty-five. Six more missions and sayonara. There were a few crews who had more missions than we and would leave before us assuming they had no unforeseen trouble. We'd been off status with wounds received some months before and fell behind. One could feel the pressure the older crews were experiencing as they approached thirty-five. The odds figured to be less each time you went into combat, but it was something you tried not to think about because you had little control of your destiny.

Our squadron made available one of their tents as a classroom. However, most instruction was given in the shade of a tree outdoors. Buildings and tents were entered only when required. The breeze outdoors was pleasant, but indoors it was unbearablely hot without any means of air conditioning.

We instructed our new charges in all facets of operations before we allowed them to fly. The one-on-one policy of training made instruction much easier and more complete. After two days an aircraft was scheduled for their first transition flight. Crews had to be certified prior to flying a combat mission. We taught procedures only. They knew their jobs before they arrived. Crews received good training in the States, but we had to teach them combat tactics and procedures. The policy of the aircraft commanders and the navigators flying as observers on their first mission would afford them the opportunity of seeing the show without worrying about the mission. We never had the luxury; we'd learned as we flew combat.

We arrived at the hardstand which housed our old plane, *Lucky Lady*. We spent over an hour going over the exterior and making the necessary pre-flight inspections. Everything checked out and we were ready to go. Our students were impressed with the decorations *Lucky Lady* had on her nose. The bombs depicting combat missions, the camels for Hump missions and the small Japanese flags for aerial victories. I conducted a short meeting with the bomb team members and after making clear the requirements we all pulled the props through and climbed aboard.

Dave was in the seat as were most of the new crew members. Only Bart remained at the controls. Working with Dave was easy. He was as his AC said, an excellent navigator. The weather was clear and bright with a few puffy clouds drifting through the area. We headed for the bombing range at one of the Japanese held islands. Our target was a much bombed runway the Japs had used prior to being neutralized. Rota was nearly as large as Tinian and was nearby.

The islands of Truk and Yak far to the south were used for the long-range training missions. We'd use one of them later in our training. Each day we flew a different profile and soon it was check ride time. They did fine and were certified combat ready.

As a new crew they wouldn't keep the new aircraft they flown to Tinian. It was decided since we were ready to have a new aircraft assigned, they would get *Lucky Lady* and we'd take the new plane. Once again the search was on for a suitable name.

Riley was lucky to have such a fine plane assigned to him. We made them promise to treat her right. If they did, she'd get them there and, more importantly, back.

We took a final vote and decided our new plane would be called *Here's Hopin*. The name symbolized our hope for a speedy end to the war and our further hopes to be around after number thirty-five. The name was painted on her nose in time for our first mission from Tinian.

The nights on Tinian were very different from what we'd become accustomed to in India. Here you heard no Jackals wailing. It'd taken some time to get used to the noises of India, but here it was quiet and peaceful with gentle evening breezes. However, there was one aspect which was unnerving. We lived in the middle of the tall sugarcane and so did some of the Japanese soldiers who were not killed or captured. They existed on K-rations and other bits of food they stole. They also stole items of clothing such as boots, shirts and pants, none of which bothered me. What did bother me was their howling at all hours of the night from their concealment. It'd come out in broken English, "Yankee, sona-bitch, I cut your throat tonight." The sounds were nearby. Thick cane made their concealment complete. We learned to sleep with our .45's under our pillows.

There was a group called the "night fighters." All Negro infantry troops who made sweeps through the sugarcane and shot anything white. It sounded like a real war outside our tents. Their sweeps sometimes produced prisoners, but in most cases bodies. The Japanese persisted, however. When the firing started everyone headed for a slit trench. One didn't want to be mistaken for the enemy. I wasn't sure which bothered me most, the intense shooting or the threat of having my throat cut.

Rumors and reports kept filtering through the area. One of the reports was of an unnamed officer who visited the latrine late one night and in the dim light of the eight holer tried to have a conversation with another visitor seated at the far end. The officer asked the other fellow a question and merely got a grunt in return. From that assumption was drawn that Japanese soldiers were using our toilet facilities late at night hoping not to be detected. The story was true as far as we were concerned. It became usual practice when visiting the latrine at night to carry a weapon.

In addition to living and hiding in the sugarcane the Japs lived in the hills and caves along the water's edge. It was suggested by headquarters to avoid sightseeing in those areas and to avoid going near them unarmed or alone. Most of us heeded the warning. However, there were those who didn't take the warning seriously. Some paid the price. Often they were never seen again.

As the days progressed, activity on the flight line picked up. The maintenance people worked hard to get us into a-one shape, knowing at any minute the call would go out to resume combat operations. Most of us were eager to get on with it; after all we were getting close to finishing our tour and flying was the only way to accomplish the task. If all went well we should finish our missions within a month.

The war news was good. The Americans on Okinawa had cracked the Japanese defenses and in Europe both Hitler and Mussolini were dead. Things were happening fast. Maybe we'd get more attention out here in the Pacific. It always seemed as though Europe was the focus of our government.

There was also bad news. Within a week, our president, Franklin D. Roosevelt and war correspondent Ernie Pyle were dead. The president of natural causes, and our beloved Ernie at the hands of the Japanese near Okinawa. Death was nothing new to us. However, the effect was one of complete sorrow.

We knew the end of the war in Europe was at hand when a new report came in recording the capture of hundreds of thousands of German soldiers by Eisenhower's armies.

* * *

Buildings cropped up everywhere throughout the area making it look more like a military installation rather than a helter-skelter bunch of tents. The CeeBee's were now replacing tents with quonset huts and with the huts came a new way of living. The CeeBee's were an industrious group with all the know how to accomplish the task of putting together the large erector sets.

We soon discovered the waters surrounding our island were deep, clear and beautiful. It abounded with color and it was possible to see the great depths and behold the beauty of the coral formations and the countless fish.

The beach was at the foot of a cliff. The Ceebee's had constructed a sturdy stairway from the plateau above to the sand and coral far below. To get to the water one had to negotiate the sharp coral. Admission to the beach was paid by removing at least one rock from the area bathers used. We became expert on the method of crossing the coral without shoes. Perched on an outcropping far above the beach was a lifeguard warning tower. The tower served two purposes: to warn of large fish, and to help swimmers in trouble. At times the flag would go up and you were prohibited from entering the water. It was during these times a new sport was invented. At the base of the cliffs for countless years the large trees lining the cliffs dropped their leaves which gathered in large piles. In the dead leaves one could hear the thunderous noise created by rats that were as large as house cats. We considered them a menace. We were required to carry our sidearms which came in handy with our new sport. We lay in the sand with our forty-fives cradled in our hands and shot the rats. When hit, the rats would explode into nothingness. Bets were made. It was safe because we only fired toward the cliff and we were eradicating the rat population. Many dollars exchanged hands during the contests.

* * *

General Ramey, 58th Bomb Wing Commander was a blustery, earthy leader. When he spoke, you listened. His vocabulary was what made him earthy. Most of his sentences were interspersed with four letter words; his meaning was never left in doubt. He was a leader unafraid of flying missions with the combat crews. He flew as commmand pilot on a number of missions. In fact bomber command wanted him to fly less on the dangerous raids. He had gained our respect as a soldier's general. He put out a standing order to the effect that no operator of a vehicle would pass a man walking if he had room in the vehicle. The order came about when he found men walking to the beach some distance away as trucks passed empty. This made the trip to the beach more enjoyable. The order included all ranks and woe to the man who disobeyed it. A visit to his office for disregarding his order could be very traumatic.

April 1945 came to an end and we knew soon we'd be back in combat. The whole wing had finished specialized training using large formations and other tactics. Good formations meant we could fight off large concentrations of enemy fighters.

May rolled around and I realized on this day I'd become a major. Not in rank, but age. I could now vote! But we had no elections in the Army, so it meant little. In honor of my birthday a nice mission briefing was held. Our first mission from Tinian was to be flown with two wings. We would attack the naval facilities at Kure, Japan with the 73rd Bomb Wing on Saipan. The 73rd had moved into our vacated facilities in Kansas after our departure for India. One hundred and fifty B-29's were scheduled for the raid. A daylight mission was planned and we were leading the 444th Bomb Group, second across the target. Getting all the planes across the target in the shortest possible time was the goal. Visibility would deteriorate rapidly as bombs caused fires sending smoke skyward. Our goal was to surprise the enemy, leaving them no time to land and rearm.

I was excited about our first mission from Tinian. It would be very different with Iwo Jima in our hands. The chances of survival were greatly improved. The islands of Saipan and Tinian so close together came to life with a roar at midnight, the 5th of May as preparations for an 0400 takeoff were under way. Sleep had been near impossible with a midnight alert. The mission would take over fourteen hours from start to finish. We referred to it as a ball-buster. After all the last minute briefings and chow, transportation took us to our shiny new plane. It looked so undressed without the symbols of combat adorning her nose. We passed our gallant *Lucky Lady* with her decorations of accomplishment displayed and knew we would miss her.

We accomplished the necessary pre-flight requirements and climbed aboard to await the signal to start engines. The signal came and the island rocked as all the engines sparked to life with a roar. We responded to the taxi signal and were first to pull out onto the taxiway followed by the deputy lead and the others according to formation position. It was a great luxury having two runways for departures and it saved precious fuel. The two lines of aircraft all turned 45 degrees to the runway and accomplished their runups. It was an impressive site to look down the long line of aircraft with spinning propellers. It sent a shiver of pride down my spine. The signal for takeoff was received and each line started to feed on to their respective runways. Within seconds the huge B-29's hurtled down the runway and into the black pre-dawn sky. Takeoff interval was fifteen seconds for spacing. It'd take less than twenty minutes for the seventy-five B-29's to be airborne.

After takeoff timing of turns was mandatory because aircraft from Saipan would come close to our departure lanes. Mid-air collisions had to be avoided.

It went well as 135,000 pounds of machine and men lifted skyward after nearly two miles of runway passing beneath the B-29's. I was surprised how well executed the departure plan had gone as we climbed to our initial altitude of 10,000 feet. Our formation was strung out many miles behind as we winged our way north. Formations were kept loose until we neared the Japanese coast.

Dave sat next to me, eying my every move, reminding me of my first ride in a B-29. As Dave and I worked together I could see the excitement on his face. After all, this would be his baptism of fire. I tried to relax him, but one must remember you have to experience combat. No one can make it easier. It was never a lark. Fear was always present, but suppressed. One way to overcome fear was to work hard and keep your mind on the business at hand. Some people were obsessed with fear. Others lived with it and showed little. I took the attitude after the first enemy aircraft fired on us that we were in a fight to the finish. Dave and his pilot, Alex, had to see for themselves; it was part of the indoctrination. To sit and watch was far worse than taking part in the action. However, there was no better way to get the experience needed and not be burdened with decisions and responsibility. Their next mission would be with their own crew and plane.

We passed over Iwo Jima and flew on to the rendezvous point three and a half hours ahead. We circled over the imaginary point for twenty minutes allowing the planes of our group to get into their assigned spots. If a plane couldn't make the rendezvous he was instructed to join the next formation going in, but in no case was he to attack a target alone. Unlike the European theater of operation, we had what was called the buddy system. If a plane was in trouble, we tried to protect it by slowing the formation and escorting him out of the danger area. When an aircraft had to ditch we tried to stick with them until we were sure of their location, then reported the location and rendered any assistance possible.

We came toward the target from our departure point as numerous enemy fighters attacked us. We arrived over the target and the flak which had dogged us since landfall continued unabated. The black bursts exploded near us and it was fairly accurate. We escaped major damage. However, this wasn't the case for two of the 150 B-29's. Luckily, none of our group was lost. We'd dropped over 600 tons of bombs on the primary target and caused major damage. The enemy fighters suffered ten lost with fifteen probables and twenty-five damaged. Our crew had accounted for one of the enemy losses and another damaged. We hoped it'd be confirmed.

On the same day the rest of the XXI Bomber Command was busy on two other targets. The 313th Bomb Wing from Tinian hit Kobe on a night mission. The 314th Bomb Wing from Guam was bombing Kamikaze fields on Kyushu, a day mission. In all there were 289 aircraft bombing primary targets and ten others hitting secondary targets. The 314th lost three aircraft and the 313th escaped without a loss. Your chances of survival were greatly enhanced at night. Two B-29's of our group landed at Iwo Jima for repairs or fuel and all others continued home without further incident.

"How do you feel Dave, now that you have your first mission under your belt?" I asked as we reached the ground.

"It scared the shit out of me! I'm glad I was with you. You're a cool cat under fire. I'm not sure I'll be able to stay as calm as you guys. You acted like it was a training mission, so damn calm!"

"Looks are deceiving."

"Well, I'm impressed. You used to get more excited in navigation school when we flew the old AT-7."

"Here comes our truck. Let's get aboard so we can get to debriefing. Remember, don't be afraid to speak up during debriefing. They want to know what everyone saw. Our doctor, dentist and chaplain will have all the booze drunk if we don't hurry."

"You're kidding!"

"Like hell. They meet all missions and they serve up the mission booze. Remember the briefers will want to know color of flak, number of bursts, number of fighters, damage to either friendly or enemy and stuff like that. They plot flak corridors and flak concentrations. Do you remember those red circles on the briefing maps in front of the briefing room?"

"I sure do!"

"The info comes from mission reporting. It's damn necesary if you want to survive."

We entered the large tent pitched next to the briefing room.

The debriefing had gone well and now it was time to relax and have some booze to calm the soul. Just as I'd told Dave, our three greeters were already fairly well oiled. Bart raised his glass for a toast. "Here's hoping all our missions go as well and here's hoping that you two will have as much good luck as we have. Oh, I almost forgot—a toast to Johnny on his birthday, even if it was a couple of days ago."

"I think we ought to drink to Pops for his confirmed kill today," I added.

Pops was so damn proud he looked like a strutting hen after laying an egg. "The next one's on me," he drawled.

We were feeling no pain as we left the tent and started toward our tents two blocks away. Riley's crew had met us as we emerged from the tent and greeted their returning heros with gusto. We could hear the excitement in the tent next door as the old combat warriors told of their great experiences.

27.

Life on Tinian improved in spite of outdoor privies, cold salt-water showers and the tents we called home. It was hard for the newcomers to understand how much better the quality of life was here compared to India, but they had nothing to judge by. However, no matter how bad it was, I'll always remember my experiences while being assigned there.

Work was being completed on the new consolidated mess, a large ugly building which looked like a huge screened porch. All buildings constructed here had one thing in common. Except for the briefing room, they were built in such a way as to take advantage of the sea breeze. The briefing room was a long building which had to be secured during briefings which made it a very uncomfortable place to be for very long. When section briefings were held which didn't require the large plexiglass boards briefings were held outdoors.

The one activity always conducted outdoors was the nightly movie. It had the appearance of the drive-in movies of today except there were no vehicles. The weather was no factor. Most pulled their ponchos over their heads when the rain came down; few left. Being wet was a way of life on the islands of the Pacific.

The highlight of the night was watching the Marine Corps anti-aircraft units in action. A tow-target would be pulled across the blackness of the sky at an altitude hardly visible. First the search-lights came to life and stabbed through the black void followed rapidly by the firing of the 90mm gun batteries located strategically in the area. The big guns fired by proficient crews usually cut the tow cable instead of hitting the sleeve. The noise and vibration was thunderous. Many of us thought the rock was going to shake off its foundation and slip in to the eight mile depths called the Mariana's trench. The big guns fired rapidly and the bursts lit up the sky with a display of flashes and color hard to duplicate at a fair. We knew the marines were good as we watched the sleeve slowly fall to earth while the searchlights followed it down.

The 444th Group Officer Association had been collecting dues from the officers since its inception and little had been expended to date. It was decided we'd put the money to work by building an officers and a separate enlisted club. Each club was designed to look over the beautiful waters of the blue Pacific and to take advantage of the cooling breezes. The officers club was designed and built by the officers. Jim was one of the honchos. There were bars, gaming rooms and rooms for relaxation. Three airplanes were dispatched to Honolulu, Hawaii to buy all types of furniture, ice machines, crap tables, and the likes for both clubs. Everyone not engaged in flying or other work spent time working on the clubs. The buildings rose rapidly with the cheap labor and soon the doors were opened and life improved again. Our club was the jewel of the area; none came close to its design or beauty. It drew officers, civilians, and nurses from every corner of the island. It was a treat to see real American women. The opposite sex had a great effect on morale. The club grew in popularity and on any given night you'd see every type vehicle Uncle Sam had in the inventory parked outside. Opening night, a gala affair, was held and everyone had a ball. Being able to sit down on a real chair and sip a drink was a great treat.

All beer and coke was rationed, however little was obtained in this manner. An institution called the Tasa Officers Locker Fund came into being. For forty dollars officers could become members. A bottle a week could be purchased at ridiculously low prices. Most name brands cost around one dollar and had a street value in excess of two hundred and fifty dollars or more to Ceebee chiefs. I was approached by a Navy chief, but I wouldn't sell the booze for a profit. I thought it unfair. The chief didn't care what the price was: he had more money than he knew what to do with. They made trinkets from sea shells and watchbands from aluminum. They had a lucrative market. Most carried rolls of bills that would choke a hog. The watchbands went for twenty-five dollars and were advertised as metal from a downed Jap zero. What a laugh, but they were good watchbands. I offered Walt Smith a bottle of my booze every other week. I couldn't drink much and anyway it was always available at the club. This made him and the other enlisted troops of the crew happy.

One Monday morning after I had picked up my ration of booze

a salty old Navy chief approached me in his pug nosed weapons carrier. He said he'd like to buy the bottle I'd just purchased. "Chief, it's not for sale. I'm not going to cheat you."

"Sir, you wouldn't be cheating me. Just name your price."

"I've a good idea! We don't get much beer or coke around here and I hear you fellows have all you can drink, is that true?"

"More or less. Why?"

"If you could build an ice box and keep it stocked with beer, coke and ice I'll give you a bottle a week. That is, if one of my buddies will part with a bottle every other week."

"Sounds fine to me, lieutenant. I'll get the ice box built and be back in an hour or two. In the meantime make a deal with one of your buddies."

The chief took off in a cloud of dust. He was in a hurry to get my bottle of VO. Rich was happy to take part in the enterprise. In less than two hours the chief was back with a large ice box full of beer and coke iced. I handed him the bottle. He licked his lips as he uncorked it and took a long swig. "I'll have some one here twice a day to keep this box filled. You can count on it, sir."

"Sounds great. If you keep your word you'll have whatever kind of booze you'd like," I said as he turned to leave.

I walked to the front of the tent as he climbed behind the wheel of his small truck. "Lieutenant, VO will be just fine," he said as he snapped the clutch and sped away.

The old chief only appeared on the day the booze was due. He had a sailor come by twice a day to fill the ice box. Word got out around the squadron of our deal and similar deals were made. I could never figure how the sailors got all the beer and coke, but I didn't really care.

The ninety-day offensive had been instituted by General LeMay to try to end the war by destroying the war making capability of the Japanese people. We knew we were in for some rough times. We took the news with anticipation. We had but five missions to go and if there was a balls out effort we could be finished with our tour earlier than anticipated. No one spoke of the losses. It was kind of like a team not talking about a no-hitter in late innings. We were optimistic and that was enough.

New orders of awards were published and all the crew had been awarded the Distinguished Flying Cross as well as the fifth Air Medal and the Purple Heart for Bart and I. We were real live heroes and wanted to keep it that way. Bart was funny. He pinned his new medals to his T-shirt and paraded around the tent posing as if he were Napoleon on the foredeck of a ship. He was a kick.

We had built a volleyball court behind the tents and the competition was keen. It was a great way to get exercise. A baseball field was being built as well as a chapel. The chapel was another task Jim had entered into. He'd make a good building contractor after the war.

The food was a mess at the mess. Some things never change. Our government seemed to import all the damn mutton Australia and New Zealand produced and we exported all our beef. Dehydrated mutton was the worst food I'd ever tried to eat. Bart's graphic way of expressing himself made sense. He said, "It was like eating shit." He's probably right although I'd never admitted consuming the stinky stuff.

My mother was my savior. She sent a box as often as possible. It generally contained enough peanut butter to last between parcels. Other items like cookies, caramels and cakes were also sent. Unfortunately, each box looked as if elephants had trampled it and all the food except the peanut butter tasted like diesel oil. The cakes were generally unrecognizable and the cookies were crumbs. I never told her how they were received. I knew my family was doing without just to make me happy. I tried to tell her to send peanut butter only, but it fell on deaf ears. As a kid I'd always loved peanut butter. In fact my folks told the story of how I'd pass up steak for a jar of peanut butter. The peanut butter was an all around food and it kept me from starving. At the dining hall I was very selective, usually taking vegetables and fruit when available and of course bread for my peanut butter. The island bakery made delicious bread. I usually took extra slices back to the tent to make sandwiches.

On one occasion upon returning from the beach we smelled the fresh bread being baked and stopped to visit the bakery. I was sorry I did. We looked through the screened door and saw a massive man with a cigarette hanging from his mouth kneading the dough. He was sweating profusely and the moisture was flowing into the dough and the ash from his cigarette dropped in the mixture as well. As he mixed the dough it'd come in contact with his fat stomach. I almost turned green. I wished for all the world I'd not seen what was going on. It took me a few days to eat the bread again.

Tinian was an interesting place to explore, but we had little time to see the sights. Vehicles became available as time passed making it possible to get around a little more. Tinian town or what was left of it was an interesting place. The town had ancient ruins apparently without archaeological attention to place it in history, but it was an interesting place where many photos were taken for our families to view.

It was during one of these excursions we a found a Japanese shrine in the hills. It'd been pilfered, probably by the Marines who had discovered hidden treasure in the jungle. At the shrine the foliage was thick. The trees seem to grow limbs from the ground up making passage difficult. It was an unnerving place where one had the feeling of being watched. On occasion Japanese soldiers were flushed from jungle areas, but few people were hunting an enemy thought to be harmless. We stayed in a group and kept to the paths; there was safety in numbers.

"Let's get our butts out of here; we're probably in the gun sight of some Nip right now," said Jim as he looked down from the shrine at the head of the staircase cut into the jungle.

"Not a bad idea, this place gives me the willies," said Rich as he started down the steps cautiously.

With the officers of Dave's crew as well as us the two jeeps were overflowing. None of us needed further coaxing; we'd seen enough. As we headed down the narrow road someone caught sight of something in the undergrowth. We stopped to investigate and found an old oxen wagon which had been abandoned. We pulled it out on the roadway to examine it more closely. It was in good shape. We hooked it up behind our jeep and drove toward our cantonment area to show off our prize. We parked it in front of our tent for display. Our wagon was often stolen, but we always recovered it. We finally chained it to a firmly driven stake and there were no further thefts.

The group commander ordered an officer's call. The main topic was the cut back of nonessential officers. We were told the flying officers would be assigned additional duties to take up the slack. Admittedly some were figurehead positions. However, there were jobs which carried a lot of responsibility. It was easy to see why they wanted to ship out the ground officers. Some weren't earning their keep.

I was assigned the position of personal equipmment officer, whatever that was! I got all the information possible about the duties and then headed to the flight line to examine my new command. When I arrived, I felt the hostility of the NCOIC, a master sergeant. Their command chart on the wall indicated a number of other men were assigned. The duty of the personal

262

equipment officer was to maintain and supply all items pertaining to the crew's survival. The sergeant was unhappy because he thought I was going to upset his dynasty. It was far from the truth. I had no intention of disrupting the section by petty ego trips. There were definite advantages to this position which made the job worthwhile. One was a jeep of my own.

"Sergeant, I'm Lieutenant Lea. I've been assigned as officer in charge of this section. Let's make my position clear. I don't intend to disrupt a well functioning activity. I'll not get in your way. When you need me let me know. I'll be available when not flying."

"Sir, I'd heard you were okay, but damn, if we got some damn shavetail, sorry sir, I didn't mean to infer. . . . "

"Don't try to explain. I was an enlisted man myself, you guys can run this outfit, let's leave it at that."

"Sir, you'll have to sign reports and requisitions on occasion, otherwise we'll not bother you."

"Sounds like a winner to me."

"Lieutenant, your jeep is out in front. We've got trucks and weapons carriers too."

"Good show; keep up the good work and I'll be seeing you," I said as I walked out of the quonset hut to examine my new vehicle.

The other officers assignments of our crew were made, but I liked mine best. Bart and Jim became assistant maintenance officers. Rich was appointed assistant armorment officer and Roundy was rewarded with no assignment. Sure was funny. The more you worked, the more responsibility you were given. The less you worked, the less they expected of you. All the new jobs carried with it a vehicle for use by the assigned officer for emergency. Our tent area looked like a mini motor pool.

On 8 May 1945 we were alerted for a combat mission. This mission would be for the 58th Bomb Wing exclusively. During the briefing we were informed it was V-E Day. The war in Europe had finally come to an end. Now, it was time to concentrate all the governments efforts on Japan. As far as the Air Force was concerned we had enough power to take care of our end of the business. It was the ground forces who needed a lot of help with the possibility of an invasion of Japan staring them in the face.

The target selected was O'Shima and we were designated group lead. Riley would command his own crew and would be flying our old standby *Lucky Lady*. Each of the four groups would input twenty-two aircraft with the remainder of the wing flying with the 73rd and 313th Wings. Every combat crew in the group would be flying. O'Shima was a long mission requiring the use of bomb bay tanks which cut our bomb load to twenty-two 500 pounders. We'd drop GP's from 17,000 feet in daylight.

"Johnny, can I work out my flight plan with you?" asked Dave.

"Sure thing brother. It's a good idea for all the navigators to flight plan together. This keeps us on the same wave length," I explained.

"Great."

"Daylight missions are more complex and require more planning. Don't worry, we'll hit all the important highlights."

"One thing has bugged me about the daylight missions."

"What's that, Dave?"

"Why do you rendezvous on the coast of Japan rather than at sea?"

"That's easy. We pick a point easy to recognize. We've had little or no trouble with Japanese fighters while we are forming up. Why, I don't know."

"You'll notice the rendezvous point is always near the IP. From the rendezvous we leave on course for the IP."

We completed our work and headed home. I was most happy to drive some of the others in my new convertible. We had to get some rest for the 0100 alert.

The alert came and I awoke from a sound sleep. We had three and a half hours before takeoff and much had to be done. We ate and got our final briefing; then it was time for us to head for our birds. Transportation picked us up at ops and delivered us to the birds. We were greeted by my personal equipment troops making sure everything was okay and checking to see if there was anything special I wanted. I'd gained their confidence and all went well with Sergeant Walker running the show.

The tough part of our missions was the takeoff. On occasion a plane would not develop enough power and would crash into the hill at the end of the runway. Unfortunately, the hill was near the marines living area. When they heard the sound of engines starting there was a mass exodus until the last plane took off. With the planes at their maximum weight, engine failure could spell doom if it happened too far down the runway. We taxied past *Lucky Lady*. I said a silent prayer for my friend's safety. In a way it made things tougher on me than before they arrived. Before I had only our crew to worry about; now I worried about my closest friend, too.

The signal came and we gained takeoff speed as full power was applied to the engines; she responded and we climbed and headed for our destination 1,500 miles to the north.

Over the target eighty B-29's hit the primary, dropping 383 tons. There had been enemy fighter attacks, but they were ineffective and scattered. The flak on the other hand was effective but we lost no aircraft. Our claims were eight enemy fighters destroyed and twelve probables. We later found that *Lucky Lady* had been hit by flak, but not in a vital area. She had a charmed life. *Lucky Lady* landed fifteen minutes after our landing on Tinian. Iwo Jima saved ten aircraft. Our former students were a happy lot when we met them at the debriefing. The real success of the long overwater missions rested with the navigator and how he managed the bomb team. Dave obviously did well. Max Riley was sure he had the best. I personally thought he was great, but I knew one who was better!

After the debriefing we made our way into the booze tent and our greeters were feeling no pain. They were especially happy when they heard we had no losses. The excitement of the new crew was hard to describe. Soon more crews joined us and the tent was bulging with humanity. Everyone was happy, especially Walt Jenkins and his crew. They'd just completed their thirty-fifth mission and would be heading home in a few days. I dreamt of the day I'd enter this tent and know I was through flying combat and would be heading home. It shouldn't be long now.

"Let me tell you fellows; the mission was a tough one for my troops, but we made it and I'd like to present a toast to all those who'll never make it home, God bless them," said Captain Jenkins as tears flowed down his cheeks unabated.

The chaplain stepped forward and said, "You'd make a good preacher, Jenkins. I'm happy to see you and your men heading home to your loved ones. I'd like to buy the next drink."

"Padre, how come you never buy at the club?" asked Bart as he accepted the drink.

"Like hell, you say," the chaplain responded.

"That doesn't sound very ecclesiastical, padre," retorted Bart.

I knew if I had one more glass of Four Roses someone would have to carry me home. I staggered out to the company street and stumbled home followed by the others.

We slept peacefully until the noise made by the crews returning from the other mission made further sleep impossible. I got up and went out for my saltwater shave and shower. Everyone but Roundy was rising, but I didn't care. He'd done a good job on the mission.

On my return to the tent I got a big surprise. Seated before me was Hal Landis. He was talking to Bart. I could hardly believe my eyes. "Hal, am I glad to see you!" I said as he put the bear hug on me. "Where the hell did you come from?"

"Just down the road apiece. I'm stationed at Anderson on Guam," he answered.

"Wait until Dave sees you."

"Dave! What the hell are you talking about?"

"Christ, I thought you knew."

"Knew what?"

"Dave is right next door. He's assigned to our squadron."

"You're kidding! You mean with all the B-29 outfits out here he was assigned to your squadron?"

"You've got it right. He flew his second mission last night and we got a little drunk afterward. Do you think we should give him a piss call?"

"You bet your sweet ass."

"By the way, I'm sorry for not introducing everyone."

"Not to worry, we introduced ourselves."

We left the tent as I pulled on my clothes and headed for Dave's tent.

"These two guys are my pilots. Bill Laydon and Hank Thompson," said Hal. They'd been sitting in the borrowed jeep.

"Glad to meet you, both. My name is John, John Lea," I said before Hal had a chance to finish the introductions. "Would you like to come along?" I asked.

"We know you better than you think. All we hear about is you and Dave when you three were in cadets. We'll wait here," said Bill.

We turned toward the tent and pulled the flap back and entered as Jim and Bart came out to talk to Hal's pilots. All five were dead to the world. I hated waking them, but this was a special occasion.

"Piss call," yelled Hal as he approached the peacefully sleeping, Dave.

Dave, as well as the others in the tent sprang up to a sitting position as Hal let out the yell. They must have thought they were under attack. Dave rubbed his eyes and jumped out of bed and grapped Hal's hand. "What a surprise! We knew you were down at Guam and hoped to get down there to see you, but this is great," said Dave as he pulled on his short pants. The others in the tent laid back and tried to go back to sleep.

"How long can you stay?" I asked.

"We have to get back tonight," said Hal.

"Let's make the most of it, then. How about some chow and then we can all go swimming and hunting," I said.

"Hunting! What for?" asked Hal with an odd look on his face.

"Rats as big as house cats. It's a ball. we'll show you," I answered.

"You've got to be kidding. What do you use to kill them?"

"Our forty-fives. It's great fun to watch the little bastards explode."

"It sounds like great sport, but I'd rather swim," said Hal.

"We can do both."

"I'd like to get you two down to Guam. Things down there are a bit more civilized than here."

"Maybe we can wrangle a three-day pass and come down and see you soon. I've a couple high school chums down there with the Navy I'd like to see, too," I said.

"I get an itch to fly the B-29 rather than the old Gooney Bird, but we can't have everything," said Hal.

"Johnny only has a few missions to go and he'll be heading for home," said Dave.

"Yeah, the hard ones. We just had one crew finish, but not long ago we lost one on their last mission. One never knows. I try to take them one at a time and think positive."

"How about you, Hal? You've been overseas almost as long as Johnny?" asked Dave.

"It's hard to say, but I could be leaving within a couple of months, if all goes okay," answered Hal.

"It looks like you'll both be home and I'll still be struggling out here winning the war," said Dave.

"As long as we're as close as we are we can still plan to get together occasionally. And when this war is over if you two move to California we can be neighbors. There's no way I would live in Minnesota or Mississippi," I said.

We spent a marvelous day forgetting all the problems of the period. We shot a number of rats and in doing so we made the area sound like a small war. All too soon we had to return so Hal could get airborne before dark.

The three musketeers had finally got together again. We knew it wouldn't be as long to wait until our next meeting.

28.

Dave and I approached the landing field and saw great preparations being made. We knew something big was on. We drove to the personal equipment building to find out what it was. We came to a stop in front of the building and entered. Dave was impressed with my new command. We soon found there was a maximum effort mission being prepared for. Most of the men from the section were on the flight line checking all life saving equipment. Two men remained in the supply room. Sergeant Walker met us and showed Dave the facility. He led us to the rear of the building which housed a darkroom. I'd no idea it was there. The sergeant had been reluctant to tell me of its existence for fear I'd object. I was in fact delighted. They were doing good work and supplied me with film and took pictures, which I had little time to do.

Dave and I returned to the squadron area and found the mission was scheduled for the 25th, two days from now. We went to operations to see if we were scheduled. I was anxious to fly each mission to get it over with. Both our crews were on the board.

I found Bart and Jim and we decided to go down to the flight line and see if our plane was in top shape. Rich, Roundy and the enlisted troops were already there. Rich was busy loading bombs with the help of the bomb-loading people. The gunners were busy loading .50 cal ammo. I checked the navigation systems. Roundy came forward and said he'd found something wrong with the radar and was going to get the radar maintenance people over right away. He didn't think it was serious. There were crews working on all the airplanes within sight.

The following day general briefing was held and the briefing building was jammed. Each crew sat in one line on each side of the aisle and extra chairs were provided in the rear of the room. You didn't have to be an expert to see something big was on. The brass entered and the regular amenities were observed as the head briefing officer with his long pointer in hand addressed the audience. As he spoke of the mission in general terms the map behind him was uncovered and we could see where we were headed the next morning. The target was Nagoya, one of the most heavily defended targets in Japan. It was part of the iron triangle made up of Nagoya, Osaka and Kobe. The lines drawn across the large map laid testament to the number of B-29's which would participate on this mission.

The mission would be the first with all four B-29 wings striking the same target and would be the largest 20th Air Force effort to date. Five hundred and twenty-five B-29's were scheduled, 141 from the 58th alone. We'd be carrying 500 pound incendiary cluster bombs. The bombs were actually thirteen small thermite bombs which at a predetermined altitude would be dispersed via a proximity fuse. When the fuse fired, the thermite bombs were spread over a large area. The bombs could burn through anything. They were devastating. The fire bombs as they were commonly called became the most feared weapon by the Japanese, and for good reason. We were burning their cities to the ground and they could do nothing to stop us. Japanese fire fighting equipment was woefully inadequate to handle the fire storms. In most cases they let the fires burn themselves out.

The number of aircraft involved in this mission made planning complicated for the planners as well as lead crews. When arriving at the rendezvous it would be difficult to sort out our aircraft from others. I think this is the main reason they repainted all the tails on the B-29's with large emblems. We used to have a small diamond with the aircraft number painted in the center. Now a large triangle with an "N" designating the 444th Bomb Group of the 58th Wing adorned our tail. Other groups of our wing had different letters in the large triangle. Our squadron used red trim and the other two squadrons had different colors.

Within the space of three miles three wings would send over 450 planes aloft. The planes from Guam posed no problem because of their distance from us. Discipline and timing was the key to eliminating collisions.

Each wing had a separate rendezvous point, but all were near each other. Sorting out the planes was accomplished by use of color smoke bombs. The crews were briefed to join other formations if they could not meet the time criteria or got mixed up. Many times planes from different wings joined to fly over the target because of those problems. Elements of the 58th Bomb Wing left the rendezvous and headed for the IP.

There was an unusually large number of enemy fighters in the air. They had spotted the first formation and down they came out of the sun. After their initial attack they came at us from all angles. Their best pilots were here to do battle. Our gunners shot one of the enemy down and damaged at least two more. We were blessed with excellent gunners and the best gunnery system.

It was pure hell going into the target area. Flak came up, then fighters then flak again, there was no let up. Everywhere you looked, fierce and deadly combat was going on. I'd never seen so many enemy fighters at one time. I hoped some day we'd have fighter protection, mostly just to keep the enemy busy. Both enemy and friendly aircraft were dropping from the sky; it was a gruesome sight.

Our planes dropped over 2,500 tons on the primary. We'd destroyed three square miles of the city including part of the Mitsubishi Aircraft Engine Factory. Tactically the mission was a great success. We'd shot down a total of thirty-one enemy planes with thirty-five probables and 115 damaged. Our losses were also great. We'd lost eleven B-29's; two had come from the 58th Bomb Wing and worse, one of the two was from our squadron. Our good friends and lead crew partners took a direct hit in the bomb bays and the plane disintegrated into nothing. Pappy Karns and his crew were on their last mission and were planning to be on their way home within days. It was a great personal loss to us; we'd been close. It put the pressure on us, too, for we were the only lead crew left from our squadron. We felt sick about losing our friends and the thought of them being killed on their last mission put a damper on everything.

Two nights later all four wings were again after Nagoya with 457 B-29's. They dropped over 3,600 tons of incendiaries, burning out another 3.8 square miles and causing extensive damage to the Mitsubishi aircraft plant. Again, success; we had lost only three planes. However, another was from our squadron. One of our newest crews had lost their aircraft commander and navigator who were with an older crew on their orientation mission. The rest of the crew would now have to join the pool and hope to get a pilot and navigator. An eyewitness said some of the crew bailed out, but couldn't say how many chutes were sighted, it didn't look good, but there was some hope. If they were captured they might

270

survive the war in a POW camp. It sure beats the hell out of the alternative. Our crew didn't fly on this mission due to our assignment to lead the next day's mission to Tachikawa.

The great air offensive was in high gear. There was little time to consider personal feelings. I'd received a letter from Kimberly. I'd written a letter a week prior explaining I'd soon be returning to the States and could see no way of seeing her for some time to come, if ever. I encouraged her to find a good Aussie and forget me. I hated to write the letter, but I knew it was unfair to allow her to think it would be different. Her response was that I couldn't discourage her. She'd wait; after all she loved me. I loved her, too.

We winged our way through the large cloud buildups on our way to the target. I knew we were in for a special kind of hell. We were heading for the Kanto Plains, a flat approach to Tokyo just to the north a few miles. Tachikawa was the "Wright-Patterson" of the Japanese Air Force. All research and development took place there. It was well defended by numerous fighters and heavy displacement of antiaircraft guns. The Japanese had created some very fine fighting aircraft at Tachi.

Our bomb loads were HE's and would be dropped from 20,000 feet. Each wing was assigned a different altitude to confuse the gunners on the ground. Our formation was the second to attack the target. Ahead we could see the smoke rising from the target. The weather was clear except for a few puffy clouds, but the visibility was deteriorating.

The formation was good and tight reported our tail gunner from his vantage point. The flak had become more intense and increased as we neared the drop point. The fighters attacked from out of the sun. It was hard for anyone to imagine the noise produced in combat if he hadn't heard it. Everyone was performing his specialty as we crossed the target and mine was to get us away from this holocaust and safely out to sea. After bombs away we made a turn to the right as fast as practicable with the large formation behind us. The fighters pressed attacks and our guns answered. As we turned from the target we had a better view of the area. The third wing was just at the drop point and soon explosions could be seen. It was pure hell below. We made it to sea and the shooting was over. The enemy fighters had to try and defend the target from the new tormentors. We weren't as important to them any longer.

The future looked brighter even with the unscheduled stop at

Iwo Jima for fuel. The black island of Iwo Jima was a godsend. It'd already saved many planes and crews who would otherwise have perished. As time passed it was of more value. Those brave U.S. Marines who had paid the price would be happy to know their sacrifices were not in vain.

When we reached Tinian we were told we'd stand down for a few days. The word was a maximum mission was being planned. Rumor indicated we'd hit Tokyo with everything the 20th Air Force had.

Word reached us the following day. The mission was on. Tokyo it would be, and it would be a night mission. I favored night missions. The weather was the main reason we flew at night. Heavy buildups of clouds during daylight hours were predicted with clearing at night. We'd have some lousy weather getting to Tokyo and we wouldn't have the protection of formation. However, we could expect less fighter action and flak wouldn't be as accurate.

The whole crew was tight; no one wanted to admit the pressure was building as we neared number thirty-five. I knew it was only before the mission you get the willies; once on the way it all changed—we were professionals.

We slept until early afternoon. Then rose, cleaned up and headed for the chow hall hungry as bears. Being hungry helped because the food was never too palatable. After we finished Bart and I made our way to squadron operations to check on the latest. Lately, we'd had little time to do anything but prepare to fly. We were told there was a shortage of .50 caliber machine gun barrels. Many had been burned out on the last few missions and shipment of the critical items hadn't arrived. The demand was great throughout the 20th Air Force. Our wing had made an official request through channels to the Navy for their unused barrels and were denied. The Navy had a number of derelict B-24's parked in an area near our field. The B-24's were rusting away. The Navy indicated they didn't want the Army to use them because they may need them in the future.

"Those assholes don't know there's a war going on up there," said Bart as he pointed to the north.

"Christ, I thought they were on our side. It makes you wonder if they know what the hell is going on in the real world," I said disgustedly.

"Colonel, we have to have those guns, so why not go take them?"

asked Bart.

"We sure as hell can't fly against Japan without guns for protection," answered Bob.

An unofficial raiding party was assembled and after dark we infiltrated the Navy parking area and relieved the Navy of all the excess weight. When our guys entered the old Buccaneers they found many parts and instruments had been removed, but not the gun barrels. The raid was a complete success and none of the raiders had been captured. The Navy was unaware of the theft and wouldn't discover it for some time to come; then it would be too late to do anything.

* * *

We in the B-29 units got along with the Navy CeeBee's just fine. The CB's were a happy lot and they liked to fly. They would come down to the landing field and ask for a ride and when we flew practice missions, we obliged. In return we were their guests for chow at their dining hall. We were very happy to be invited; they ate much better than we did. We ate with them as often as possible. After a time the numbers of AAF personnel grew and the Navy tried to put a stop to it. The CB's devised a system where we'd be undetected. They had extra dungarees and we wore them to chow. We were coached on which unit we were supposed to be in and what duties we had. When confronted by the Master at Arms we had the right answers. On one occasion I was challenged by the MA, I convinced him I was new to the battalion and was a heavy equipment operator from company D. He was very skeptical, but had no time to check my story without holding up the line. The meal was delicious and was topped off with ice cream, something I hadn't tasted in many moons. I knew every man in the dining room knew who I was except the MA.

After we finished eating we broke out a bottle of CC and thanked our friends for the wonderful meal. They were delighted and we felt the bottle was worth a meal for eleven anytime. Soon we were back in khaki and off in our jeep to our area.

After returning I wrote a few letters. I knew my folks would be happy to know I'd be returning home soon. I spoke of my rotational plans. I'd never built their hopes, but now what could it hurt? I finished my letters and would drop them off at headquarters the next day on my way to briefing.

All enlisted mail was dropped into the box unsealed for cen-soring. Each officer at one time or another drew the detail of censoring mail. It was fun, especially reading some of the racy remarks some of the men included in their letters. Some would describe in full all the events which made up the sex act. Nothing was left to the imagination. Most were definitely "X" rated. We never cut out personal notes from the letters. We were only in-terested in the portions of the letters which divulged classified information. Some men took delight in trying to fool us. It was a no-no. Some letters looked like paper doll cutouts when we finished cutting out the classified portions. A lot of the men didn't understand what was classified, others didn't care. No one could reveal our location, speak of casualties in numbers, as well as numbers of aircraft on a mission, etc. It was permissible to tell of flying previous missions without specifics.

The following day briefing was held. All wings of the 20th Air Force would be involved and it was a maximum effort mission. There would be in excess of 500 B-29's on the mission. This was to be the largest number of B-29's to attack Japan to date. As it turned out, it was the largest number of B-29's to hit a single target during the entire war.

The mission got off just before dusk and the huge armada headed north to the massive city of Tokyo. All formations came over Iwo Jima from different headings. We only had another hour to make landfall south of Tokyo. We heard the backfire and the flight engineers panel lit up like a Christmas tree. We had an emergency! We'd just lost number four engine. We pulled out of the stream and descended rapidly to avoid any planes to our rear. We were at 5,000 feet with number four feathered and on our way back to Iwo Jima. We limped in and landed.

We felt relieved having made it back without further incident.

While we waited for the engine to be changed we were shocked to see so many planes shot up so badly. Some didn't look air-worthy.

The following day we were on our way back to Tinian. After we arrived, we were told of the appalling losses. We had lost seventeen planes. It'd been one of the roughest missions ever flown. The B-29's had laid 3,650 tons of fire bombs on the primary and had shot down many enemy fighters.

Tokyo was systematically being destroyed and we were going to send another maximum effort to finish them off. All was in readiness for another 500 plane raid. It would be remembered as the most successful mission. It would do as predicted, end the bombing of urban Tokyo. This mission and the two earlier raids laid waste to 18.6 square miles of the main city of Japan. The capital city was destroyed by 3,258 tons of incendiaries. Nineteen enemy planes had gone down.

The results would prove to be devastating to the 20th Air Force as well as the people of Tokyo. Twenty-six B-29's were lost the night of 25/26 May 1945. It was the worst loss for a single 20th Air Force mission. One of the losses would include the crew of *Here's Hopin.*

29.

Mission number thirty-four was launched without difficulty. There were thirty-five aircraft launched by the 444th Bomb Group. The concentration of air power of the 20th Air Force was awesome and it was being used to apply pressure on the Japanese war lords.

The long flight was very routine and soon we were in sight of the Japanese home islands. The pathfinder aircraft had started massive fires which could be seen many miles out to sea. The pathfinders were sent ahead of the main force and marked the targets. The pathfinder's mission was dangerous, but necessary.

The weather was CAVU and would stay clear for the mission, but it would be impossible to see the target after the smoke started rising. Only the first 40 percent of the bombers actually bombed visually.

Intense heat created by the fire bombs sent thermals thousands of feet in the air. Some of the huge B-29'S were being tossed about like paper airplanes in a heavy wind.

It became impossible to bomb below 14,000 feet. The last 300 planes were forced to climb to 22,000 feet and bombed by radar.

The target area had intense flak and over sixty enemy night fighters. It was the most spectacular sight I'd ever witnessed. The searchlights pierced the black night and stabbed at us. Weird balls of fire raised from the ground. They were throwing everything they had at us. I wouldn't have been surprised to see the proverbial kitchen sink. The battle was fast and furious and hadn't slowed since we were in range of the coast. We all flew individual runs over the target, no formation protection. I was sure every gun in Japan was aimed at our plane. I suppose everyone felt the same way. It'd seemed an eternity from landfall to the IP as the lighter automatic weapons reached our altitude with tracers arcing through the sky. The tracers were like fireworks at the fair, but much more deadly. At this altitude they could

276

throw rocks at us and have a fair chance of making a hit. As we passed out of range of antiaircraft fire we knew what to expect and they didn't disappoint us. The enemy fighters struck with a vengeance. Our gunners were calling attacks faster than we had guns to fire. It was like a boiling caldron as we pressed on toward the IP. The enemy fighters were unsuccessful in their attempt to turn us from the target, but they were taking a heavy toll. All the groups were sustaining heavy damage as we approached the IP.

"Six fighters at 3:00 o'clock high," called Roy from his vantage point high atop the plane's fuselage.

"I see 'em," answered the left scanner in an excited voice. He swung the guns around to meet the challenge. "I got him, I got him," cried John Wright.

"Hold it down," ordered Bart. Then he added, "Nice shooting John."

The fighters seemed to swarm like bees. The sparklers in their wings were deadly machine gun and cannon fire. I felt the jolt as we were hit. Then I heard someone in the rear cry, "We've been hit back here!"

There was no time to worry about it now; we were getting close to the IP and we were still flying. All of a sudden the fighter attacks ceased; we knew what to expect next. The flak came at us with all the fury the enemy on the ground could muster. I'd never seen such fire. Tokyo had one and a half times more heavy guns than Berlin.

"Pilot from nav . . . we're now over the IP, on course and altitude for the drop."

"Roger. Bombardier, have you sighted the target?" called Bart.

"Roger, dead ahead," answered Rich.

"Okay, it's your airplane," responded Bart.

"Center your PDI," called Rich as he put his eye to the bomb sight and started making small corrections. The planes was now being flown by corrections from the bomb sight.

We were getting close to the drop as the flak rocked our plane. It was like a boat on a heavy sea. On the ground it was like a boiling sea of fire, it must have been pure hell. I wondered how anyone could survive.

"Bomb bay doors coming open," called Rich.

Time seemed to hang motionless as I waited for the bombs to be released. Then Rich called, "Bombs away, doors coming closed."

Now it was time for me to get us out of here, I said to myself. At that instant *Heres Hopin'* took a direct hit. The heavy flak burst had struck number one engine; the prop was gone and fire had started.

"We're in trouble, Johnny. Give me a heading and altitude," cried Bart as he, Jim and Walt fought to get the fire under control.

I was ready with the information. I had it all figured out well before he called. "Fly 120 and let down. I'll tell you when you can level off," I answered.

"Roger, coming around to 120." The plane was sluggish and slow to respond as we turned into the dead engine. We were losing altitude as Bart fought to control the big plane. The flak again slackened and enemy fighters pounced on us sensing the kill as the fire from the engine trailed behind. The flames acted like a magnet to the enemy fighters waiting for cripples. They attacked from all quadrants. We fired back, but there were too many. We continued to dive for the water.

"Jim, hit the other fire bottle. We've got to get the fire out or we will buy the farm," ordered Bart.

One fighter came so close it seemed as though he were trying to ram us. As he passed toward the rear, we heard Pops call, "I got the son-of-a-bitch."

The fighter exploded and disintegrated and the pieces floated toward earth. We'd shot two down. If we could get down on top of the water we'd have a lot better chance, I thought.

"Bart, come right to 220 and level at one thousand. Maybe we can get the fighters off our back down there," I said crossing my fingers.

"Roger, 220 and a grand."

"Add all the power you can; we're going pretty slow," I called. I wasn't sure we could hold 1,000 feet, but we had no chance at 8,000 feet.

"Pilot, this is engineer, over."

"Go ahead, Walt."

"Sir, we have another problem. We must have got hit in number two also. We're losing oil pressure and the CHT is rising. We'll have to reduce power on number two and be ready to feather if it gets worse."

The noise decreased, but not where I was sitting. The turrets next to me were rattling as the expended shell casings and the ammo clips slid down the chutes while the four gun upper turret fired on.

"Radio, get this emergency message out right away," I called to Ray over the interphone. I reached around the turret and he took the message. I'd planned my calculations of where I thought we'd probably have to ditch. If we didn't ditch I'd update the message later. I felt every man on the plane must have known we'd probably ditch and I wanted us as far away from Japan as possible.

"Pilot, we've cleared the coast. Are you going to be able to maintain the altitude?" I asked.

"Going to try like hell. It depends on number two," answered Bart.

"I have it planned where we should try to ditch. We need another hour of flight to make it." Now, the whole crew knew of our impending ditching. I was sure they were praying we could reach Iwo Jima, as I was, but we'd lost too much fuel and we were lucky the plane was still flying. There wasn't any doubt we were going to get our feet wet very soon.

"Lieutenant Ellis," called the tail gunner.

"Go ahead, Pops."

"I think most of the fighters have left, but there are a couple dogging us out of range."

"Probably low on fuel. I didn't think they'd follow us out to sea. I want everyone to make an estimate of damage in your section of the airplane and report back to me ASAP."

"Sir, this is the CFC. I have some pretty bad news to report."

"Go ahead, Roy, what's up?"

"We got hit real bad on the left side by one of the fighters and John Wright took a 20mm shell in the chest. He's dead. No one realized he'd been hit, we were all so busy. But I found him slumped over his gun sight. It's a mess back here, sir."

There was dead silence on the plane. What a terrible blow, John Wright was our newest member and a damn good gunner. I felt heartsick thinking of him lying back there, and with only one more mission to fly. My mind was full of thoughts about the letter I'd just sent home. How I wished I hadn't written I'd be home soon. I shuddered at the thought of my mother opening a telegram from the War Department explaining I was a MIA. She'd suffered through the war with me over here and it'd caused her to come down with with shingles. My damn letter sure would confuse things at home. The telegram would probably get there first. No more daydreaming. I had to get back to work. We were in big trouble and it was up to me to make sure we did everything we could to get close to one of the submarines on station.

I prepared a Mayday message; then worked out a course to the spot where the submarine was last reported to be, according to our intelligence folder. Next, I had to get all my gear ready for a ditching. The silence was finally broken.

"Roy, this is the AC, I'm sending Lieutenant Ellis back to help out and see what he thinks about the damage you reported, over."

"Right, sir, we're trying to clean it up. The damage doesn't seem to be too serious. We've a bunch of holes. We're trying to stuff things into them."

"Roger."

As Rich passed my desk I had to raise the hinged part of my table to let him pass. He said, "We're really in a mess, aren't we?"

I nodded and said, "We can make it if we're lucky!"

Rich called from the rear soon after he had crawled down the tunnel. "Bart, Roy didn't mention it, but he and Pops are wounded. Roy's wound was not too serious except for the burn on his forehead. He was probably grazed by a shell, but we aren't sure how bad Pops is; he's still in the tail gun position."

"Bart, how is it up there?" I asked.

"It doesn't look like we'll have number two engine very long. Do you have a course to the submarine?"

"Roger, turn to a heading of 240 and it's about an hour away at the speed we're traveling. Can you keep her in the air that long?"

"Beats the hell out of me. I can only try. But I'm not optimistic."

"Do you want me to send the Mayday message or do you want me to hold off?"

"Walt tells me we may have trouble flying much longer due to the strain we are putting on our two good engines; they're running hot."

"I'll keep updating the message and when you give me the word I'll have Ray send it, okay?"

"Righto, we'll fight it as long as possible, but I'd rather ditch with power than with a dead stick."

"Pilot to crew, everyone listen up. As you're all aware, we're going swimming soon. Things are going to hell in a hurry and I want to ditch under the best conditions possible. I think we may be able to stay airborne for maybe thirty minutes, if we're lucky.

I hate like hell putting this plane in the drink at night but we've no choice. I don't want to minimize the danger of an open sea ditching. You're aware of how people have done in the past. We're trying to get as close to submarine as possible. Remember there've been over 600 B-29 crewmen saved at sea, so we have a good chance if we're on the ball and don't panic. Everyone gather up your survival gear, first aid kits, water and food. Make sure you have your Mae West and survival vest on and when we get ready to ditch, it would also be a good idea for each of you to pop your chutes and use them for padding. Any questions?"

"Bart, this is Rich. We got Pops out of the tail; he's conscious, but bleeding. I'll see what we can do to stop the bleeding and maybe give him a morphine shot for the pain. He's hit in the left side. I'm no doctor but I'm really worried; it looks bad to me. Try to land this thing as smoothly as possible; he can't take too much of a shock."

"Righto, I'll do my best. Remember, I'll give the ditching signal with the alarm bell as well as telling you what's going on, time permitting."

"Johnny, how are we doing?" asked Bart in a casual voice.

"Not too bad. We're progressing slowly and will be about 150 miles closer to home if we can stay in the air another twenty minutes, over."

"Roger, take time to get yourself ready, we want to make a fast exit after we hit the water. Don't forget the flare gun and the flares."

We continued to fly, but we were slowly losing power and altitude. I could almost feel the cold water of the northern Pacific. Every minute we stayed in the air took us closer to the sub and further from the shores of Japan. I got the intelligence flimsey out again and studied all the information provided about survival and air sea rescue. I turned the sheet over and was horrifed at what I saw. Oh, my God! The submarine which we were heading for was off station due to mechanical difficulties. There'd be a replacement as soon as possible. What stupidity! I hadn't seen the notice in my haste; however it wouldn't have changed anything. I was afraid with Japan so close they wouldn't send a flying boat for us. I reported to Bart the new information and told him I hadn't seen it because it was on the rear page.

"It's not your fault; you did everything you could. From the looks of the sea below, it's going to be rough. No seaplane will be able to land. Maybe it'll smooth out after dawn. Let's hope so. They may send a B-17 Dumbo out from Iwo after daylight if they got our message."

"Pilot from engineer, over."

"Go ahead, Walt."

"Things are going bad. I'm sure we won't be able to keep flying more than ten or fifteen minutes. I recommend we set up for the water landing before we lose all power, sir."

"Pilot to crew, you heard what Walt said. Get everything ready; we'll be landing within five minutes. Johnny, get the Mayday out now and fasten everything down. What do you have for a surface wind?"

"The wind is 270 at twenty-five knots, that should help a little," I said.

"Okay everybody, this is it. We're turning into the wind right now and should be in the water in minutes; good luck!"

"Sir, the engine just crapped out," called the flight engineer.

I was sweating like all the others, but I was ready for the entry into the dark sea. Lord be with us.

30.

The total darkness made one think of a black abyss, a bottomless pit as the huge crippled B-29 descended toward the angry sea below. The landing lights were lowered and turned on when we were within a hundred feet of crashing into the sea. The white caps were breaking on the surface with a vengeance. The sea was very turbulent. It looked as though it were waiting to swallow us up; what a bad break! But no use crying over spilt milk; the time of reckoning was at hand. My life didn't flash before my eyes, so I figured I'd make it.

The silence was broken as Bart called, "Get ready for the shock and remember after the first contact the plane may skip along so keep your place until we come to a halt and then get your asses out as fast as possible." The interphone went dead and now it was time to pray.

Heres Hopin' struck the water tail low and skidded along the surface for a short time then the nose came down and we went below the surface. I prayed it would not keep going down. The second shock was firmer than the first. Then the nose came back to the surface. What a landing in the wild sea! The plane was floating nicely as everyone scrambled toward his assigned escape exit. I exited through the astrodome atop the plane at the head of the tunnel and soon I was standing on the center of the wing trying to keep my balance on the slippery surface as the plane bobbed up and down. I rushed over the fuselage to help with the wounded. Everyone was out except Staff Sergeant John Wright who would forever be part of this B-29.

After we assembled on the wing the two rafts were inflated and lowered into the sea at the rear of the left wing. There was no panic; everyone took his time and in a matter of seconds we were all aboard.

"Bart, since everything looks normal I'd like to go back in the plane and get a few items we can use, like my sextant and a chart.

They may come in handy," I said.

"Okay, but don't take too long; this plane could sink any minute."

"Roger, I'll be back in a flash." I pulled myself back to the wing. The two rafts were secured together and tied to the extended flap. As I dropped into the hole where the astrodome used to be I waved to the guys as they watched huddled together for protection against the sea spray.

I entered the tunnel and looked aft and thought of John Wright back there all alone and shuddered. I slid down to the floor of the cabin and collected the items I needed and as I started to climb back to the tunnel I looked into the forward bomb bay and could see the water slowly rising. I poked my head through the hatch and called, "Here I come . . . " My words were heard by no one. The two large rafts weren't where I left them and a quick search of the black sea revealed nothing but threatening water. I yelled at the top of my voice, but no response was returned. They were gone and I was all alone! I yelled again and I thought I heard something over the howling wind, but it was probably my imagination. I felt a shock of fear go up my spine. What to do? I couldn't believe they'd run off and leave me. They knew I'd be right back. The line must have pulled loose and they couldn't get back to the wing. The current must be strong as hell.

I reentered the plane to get out of the wind and spray and tried to think, I had to settle down and use all the training I had, and then some. I was intimidated by the angry sea which waited for me but knew I had to make plans for the danger that awaited me.

I slid down to the forward cabin deck and took stock of what I had to work with. I gathered up every useful item of survival and then decided what I'd carry with me and started packing my survival vest. I decided to take two one-man life rafts and use the second for extra items. One item I was happy to have was my pocket size survival manual. It should make future decisions easier. I stuffed my chart in my flight suit, then decided to go aft to see what I could use. First I looked into the forward bomb bay to see how much further the plane had settled. To my amazement the water had not risen appreciably. I climbed into the tunnel and crawled to the aft cabin. I saw John Wright still seated at the scanners position with a parachute draped over him. There was considerable blood and other distasteful remnants of the disaster. I decided there was little use looking around the area and returned to the front of the plane.

I looked at my watch and realized it would be getting light within a couple of hours. It was time to get in the water. I cut some parachute lines and stuffed them in my pocket then pushed the two rafts and all the other gear I was going to take, including a spare parachute, up the tunnel. It was time to go.

I poked my head through the open astrodome and immediately felt the strong wind and spray. I pushed my two uniflated boats onto the wing and climbed out after them. I inflated the extra raft and placed all the items I'd taken from the cabin in it and secured them as best I could. I hoped I could keep the parachute; it would help in so many ways. But it was heavy and could easily be lost. I inflated the other raft and then I tied them together and pulled them toward the rear of the wing. The sea was running from the front of the plane toward the aft and my first boat extended to the full length of its line as soon as it hit the water, almost pulling me overboard. I tied another line to the wing flap and then stepped into the raft. I untied the line and floated rapidly away from the B-29.

Within minutes the plane faded into the mist and I was riding the rolling sea. I again thought of John sitting in his seat. I was sad and frightened. I wanted to stay on the B-29 until daylight, but couldn't afford that luxury. The enemy might find the plane or it could sink. I wanted to get as far away from the plane as possible. I didn't want to be taken prisoner.

It was hard to think clearly. I was drenched and almost seasick. I knew the sun would dry me out fast and hoped the ocean would calm down. I kept thinking of how alone I was and what a bad break to be separated from the others.

I decided to get everything shipshape. I started by tying a line from my leg to the raft in case I was tossed overboard. At times I'd see my spare raft on the rise or going down one of the deep troughs, but she was still with me. The white caps and swells were enormous; they towered above me eight or ten feet. Being at absolute sea level made my visibility limited. I could pass right next to a ship and not see it. I was fighting to stay in the raft as the sea tossed me around like a cork. I was lifted by the mountain of water and then dropped into the watery valley. I decided to inflate my life vest just in case I was thrown out. Just as I pulled the second cord to inflate my vest, I flew out of my small boat and landed in the cold water. I was glad I'd tied the raft to my leg, although it was pulling so hard I thought my leg would come out of the socket. I pulled on the line and soon I was holding the side of the raft. The sea motion made it impossible to determine which way I was going as I swirled around. It made little difference. I had no control over my direction; maybe by some miracle I wasn't too far from the others. There was little use trying to reenter the raft. I'd only be dumped out again.

After three hours in the water I saw the gray of dawn and was finally able to determine direction. The best part was that as it got lighter the sea calmed down a great deal; it gave me hope. I looked for my second raft but it was nowhere to be seen; it had pulled loose and now I had lost the parachute, the big water jug and a few other items which would make my voyage more enduring. I still had the water in my survival vest, two whole pints. I tried to remember how long a man could survive on two pints of water, but it was academic. I'd be able to capture water when it rained and it surely would!

I busied myself taking inventory of my gear. I didn't have much, but I had enough to survive, assuming my raft didn't sink or get away from me. I felt sure I'd be rescued soon, but had to plan as if I were going to be out for a while. I recalled a couple weeks prior when we'd received a distress call from a downed B-29 two hundred miles north of the Marianas. We'd diverted to their reported position and came right over the two large rafts. We got our sea marker dye ready and made a standard rate turn so we would come back over them. I timed the turn and knew we hadn't varied, yet the rafts were nowhere to be seen. It took fifteen minutes of concentrated search before we again spotted them and dropped the marker dye on them coloring the ocean yellow-green. As I thought of the event I knew how difficult it would be for anyone to find me in this immense ocean, and I wasn't within two hundred miles of Tinian. I was sure our distress message had been received; therefore I felt they had pinpointed our ditch location and would have little trouble finding me. I was cold, wet, hungry and exhausted. I pulled myself into the raft and reinflated my Mae West. I tried to remember how long it had been since I'd slept and with those thoughts I fell into a deep, but troubled sleep.

The day broke with scattered clouds and a slight wind. The swells were still big and the troughs deep, but nothing like the night before. My little craft rode up and down and after the sun had been up for two hours a noise woke me. I searched the sky for the engine I'd heard; then I saw the Japanese patrol plane as it circled to the north of my position. I estimated the distance to be approximately four to five miles. It dawned on me, they'd found our plane! I hoped the Jap pilot would think we all perished in the ditching, but I knew better. They knew the B-29 was a good ditching aircraft and stayed afloat for a long time. I wished the plane would've sunk; now they'd expand their search and probably send out a surface vessel to look for us. As the Jap plane searched I went under cover. I figured the others had heard the plane and would take the same action. I pulled the rubberized raft cover with the green on one side and the yellow on the other over me. The green would blend in with the sea around me.

The plane circled and came over me as I held my breath. If they spotted me they'd probably strafe and I'd have little chance of survival. I was glad I didn't have the other raft; it would've made it easier for the enemy to spot me. I couldn't chance a look, but I heard the plane as it hung over my position; then I heard the noise diminish as they widened the search pattern. I was delighted. They apparently hadn't seen me. I had the feeling that all the eyes on the search plane were looking directly at me. If you'd ever heard a Japanese twin engine plane you'd know what it sounds like. They seem to have trouble synchronizing their props. It reminded me of an old washing machine when I heard the "wah-wah." In the American flying services you were always taught to synchronize engines from the very beginning of your training.

The immediate danger had passed, but I had to stay alert because I was convinced they'd send a surface ship to investigate further.

All the excitement had dulled my senses. I'd forgotten the hunger and thirst, but now after being under the rubber cover I felt parched and hungry. I took a very short drink from one of the two tins and fastened the lid tightly to avoid any leakage. I decided to take inventory of my cache. I was sure I'd lost some of the items as well as the luxury items I'd stowed in the second raft. I had one life vest, still inflated; I stopped my inventory to deflate the vest. Two containers of water, one pint each; a small fishing kit, a first aid kit, lifesaver candy, signal mirror, a jar of peanut butter, three K-ration dinners, a soggy map, knife, and my .45 caliber automatic encased in its plastic water proof cover which hung under my left arm in the shoulder holster. I almost panicked until I found the repair kit for the raft. I prayed I wouldn't need it. Chances were I'd be found before too long, though I knew I'd better plan for a long stay by rationing all my stores.

I remembered the instructions I was given concerning conservation and rationing. Always plan for the long haul. Never take an early rescue for granted. I thought for a few seconds; water should be plentiful providing it rained and food should be available directly below me; time would tell. I'd found the plastic water container in the lifesaving kit for water storage. I knew it would come in handy. It was a damn shame I'd lost my five-gallon jug of water and the other items on the second raft, but there was nothing I could do about it. Hindsight would only drive me crazy; I promised myself not to agonize over the losses any longer.

After I finished my inventory I secured each item as best I could, it would not do to lose any more of my precious equipment. Now it was time to eat, and I was hungry. I thought of how hungry I'd get if I didn't catch a fish in the near future. I was glad I still had my peanut butter; there was a lot of nutrition in that jar. I selected the breakfast K-ration and decided it would be more fitting to eat the morning meal since it was morning. We'd always kidded about K-rations being the same and interchangeable. The taste was secondary, the nourishment was the important thing. Half of the meal should hold me. I'd eat the other half later.

The nylon line I'd cut from the parachute before departing the sinking plane would play a large part in my survival, I was sure. After I'd finished my first meal on the ocean I thought of how the small craft was my only means of support. Without it I'd be doomed. Extreme care must be exercised to be sure no sharp objects came in contact with its surface. When I used my trench knife I was very careful and returned it to the scabbard immediately.

The sun was now overhead and the sky was as blue as the water. Under other circumstanes I would have enjoyed the beauty of it all. I wanted to take off my flying suit and wring it out, but it was too difficult to move in the small space. Taking off the suit would be too much of a challenge. It'd be difficult to keep the raft from turning over and I'd had enough of that during the night. The sun had only dried the upper portion of my clothing. I would've liked to put my butt up in the air and dry it too, but again I couldn't maneuver.

The sea had calmed and the swells were approximately three to four feet making the ride more comfortable. I felt the side of my raft and decided it should be inflated more. I pulled the protected small hose from its housing, took a deep breath and blew. I could feel the raft tightening and was happy to know it held all the air.

One of the most important things was to keep myself busy and that was difficult in the space I had to operate in. Fishing would be a great time waster as well as being beneficial. I took the small fishing kit and examined its contents. The kit only measured three by four inches, but it had many useful items of tackle. Line, hooks, lures, leaders and colored cloth to use for bait. I sure hoped it'd catch fish! I wondered what kind of fish I'd catch? I pulled out my water soaked survival manual and carefully searched through the book for the information. I came across a picture of sharks. There was no way I wanted to see one of them! The Japanese are great fisherman so I was sure there were edible fish in these waters. Then I remembered that the Japanese ate a lot of shark, Christ! I hoped there was more than shark out there! I didn't want to think about it. I prepared a line and started fishing. After two hours of having no luck and trying almost every combination I decided to quit for the day. Maybe they'd bite better tomorrow.

I had to fix a routine, but what would I include? I knew I had to keep busy. It would help the time pass quicker if I included fishing and singing; what a life! It was then that I heard the faint sound of aircraft engines. I scanned the sky and finally saw the planes high to the west; they were B-29's heading for Japan. It made me feel better thinking of them going up there to kick some ass. I sure wished I was up there with them instead of down here bobbing like a cork. I knew it was useless to signal; they were too far away and they wouldn't be looking for a tiny raft out here in the middle of the ocean. I strained to see the tail markings, but they were too high and far away to distinguish. If what they told us at briefing was true there would not be many more missions to Tokyo. After what I saw last night I believed it.

I settled back and rode my small boat over the waves as the afternoon wore on; then I had a familiar urge which in the past caused little thought, but now I had to figure out what to do about it, and how! The unmistakable feeling got stronger and there was no time to waste, but how would I accomplish this biological function? I pondered the problem for a few seconds and decided the only way to take care of it was to take off my flying suit and let myself into the sea. I wiggled and struggled and wiggled some more and finally got the one piece flying suit down to my waist and then over my boots. I then removed my boots and all other clothing and secured it neatly in the raft. I had to be most careful not to overturn the raft as I slipped into the water. I went over the low end of the raft and into the chilly sea; it almost took my breath away. I'd become used to salt water baths, but this was ridiculous! I'd never tried to relieve myself in this manner and it took a few minutes for me to empty my bowels. I hoped the debris wouldn't attract a big fish. I'd fastened the raft to my upper arm so it wouldn't get away from me. I then pulled myself around to the opposite side of the raft trying not to cause too much confusion on the surface. It was known that sharks sometimes attack when they think they have a wounded fish near the surface. I quickly pulled myself aboard and wished again I had the parachute to use as a towel. I'd have to stay naked and let the warm sun dry my body. I knew I'd have to enter the ocean at least once a day and the thought of not knowing what was waiting for me was unnerving to say nothing of freezing my balls off!

It took but a few minutes for both my body and the clothing I left in the raft to dry. I knew I'd get better at this ritual, if I had to repeat it for very long. I was a regular guy.

I was gaining confidence in my little raft as time passed. I prayed I wouldn't have another hellish night. Each time my raft had turned over I had to pull myself back into it after deflating my Mae West and then reinflating it after I was safely aboard. The trouble was that I didn't stay aboard for very long. It was most tiring to reenter the raft time and time again. The maneuver was accomplished by holding the small part of the raft with both hands and then pulling it down as you raised your body. After fighting the ocean and pulling myself onto the raft a few times I was exhausted. I'd gone through a self debate whether to keep my pistol and after pondering the question for some time decided I might need it to ward of the enemy or possibly a large fish. The discomfort of wearing the heavy pistol would have to be endured. I'd removed it from my shoulder holster and stowed it securely in the raft. I hoped I wouldn't have to use it. After dressing and enjoying the warm rays of the sun I started to daydream about my love, far off in Australia. I felt things would prabably never work out for us, but her lovely vision was available by merely closing my eyes and it was most comforting to me. It was at that exact moment I heard the sound of an airplane. I immediately prepared to either cover the raft from view, or turn the yellow side up to make myself more visible. I was having trouble determining what direction the plane was coming from. If it came from the north it would surely be the enemy; however, if from the south it could be friendly. I reached for my signal mirror and was ready in any case. Yes, the plane had a smooth sound and was coming from the southwest. It was a PBY, a Navy patrol plane. Oh God, let him see me! I flashed my mirror and waved the yellow cover. He circled some distance from me then headed further to the southwest. He was going away; I prayed he'd come back. I could barely hear the engine, but there was no doubt in my mind the plane had made a landing.

Within minutes I heard the engines reving up as the throttles were advanced. I was out of eye view and could only pray they would search further. Then off in the distance I saw the big float plane rise into the sky and fly off in the same direction he'd come. They must have found Bart and the others. They probably couldn't spare the time to look for me because of the wounded men. I told myself, as fear and anger overtook me. After a few minutes of total frustration I tried to rationalize; they must have felt the need to rush the wounded to the hospital which means one or more of them were in pretty bad shape. I was sure Bart would know I wasn't too far off and would get a rescue team back for me, but I was very disappointed at what had just transpired and knew it would take some time to get back to normal, if there was such a thing floating out here in the north Pacific in Japan's back yard.

31.

The two large hexagon shaped rafts tied together leisurely rode up and down the swells and troughs of the blue ocean. The nine occupants were distrubuted five in one and four in the other. Each raft had one wounded man to care for. Both of the wounded men were in a state of shock; they'd lost considerable blood. "I can't figure how it could have happened! Leaving Johnny out there all alone. I'm sick over it," said Bart from the lead raft speaking to Rich who sat next to him on the floor of the raft.

"I know how you feel, but we tried to get back to the plane in every way possible after the line pulled loose. Don't drive yourself nuts thinking about it, Johnny's a tough customer and should do okay by himself. We yelled so hard I almost lost my voice. I guess the wind drowned us out, it was impossible," answered Rich as he looked through the field glasses in all directions trying to see something, anything.

"I know Rich, but it doesn't change how I feel. After all I was supposed to be in command and I let us get separated. I was in hopes we would be able to see him out here, but you can't see beyond the next swell. If we could stay on top of one of these swells for a few minutes we might get a better look. Just keep looking that way, Rich." He pointed in the direction they had come.

"You know Bart, he's probably pretty pissed off at us right now and I can't blame him. I know if I were alone on this damn ocean in a one-man raft and no one to talk to I'd be ready for the funny farm."

"The damn one-man life raft is so small, at least we can move around. Can you imagine how it was in the dinghy last night? We did everything but capsize; he was probably in the water all night, the poor bastard. But like you say if any one can hack it, its Johnny, he's a lot tougher than one would imagine. You should have seen him in the fight at Calcutta, he fights like a demon

292

when pissed off. He may punch us all out when he sees us."

Bart slid up to a kneeling position and looked over to the other raft. It was only four or five feet away. "How's it going, Jim?"

"Everything's fine except for Pops, he's pretty weak. I hope we can get him to a hospital soon. We've done everything we can for him, but if we don't get him to a doctor soon, who knows? How's Roy doing?"

"Not too bad right now. We got the bleeding stopped except for a bit of oozing around the bandage. He's asleep now, but last night he got a little seasick to make things more complicated."

"Bart, we're out of morphine and Pops is moaning, he's delirious, kind of like he's lost his marbles. How are you fixed for morphine?"

"We have one left, I'll pull us together and give it to you," answered Bart.

"We must be a lot better off than Johnny. I sure feel bad about leaving him. I thought the line was tied off better than it was, but we can't cry over spilt milk," answered Jim.

"Did you hear something, Bart?" asked Rich as he searched the water and sky with the glasses.

"I sure as hell did. It's an airplane. Can you tell which direction it is coming from?" asked Bart.

Jim had heard the twin engine plane also. "I heard something and it sounds like it is coming from the south. Did you hear it?"

"Sure as hell. It has to be a US plane you know how much trouble the Japs have synchronizing their engines and this bird is purring," said Bart excitedly. "Jim, you have the flare gun get it ready with a red flare. As soon as we see them fire it and get another ready, this may be our lucky day," cried Bart.

Everyone, including the two wounded men were searching the skies for the plane. Pain and seasickness had vanished. Rich was the first to spot the lumbering flying boat. "There, there to the southwest. Do you see it?"

"I sure as hell do. Get ready, Jim."

Jim held the pistol above his head ready to launch the first missile. "Okay, let her rip, Jim. I think they see us," said Bart in a voice as excited as anyone would ever hear from him.

"It's Navy but we won't squawk," yelled Rich.

The red flare flew high overhead and exploded in a dazzling red display. The aircraft spotted the location and followed it back to the two rafts adrift. Every man was up flailing his arms or whatever else he had handy. All the motion made the rafts sway to and fro. The PBY made a turn into the wind and started down for a landing. The pilot skillfully touched the sea between swells and landed as the spray flew up behind. The plane slowed then turned toward them and taxied close to the rafts. There was bedlam aboard the two rafts; even the wounded forced a smile.

The hatch on the side of the plane opened and two sailors were ready with a line. One tossed the line and it was caught by Bart and soon the boats were alongside. "Hurry, sir, the skipper wants to get off as soon as possible," yelled one of the sailors.

The ablebodied men helped the wounded aboard and then clambored aboard themselves. As soon as everyone was in the plane the sailor took his knife and cut a long slit in each raft and soon they were beneath the surface and out of sight. He hurriedly slammed the hatch closed and called forward to tell the pilot that all was secured.

The plane turned into the wind and soon the engines were revved up to their full capability and the big plane moved slowly on the surface. It seemed to take an inordinate amount of time to get airborne, but airborne it finally was. The plane turned toward the direction it came as it climbed to altitude. Bart rose and went forward to thank the pilot for rescuing them and to introduce himself. Then he said, "Lieutenant, my navigator is down there somewhere behind us. We got separated. He should be close by; he's in a one-man raft. Can we make a pass to the north and have a look for him?"

"Sorry, lieutenant. I have my orders to get out of this area as soon as possible. There are a number of enemy ships in the immediate area and to top it off there's one hell of a storm due to hit, real soon."

"That's all well and good, but I have an officer down there and I'm not about to leave him out there all alone in a small dinghy. He won't be able to survive a major storm," yelled Bart to be heard over the drone of the engines.

"Sorry, we'll have to let someone else rescue him," answered the pilot.

The plane continued in a southerly direction struggling for height when the first burst of flak exploded to port. "Holy shit, where did that come from?" asked the pilot as he turned to his co-pilot.

"Beat's the hell out of me," he answered as he looked down to find the antagonist.

Another burst came a bit closer and rocked the flying boat. "There, the son-of-a-bitch is, off to our starboard. It looks like a fishing boat. Maybe, we interrupted his fishing," said the ensign.

The third burst was no closer than the first and the firing ceased. Soon the PBY was out of his range and everyone relaxed for the long flight back to Iwo Jima.

"Did you see the slug of fishing boats around the gun boat?" asked the ensign.

"Yeah, those crazy bastards are out in numbers fishing while the shooting is going on. I guess they have to eat!" answered the pilot.

Bart saw the impossibility of trying to persuade the pilot to turn back. He turned without another word and left the flight deck with a scowl on his face.

"What's up, Bart?" asked Jim anxiously.

"The asshole won't spend any time looking for John. It sure pisses me off to think we could probably find him within a few minutes and we're leaving him out there with the damn storm coming and a fleet of enemy boats nearby," said Bart as he threw his cap down on the deck.

"Don't take it so hard, you're punishing yourself and it's not your fault," said Jim trying his best to console him.

"If it is anyone's fault it's mine. After all, I let the line come loose. I guess I don't know how to tie good knots," said Ray Siverson the radio operator.

The statement had an effect on Bart. He explained to Ray, "It wasn't your fault, a lot was happening and there was a lot of excitement. Circumstances must be considered. I feel bad about leaving him for a second time, it's not fair to fly off to safety while he's down there fighting for his life. I'm sure he must have heard the plane too and is wondering why they didn't come for him."

"Well, Bart, at least we'll get Pops and Roy to the medics. I don't think Pops would have made it through another night at sea, especially if a storm came up. We can get a search party out for Johnny right away, I'm sure," said Jim.

The Navy crew included a corpsman which was a real break. He did an excellent job of making them more comfortable and administered pain killers. He worked on the two from the minute they were lifted into the hull of the flying boat. They'd be in a military hospital within a few hours.

32.

The sun fell near the western horizon and I was as low as a man could possibly get. I was now all alone; they'd left me to spend another miserable night on the open sea. I was thankful that at least the sea was calm.

My mind worked on the rescue. I kept trying to rationalize the situation. Why they'd left me was hard to understand unless the wounded were so bad off they couldn't waste a minute; otherwise they could have spent a few minutes looking for me. Since the rescue plane spent so little time looking for the others they'd obviously had a good fix on our position. I shouldn't worry. Bart would have them back after me at first light I was sure.

What bothered me was the noise like gunfire I'd heard after they'd taken off. Maybe it was thunder! I knew I had to get myself ready for night. It was getting dark rapidly and I didn't want to get caught trying to tidy up in the dark or waste my flashlight batteries. If the night was clear there'd be plenty of light from the moon and the stars. My biggest desire presently was water. I knew I had to conserve, but I was very thirsty. I took out my small can and wet my mouth, swishing the fluid around and around before I swallowed it. I could get along without food for a long spell, but water was another thing. I looked skyward and there were clouds, but none looked as though they had enough moisture to produce rain. Possibly rain would come tomorrow and I could get refilled and also drink my fill. The thought weighed on my mind. Then I remembered. Tomorrow they'll surely find and rescue me and I would look back on this as just an adventure.

Darkness had set in and I was in a black void. The feeling was without question very difficult to relate to. I could hardly see my hand in front of my face. The moon would come up later and soon the stars would provide some light, I hoped. I laid back and enjoyed the stillness of the sea. The only sound was the gentle lapping of the sea against my tiny raft. My mind worked on the old seamen's adage, it was always calm before the storm. It didn't look to me as if a storm was brewing especially after last night's blow. I was just imagining things.

I decided to try and get some sleep, I was very tired and maybe, after a time the moon would bring light and I'd be able to eat a little. My eyelids were very heavy and soon I was asleep.

I woke to a startling amount of noise. A raid was in progress and the multiple engines of the formation off to the west were quite noisy. I couldn't see them due to the lack of running lights on the B-29's. I made a silent prayer for them and wished them good luck. With all the B-29's so near, I had the feeling of not being so alone.

The wind had freshened during my nap and as the waves broke against my raft a little water trickled over its side. I didn't want it to get any stronger; the last thing I wanted was to have to spend the night in the water again.

I felt well rested after only three hours of sleep. There was nothing to do. I was bored. I tried to get some more sleep, but it was impossible. I ate the rest of the open box of K-rations and then noticed what light I'd had seemed to disappear. I relaxed and fell into a deep sleep once again.

I awoke with a start from a sound sleep, the noises I heard were human, but not a language I understood. I was so startled it was hard for me to think clearly. I wanted to flash my light in the direction of the voices, but the voices seemed to be coming from more than one direction and there was no doubt, they were speaking Japanese. I was terrified, what was going on? How could this be, was I dreaming? It was no dream, as my eyes became used to the night I made out a number of wooden fishing vessels. I was completely surrounded. They had not spotted my small dinghy in the darkness. Lights were being lit on each of the boats and the light reflected on the sea seemed to be pointing at me. It was only a matter of time before they spotted me. Then the fat would be in the fire; they'd have fun with this big fish, I was sure. I wondered what they'd do with me, probably torture me then use me for bait. Emperor Hirohito would most likely give them a medal. What a fix I was in, I needed to think fast before I was discovered. If I hadn't gone to sleep I might have avoided this mess, but that was like looking up a dead horse's ass, as Bart would have said.

I had to get out of the circle and and away as soon as possible.

The lack of activity aboard the boats meant most of the fishermen were in the rack. After all, they had no reason to be alert, but I was sure each vessel had at least one watch. However, since there was no reason to suspect any foul play they probably wouldn't be very alert.

My sea anchor which I'd had out since early evening for stability, and to cut drift had kept the raft from floating against the hull of the ships. I knew all I could do was stay quiet until I was sure they were in bed and then paddle away to the safety of the open sea. An hour passed, it was now or never. I headed for the nearest boats and would try to go between them. I figured they couldn't see me and if I made no noise I could escape without them knowing they had a prisoner of war right in the palm of their hands. I thanked God I hadn't thrown my .45 away, I might need it after all, if I was captured I wanted to take some of them with me, at least I could make a fight of it. I wondered how well armed they were, I didn't want to find out.

It took some time for me to negotiate the distance to the boats, I'd made slow progress. Then in the dark I accidently hit the side of one of the boats with my hand, it was so damn dark I didn't see it. The bang hadn't made much noise, but to me it sounded like a shot. Then I heard two people talking, I froze where I was, I was sure they could hear my heart beating. Luckily, no lights came on and it again became quiet. Maybe the Japs were just exchanging dirty jokes, who knows! The back of my hand where I'd hit the side of the boat hurt, I hoped it wasn't bleeding. I then reached down and pulled the .45 close to me just in case. I knew if I fired the weapon all hell would cut loose, but it might start enough confusion for me to escape. The plan was only to be used as a last resort.

The voices continued as I held the pistol in one hand and the paddle in the other. All Japanese voices sounded as if they were excited, so I'd been told. After a few minutes the voices were quiet and I knew I'd used up some of my luck. I pushed the automatic back into its protective plastic case and once again realized I'd done the right thing by keeping the weapon.

A door closed on the fishing boat, it had not been slammed. It made me acutely aware of how noise carries across the water. I must be very careful to avoid any further disturbances, my life depended on it. I started to paddle toward the bow of the fishing boat and after a period of fifteen minutes I reached the spot to go between the boats. My raft hit something under the surface; it puzzled me. I reached below the surface and found a large fishing net had been drawn between the two boats. I surmised the whole inner area was part of their fishing system. I had to make a new plan as there was no way for me to escape by paddling between the boats.

I studied the situation, but without being able to see clearly I was at a disadvantage. I was lucky for the dark night in one way and not in the other. Things were about to change, however, the moon was starting to rise. I could now see the faint outline of all the boats. I estimated the circle I was trapped in measured approximately 100 yards across. The boats were uniformly about fifty feet in length and there were at least five forming the circle. Each boat had a dim light on its fantail.

I removed my boots and tied them together and secured them in the raft with my other precious items, then slipped into the cold water pulling the raft behind me. I swam until I felt the net under me and then I merely climbed the seine as you would a ladder. I was now out of the water pulling my boat behind. To my surprise another net was laid to sea. I climbed down the outside ladder and when it fell below my reach I stepped back and climbed into my raft. I paddled as fast as I could away from the circle, but was making little headway due to the current. When I was far enough away I went with the current and started to put some distance between me and the fisherman. All at once I hit an object; what could it be? It turned out to be a floating glass ball which held up the outer reaches of their nets. I took my knife from its scabbard and cut the line holding the float and tied it to the outside of my raft, then I looked for another and repeated the act. They unwittingly helped me to stay afloat, any buoyancy would help in a big blow.

My arms ached as I looked toward the enemy and now the light from the moon was making the area visible. I didn't think they could spot me now, but I was taking no chances, I kept paddling. I wondered what else could happen to me. Being this close to the Japanese mainland was of no comfort. I thought of the perilous situation I was in, if only the PBY had picked me up! I was in deep shit and knew it, what to do?

A huge light beam flashed across the surface and I almost pissed in my pants. I ducked instinctively, there was another fishing boat, larger than the others with a light and it was scanning the surface outside of the fishing boats. I assumed it was checking the floats, I hoped the two I'd stolen wouldn't be noticed. It may be a protective boat and possibly armed with a deck gun. The thought scared the hell out of me. Instead of resting I put all my energy into making distance between me and them. After sweeping the area the light went dead and with it a blackness I cherished. I had been a victim of "Murphy's Law" everything that could go wrong did, but I was still lucky and alive.

As I got further from my adversaries I could see the light of dawn starting to streak across the dark sky, a beautiful sight to behold, I enjoyed it momentarily and then after a short swig of water settled back to rest. As the adrenalin drained from my body I fell back in exhaustion as I covered my raft with the green side of the cover up.

I was dreaming of home and then of being in a large kettle of water, things were screwed up. I had another dream about people all about me and I was trying to reach them and they ignored me as the tide was pulling me away.

I was sleeping soundly when I woke to the sensation of being spun around, then I heard the noise. I cautiously peeked out from under my covering and saw a fishing boat heading in the direction of the others, then all at once my raft turned over and I was tossed into the cold sea once more. I realized what had happened after I'd righted the boat and climbed back aboard. The guy who was guiding the fishing boat hadn't seen me and damn near ran me down, lucky again. What made me mad was that the Japs couldn't kill me on purpose while I was helping to destroy their ancient land, but they were doing a damn good job accidently. It really doesn't matter how they kill you as long as they get the job done. I was damn lucky the props on the scow didn't pull me under and chew me up; prayers were in order.

33.

I was still adrift on the open expanse of the north Pacific Ocean away from land and people. The shooting war seemed remote now that another war was being fought, a war between me and the elements of nature. I wondered if I could win if for some reason I had to stay out here for more than a day or so, time would tell.

At the present I felt no immediate danger since the fishing fleet was no longer in sight and the ocean was not misbehaving. My experiences thus far had been anything but pleasant, maybe the future would show the other side.

It seemed as the sun rose so did my spirits. My escape during the darkness had shown I was resilient. I felt confidence returning as I prepared for my first meal of the new day. I decided to eat some peanut butter knowing it contained plenty of protein and vitamins. I thought of the wonderful bread the bakers prepared on Tinian. Funny, Tinian had been my new home for only a short period of time, but mostly it was a pleasant place to be; in fact, I longed for it.

It was so quiet here in the middle of nowhere. The only noise other than my voice was the gentle slap of the water as my raft drifted from one swell to another. I was happy I'd taken the two floating glass balls if for no other reason than as a momento. After my gourmet breakfast I felt two urges, one to drink and the other to relieve myself. The drink was easy, the other wasn't. I put off getting into the water as long as I could, but there was no escape, I had to disrobe once again and go for a dip. The water was cold as I finished my defecation. I pulled myself back aboard and went through the difficult task of dressing in a three foot raft while seated.

I planned my activities for a two day stay, I thought of the old quote and I'm not sure who said it, "live today to fight another day." My thoughts ranged from how I would finish my last mission to Kim and most of all to seeing my family. By now my family had been notified, I was sure.

Talking aloud made me feel better. I also sang songs even if I didn't know all the words. Included in my planned activities were fishing, singing, praying and looking for my rescuers, not necessarily in that order. I prepared my fishing line; I was serious about the fishing it was not only therapy, but a source of food and strength which I knew I'd need. I dropped my line over the side knowing it would be difficult to catch my first fish, but not impossible. I'd sure hate to attract a large fish it might get the idea I was the bait. I fished for several hours without any results. I'd tried every combination of bait I had, I tried fishing deep and shallow, nothing seemed to attract any fish, big or small. I was a little discouraged, but not alarmed. I decided to stow my gear and try later in the day.

I laid back to rest and conserve energy, I thought of better times. My fingers were dangling in the cool sea water and I was nearly asleep when I felt an odd sensation at the tips of my fingers. I rose with my fingers still in the water and saw a peculiar looking small fish nipping at my fingers, apparently attracted to the movement. The fish had small teeth and hadn't broken the skin as it nipped at my digits. I decided to try to capture the fish by scooping him into the raft. After repeated failures I tried the fishing line once again. I knew if I could catch one of these little beauties I'd have bait and would be in business.

As the day dragged on I couldn't understand why no rescue planes were to be seen. Certainly the weather was not the factor. It was possible they felt I was too close to the Japanese coast, but we were no further yesterday when the PBY came in for Bart and the others. I was sure they must have good reason unless they didn't think I was worth it. I figured they must have known about the fishing fleet and felt I was too close to them for safety, yes that had to be the reason.

By late afternoon I noticed the wind picking up and the swells growing in size. White caps were breaking and I was taking on water, not a lot as yet, but things definitely did not look good. I was riding up and down from the peaks to the valleys in an ocean that had turned from docile to angry. The sky had taken on a much different look also. Large cumulus clouds were forming. I didn't like what was happening, this had all the appearances of a bad Pacific storm, hurricanes were not uncommon in these latitudes. It all depends on the barometric pressure and the force of

302

the wind. God help me if I got hit by a hurricane, I'd be a goner for sure. It was then the thought entered my head, they didn't send a plane for me because they knew a hurricane was coming! I hoped I was wrong. A little rain would be okay, but no heavy weather, please.

The wind continued to gain in velocity, it was blowing with vengeance. I felt as if someone up there was picking on me, I needed a break, I'd already paid my dues being out here for a couple days and nights. The water coming in to the raft was alarming, I bailed, but couldn't keep up. If things got any worse I'd have to get back in the water. The heavens opened up and it started to rain. I hated even thinking about it. It came down so hard it reminded me of the terrible monsoon rains of India. I'd planned to bathe with the first rain but there was no need, I was already wet to the bone and cold. I put the cover over me and as the rain fell I washed the salt away and refilled all my water containers. I dumped all the old water and as I was filling one of the pint tins a wave hit me and the container went overboard and sunk. I was pissed off at my clumsiness though I'd had little control, my mistake was dumping the old water when the huge wave hit me. There was no use crying over spilt milk; now why did I have to mention milk? I tried to keep the water from filling my boat, it was like shoveling shit against the tide, it just kept coming back.

I had my hands full trying to ride out the storm. Luckily thus far I hadn't been tossed into the wild ocean. I believe I was learning to ride the raft with less rigidity, sort of flowing with the water. I tried to relax, but it was difficult. The storm raged on and gained intensity, if that was possible. It hardly mattered if I were afloat or in the water, I was swallowing so much salt water. Visibility dropped considerably as the wind and sea churned around me. It looked as if mountains of water were hanging over me, they seemed to come from all directions. I tried to lower myself in the raft to maintain a center of gravity. I had the feeling of being on a gigantic roller coaster as I rode down the mountain of water toward the uncertain bottom of the watery valley. As soon as I got to the bottom of the trough I started to climb the next mountain with great speed. As the raft got to its apex I was spilled out into the wild water. I was still tied to my raft and I held on for dear life. I tried to get the water floats which were also tied to the raft and after many unsuccessful attempts got

303

them next to me. I tied the ropes together and then fastened them under my arms, they floated behind me closely. I didn't have to fight so hard with the floats and my Mae West fully inflated. I hung on, I wasn't about to give up. I made no further attempt to reenter the raft, it would have done no good. My survival instincts kept me going as I bobbed up and down like a cork. My hopes of surviving were fading, I didn't think my chances were too good, but I refused to give up, I would fight it as long as my body had a breath of life left.

If I lived through this tempest I'd be one lucky son-of-a-bitch. I hung on and tried to get a good lung full of air each time my head was out of the water. I tried to conserve as much energy as possible, but just fighting for the surface was draining me. I knew nightfall would be upon me soon and I was in for the greatest trial of my life.

There was little I could do to improve the situation so I rolled with the punches. As far as I could tell I hadn't lost any of my precious gear, but I could be wrong the way the waves were washing over my small vessel every few seconds. My mind brought me back to the ditching and how unlucky I was. If I hadn't gone back into the plane I'd have been with Bart and the others safe in some dry quonset hut on Iwo Jima.

I was so cold I shivered uncontrollably. Still, my biggest problem was swalling salt water. I'd have drowned long ago without my life vest and Japanese floating balls. I could feel the swirling water trying to pull me beneath the surface. The floats kept me from being pulled on my back, I had equal buoyancy forward and aft, as they say in the Navy.

I had been so busy fighting the elements that the thought of food never entered my mind. Even if the ocean wasn't so rough I couldn't eat anything, I'd be lucky to keep anything down.

Night fell and nothing improved immediately, in fact it was more difficult. I thought the wind had died down some, but couldn't tell for sure. The worst thing about darkness was I couldn't get ready for the next big wave, at least during daylight you could prepare by getting a fresh breath of air.

The terrible ordeal went on for countless hours, but I still hung on. I knew I'd withstood the worst of the storm, I was sure the front had passed and even though the weather would continue to be foul I'd survived and had a good chance of making it.

Early in the morning, about an hour before daylight the storm broke. The wind and waves were decreasing in intensity. I had to try and reenter the raft, but I was so tired I wasn't sure I could pull myself aboard. I reluctantly released the air from the valves of my Mae West, grabbed the sides of the raft and pulled it under me as I raised up as far as I could. I was so bushed it took a super human effort to accomplish the simple task. I laid face down in the raft trying to get up enough strength to turn to a sitting position. It took some time, but finally I'd accomplished the task. I did my best not to rock the boat, I sure didn't want to go through that again. I immediately inflated my life vest and tied the floats to the side of the raft and tried to relax.

The sea was still wild, but I was still in the raft. My big problem now was a combination of motion sickness and the salt water I'd swallowed. I didn't feel too well and nothing in my stomach made the matter worse. I'd never been seasick prior to this raft ride, but that had come to an end. I felt miserable and my pangs of hunger were long forgotten. I could do nothing but lay there and hope for some relief. I was totally exhausted, I'd fought the sea for many hours in my bid for survival. I'd always been a strong swimmer, but it did little good under these conditions.

I gave up the idea of food, all I wanted to do was rest. I retched a few times and only liquid came up, this totally taxed my body. I laid back and within seconds was asleep.

The motion of the boat acted like a cradle rocking to and fro. Some hours later I woke, it was still dark and the seas were still rough, but nothing to compare with what had just happened. As time passed the wind died down and so did the sea. I prayed the storm would not linger. I thought it could be a fast moving cold front as many hit this area. By daylight things had improved greatly. I'd met and survived the greatest challenge of my life, it would be all downhill from here.

I ate a portion of one of the K-rations meals and believe it or not it tasted good, anything would have at this point. After finishing my meal I thought I might live. I felt relaxed and I had recovered some of my strength. I wondered what ordeal God now had in store for me. I looked at my watch and to my great surprise it was still running. The old GI Hack watch was better than I thought. I had actually come through the ordeal without losing any of my belongings. Okay, Lord, I made it, now how about some help!

34.

The United States Submarine Base on the island of Guam on the morning of 28 May 1945 was a very busy facility. Loading of one of the fleet submarines was being completed as it was being made ready for sea. The crew as well as others assigned the task wasted little time as they were watched by the skipper, Lieutenant Commander Michael A. Watson.

The *Seabat* was a new boat with a new skipper. The old man, as he was commonly called in the sub service, was eager to get under way so as not to miss the tide. He had received his official orders by messenger and descended to his cabin to read them. All eyes watched as he returned the salute of the messenger. They knew the messenger was delivering their sailing orders. The crew was ready to go to sea and get away from the rigors of the beach.

The skipper observed the activities of the men as they put the final touches to the loading and securing of the equipment and supplies. "Chief, how's the loading coming?"

The chief on the deck in charge turned, looked up and answered, "Fine, sir, we will be secure in five minutes."

"Very good." The captain was pleased as he scanned the length of the dark painted sub. The submersible was sleek and of the latest class, designed near the end of the war, the "Ray Class". The boat was capable of making 20 knots on the surface and a little less than half that speed when submerged. The boat to many was considered small for a man of war, however, it was anything but small. It measured 311 feet in length and loaded displaced 2,424 tons. When comparing fighting ships it should be remembered this submarine was a third the length of US battleships. Mike looked at the submarine as a thing of beauty and was delighted about his first command. The manning of the boat was 85 officers and men. Seabat carried 24 torpedo's and had one five inch deck gun as well as one 40mm and two .5 inch antiaircraft guns. A potent vessel capable of staying at sea for 2 months.

The fleet submarine had one primary mission and that was to sink enemy ships, however, additionally some were also involved air-sea rescue. Both missions were considered essential. The men of the Seabat relished the thought of going to sea to sink ships of the Empire of the Rising Sun.

The skipper picked up his megaphone as he observed the forward hatch being secured. He turned to the tube which went directly below the hatch to the conning tower and said, "Stand by." A talker waited at the other end of the tube for further orders. He monitored all orders from the bridge and was ready to relay all orders as received.

"Maneuvering, ready on number one engine . . . Single up all lines," he barked into the megaphone. He turned to the tube and ordered, "All ahead one third . . . Starboard back one third . . . All stop . . . Shift your rudder . . . All ahead two thirds, ease your rudder," his commands were clear and understood.

The dark slinky sub slid forward and was heading for the mouth of the harbor and out to open sea. It was still dark, the skipper wanted to clear the harbor and be well to sea before daylight. He, like all other submarine captains, liked the solitude of the open sea especially when near other Naval and Air Forces. Accidents had happened in the past and subs had been attacked by friendly forces. It seemed to most that any submarine is fair game, they fired first and asked questions later, he wanted no part of that.

Mike had graduated from Annapolis in the top third of his class. His class was the last to graduate prior to Pearl harbor. He had just celebrated his birthday and that of his son, born after his fathers departure. The child had his first birthday on the same day as his father who was now twenty-five, young for a skipper of a submarine. His family awaited his return to San Diego. Mike was born in San Diego and from a small tot had hankered to go to the USNA and become an officer. His dream had blossomed and now he commanded his own ship. His wife had been his one and only girl friend, they had planned to be married since childhood. She too came from a Navy family and was accustomed to the life as wife of a naval officer.

He felt confident with is new ship and crew. He'd been in command for only three days, it had come with is promotion. He slid down the ladder to the conning tower. The eyes of the ship were left to the duty officer who rode the bridge with the lookouts. This ship was equipped with radar which scanned the sky and sea.

Lieutenant Tom Webster, the boat's executive officer was at the navigation table laying out the initial course which would take them near Iwo Jima. Mike turned to his executive officer and friend of many years and said, "Keep your fingers crossed for me."

"You must be kidding, Captain, you'll have no problems with the boat or the crew. Have you read the orders?"

"Yes, I wanted to talk to you alone before we announce the mission."

"I'm at your service, Mike."

"No time like the present. Let's go into the wardroom and have a cup of coffee while we talk."

The two walked into the wardroom and the mess steward was ready with two large mugs of steaming hot black coffee. "We, as I'm sure you and the others know, are heading for the waters off Japan." He was interrupted by the chief of the boat.

"Captain we have cleared the harbor and have set a course for Iwo Jima, any further orders?"

"No chief, good work, we'll be with you in a couple minutes and then we'll tell the crew what we're up to." The chief returned to the operations room.

"Now, where were we? Oh yes, first we're heading for this location to pick up an Air Force flyer, if he survived last night's storm, then we're going to try to do some damage around the southern part of Japan."

"Sounds, great."

Both men finished their coffee and walked to the control room.

Mike approached the comm and all eyes and ears were on him. "Now hear this, this is the captain. I would like to tell you all of our mission and the importance of speed. We have been assigned to find and pick up a B-29 flyer who has been in the water for three days after a ditching. We hope he is still alive after the terrible storm which hit the area he was in. He is approximately 125 miles off the Japanese coast. The Japanese have many coastal vessels and fishing boats in the area which will make our mission more difficult. We must keep our heads out and make sure no enemy aircraft or ship gets to us before we see them. We will travel at flank speed as long as we can without stressing the engines. After we pluck the airdale out of the water we will do our best to destroy as many Jap ships as possible as well as looking for other downed airmen. That is about all I have, good luck and good hunting."

Tom turned to Mike and asked, "How the hell did he get separated from the others or is he the only survivor?"

"They ditched and apparently he went back into the plane to get supplies and the rest of his crew was pulled away by the current. They were picked up by a PBY after daylight and the PBY had to leave due to gravely wounded and the enemy ships in the immediate area."

"Poor bastard, he'll be lucky if he made it through last night. I just saw the weather report and they had a fast but furious storm hit the area."

"I know. All we can do is get there ASAP and hope he's still alive. There's usually a sub at a location near where they ditched, but they had to return to SUBCOMPAC for repairs, that's how we got into the act."

The chief was listening to the conversation and added, "That Air Force type must have had a bad time."

"He sure did, chief. He was on the mission to Tokyo, a rough one, they lost 26 planes. He was on one of the lucky ones who got out to sea. I hear the damn fighters followed them and lost a couple for their trouble, serves them right."

"Christ, skipper, I would rather be down here. They can have that flying, every son-of-a-bitch shooting at you, it scares the hell out of me, yes, I'd rather take my chances under the sea."

"It's a damn shame we had the three day delay or we'd be there now picking him up, but that's the breaks, who would figure a new boat having turbine trouble," said Mike.

"Well, the boat is fit as a fiddle and we're making 20 knots, right now," answered Tom.

"We're still looking at three plus days before we get there depending on how long we can stay on the surface," said Mike.

"We can't cry over spilt milk. We'll just have to do our best and hope he can hold on," said Mike.

"By the way, the report of large numbers of boats in the area can mean anything. The Japs have been converting fishing boats to sub-chasers, I hear," said Tom as he headed back to his navigation table.

"Captain, a message from the bridge," reported the talker.

"Go ahead."

"Sir, we've cleared the harbor and they report daylight is about to break."

"Very good, make sure you keep a sharp eye peeled, I want to stay on the surface as much as possible," called Mike into the tube.

"Aye, aye, sir."

35.

The sea and wind had calmed, but my sleep was disturbed by
an odd sensation. I felt as if my raft was being raised and pushed
at the same time. I sat up and looked about but everything seemed
normal. The sky was a deep blue with scattered fluffy white
clouds. I rubbed my eyes and waited motionless for a repeat. All
at once I felt my raft being pushed once more. I looked over the
side in the clear blue water which matched the color of the sky
and almost fainted. I was surrounded by a small school of large
fish. They were not being aggressive; however, they were rubbing
the sides and bottom of my small craft. I concluded the fish were
some type of large shark which did little to calm my nerves. They
were possibly basking sharks known not to be aggressive toward
man but that did little to comfort me. I was never crazy about
sharks of any type. What bothered me more than anything was
that their rough hides could cause a leak or worse, a tear. My
second concern was, they may dump me out of the boat then who
knows what would happen! I gently tried to paddle away without
success, I was at their mercy.

They continued to rub the life raft which I concluded was making them feel better, but did little for me. I was sure if they wanted
me in the water there wasn't much I could do. I tried to remember
the survival lectures concerning nonman-eating types and concluded that they knew very little. I pulled my survival manual
out and scanned the pages for any clue, none were to be found.
They were very gentle in a way, but the large dorsal fin was one
of the things bothering me, another was their size, I estimated
the largest to be in the fifteen-foot class, however, in the water
size was deceiving. I tended to discount the stories of sharks not
being dangerous, anything that large might just decide to go into
an eating frenzy. I considered for less than one second shooting
one to see if they might leave, it was just a fantasy which I
immediately erased from my thoughts.

Murphy's law was still at work. The big fish refused to leave and I could not leave, it was a Mexican stand off. Too bad they were not porpoise rather than shark.

I felt as if they liked my company after a couple hours. I thought I was going dingy, after they'd been with me an hour I started talking to them trying to coax them away. Maybe, it was best, at least I had some company. I knew I couldn't fish and I would have to hold off on entering the water to take my constitutional. It was hard to figure with all this ocean why they wanted to keep me company! I knew one thing, I was going where they wanted and not necessarily where I wanted. I actually got enough nerve up to reach over and put my hand on the back of one of the beasts. I pulled it back rapidly when I felt the abrasive skin it was like a heavy coarse sandpaper.

I was feeling very hungry and thirsty. I had only a small bit of the last K-ration and most of a jar of peanut butter. I finished off the K-ration and dipped into the jar. Then opened one of my water containers and sipped a small amount of water which I washed around my mouth a number of times before I let it slip down my throat. After eating I slid down and relaxed and read my survival manual. I was sleepy and soon drifted off.

It seemed but a short time I had rested my eyes, however, when I looked skyward the sun had passed beyond its zenith. It was then I realized the fish had disappeared, I was alone again. I wasn't sure if I felt better now that I was alone or worse. I made a careful survey of my raft as far as I could reach and was happy to find no damage. My mind off the sharks I again wondered about my rescue. I fantasized if it were possible that another B-29 crew had ditched and were the ones picked up by the PBY! I knew we had lost some planes, but not how many and had no idea if any had made it out to sea. After thinking about it for some time I concluded the PBY had to have picked up Bart and the others because of their proximity to my position. My delay in departing from the plane had caused us to be separated by at least a mile.

I tried to think back on the reports of downed crewmen and remember how they kept the search up until all possibilities had been exhausted and certainly no one could say they have exhausted all possibilities. I felt they would not give up the search for me. I also felt they must have had good reason for not flying over, it was possible the enemy was close by and waiting for them to tip their hand. Christ, the possibilities were too numerous to figure. I would just have to try and keep going. After all what could be worse than what I'd gone through the last few days?

I wanted to get my mind off the rescue so I decided to fish. I prepared the line and noticed in place of the large sharks small fish were darting to and fro. I dropped my bait as close to the larger concentration as possible without spooking them. I knew if I could catch one I would have live bait, but they seemed to be disinterested in any of the combination of lures I tempted them with. I fished for three hours trying to lure or snag one without success, I knew I had to be patient, but there is a limit. One thing was sure; it was imperative I catch a fish.

The sun started its race for the horizon and soon would dip below the edge of the world and I would be in darkness once again. I felt a small tug at my drop line. I wasn't sure if I should let him take the lure or to pull hard and set the hook. I decided to pull gently to see if the fish was still on my line. I felt a hard tug and jerked the line. I had indeed set the hook, now all I had to do was land him. I pulled the struggling fish to the surface after a few minutes of playing him. He had given a good account of himself, but I was not to be denied. I pulled the fish into the raft. I had put the raft covering in my lap to lay him on. The fish flapped on the cover to show his displeasure with being taken from the water. He was a pretty fish, a variety I had never seen. I'd have to check in the book after I secured him. There are some fish which are poisonous and shouldn't be eaten. I struck the fish a hard blow with the handle of my trench knife and he finally was through flapping about. I couldn't identify the fish from the manual. He was multicolored blue and green. It was a shame to kill such a beautiful fish, but it was survival that drove me. The fish was eight inches in length and after I skinned it and removed the entrails I could see the meat was white and looked good. I had never eaten raw fish, but understood the orientals enjoy their fish raw, that's the difference between us and the little yellow men, I guess. I carefuly saved the entrails of the fish in a plastic bag after cleaning away all the debris and stowed it for future fishing expeditions. After the fish was completely cleaned I washed it in the ocean and prepared to taste my first fish dinner.

I cut a piece off put it in my mouth and chewed until it was pulp, I spit out the residue. The taste was not important, the nourishment was. I carefully wrapped the skinned fish and put it in the bottom of the boat to keep cool. The survival book was right, I took a small piece of entrails and put it on my hook carefully and dropped the line in the water, within seconds I felt the fish take my hook. The fellow who wrote the fish article knew what he was talking about. My second fish was of the same variety but a little larger. The fish was flat like a pan fish and the meat was firm. I was now sure I could survive on fish I could catch. Water was my most important concern.

I thought about putting the fish over the side to keep it fresh, but decided it might attract larger and dangerous fish to me and that was the last thing I wanted to do. The afternoon slipped into the reddish water of the Pacific with streaks of crimson across the sky. I watched it as it sunk below the horizon and within a short time I was again in darkness, my fourth night at sea, I had to relieve myself and decided to hurry and take care of it before it was totally dark. I was lucky, all went fine and I pulled myself back into the raft effortlessly. I'd spent enough time in the water to stretch my limbs and gently exercise my legs, they were getting stiff stretched out in the small raft.

The water surrounding me was flat and calm the only sound was of the gentle lap against my raft. I felt strangely at peace. I looked toward the heavens and said a prayer of thanks for delivering me from the apparent disaster of the night before and for letting me catch my fish. I was determined to continue my struggle until someone came for me. It was me against the elements and my chances had improved, it was not my style to give up.

36.

The morning came alive with spectacular brightness; there were no clouds to hinder the brilliant sun. The gentle rocking of the raft acted as a hammock as it swayed to and fro. The night had passed and no calamity had befallen me, I'd slept without interruption and felt completely rested and ready for the new day's challenge.

My prayers were centered around the fervent hope that today would be my last day on the open sea. Visibility would not be a factor and the ocean was being very cooperative as well. It should be easy for a search plane to spot me; yes today has to be the day.

I decided to chew some raw fish, have a little water and take care of all the other necessities of everyday life. I never liked going into the cold water voluntarily, but knew I had to keep fit and one way was to keep regular. A good salt water bath may spark my spirits and if done early I could avoid additional sunburn.

The raw fish tasted better. I was very hungry and this time I was able to swallow the meat. A little peanut butter followed by one of my small candies finished off my meal. It was now time to get into the water.

I emerged from the water feeling better than at any time since my departure from *Here's Hopin'*. I set up my routine and fishing was high on the list of activities. My head moved constantly as if I were in a cockpit looking for enemy fighters. I was sure I'd spot any aircraft long before they saw me. I had to be prepared and ready on a second's notice to start signaling. I had to be sure the enemy was not the one I beckoned, however. I was in a very vulnerable spot a hundred or so miles off the mouth of Tokyo Bay where I was sure traffic was the heaviest in the main island of Honshu.

There was no sign of life anywhere north or south not even the basking sharks were companions this day. As the day dragged on

315

I became despondent. For the first time I had sunk to the point of despair. I could not figure how they could leave me out here; not a plane had ventured anywhere within miles. There had to be a reason, yet it was difficult for me to understand. I knew in the past no stone was left unturned in the quest to save downed airmen and I certainly fit the category. As I fished and pondered the question the same answer kept coming back, did they think it was useless after the terrific storm or did they decide since I wasn't with the others when picked up that I was lost before the storm? If they gave up the search I was in big trouble, only a miracle could save me. I had to believe they were still coming for me, there had to be a damn good reason and none of them I liked.

I tried to get my mind off the search and fished in earnest. I wanted to be sure I had a good supply of food because I now realized I may be in for a long stay on this huge expanse of water. I fished for two hours without result then decided to lure the fish to me by singing, still they shunned my bait. I knew I had to keep my mind active. I went through some of the math drills we had to learn in navigation school. It worked for a while then I tried to remember my favorite poem, "The Charge of the Light Brigade," by Tennyson. "Cannons to the left, cannons to the right, into the valley of death rode the six hundred." I was unsure if I had remembered the lines correctly, but it made little difference, it was a wonderful work. I wondered if I were charging into the valley of death! Time would tell, but there was one thing for sure I wasn't ready to sacrifice myself as yet. I had to keep fighting and thinking positive.

The day passed without incident; not even the fish had cooperated. I put my fishing gear away and then tried to talk to myself, not even my voice helped the loneliness.

The Bonin Islands lay approximately 600 miles to the southwest. I was probably northeast of Iwo Jima, two and a half flying hours away. Even if I had a way of navigating I wanted to stay away from the Bonins, they were Japanese. Only lonely Iwo Jima was American. Being a navigator I mentally adjusted everything to latitude and longitude. I figured I was just about at the same latitude as Southern California and it made me feel better. The trouble was it was 6,000 miles away. How I wish I could be there with my family. I had to keep my mind off them for now it only depressed me, but still there was no way of suppressing those thoughts. I also knew Kimberly was at approximately the same latitude, however, she was in the southern hemisphere thousands of miles away. I hoped Bart or one of the others had written her, but maybe they hadn't thought of that. I again thought of my folks and wondered if the War Department had sent one of those telegrams, I sure didn't want them to do that, but I didn't know how long they would wait after I was declared missing to inform the family of my status. I'd always tried to play down the dangers of flying combat in a B-29. I'm not sure if I succeeded, but now it was academic. I tried to be philosophical, there was nothing I could do, so why worry.

As the sun started its last fling at dominance of the day the wind started to freshen and this created swells of increasing size. I noticed the sky now starting to show signs of becoming cloudy. I wasn't sure what it meant, but I didn't like the change. I hurriedly made fast all my loose gear in preparation for any eventuality. I raised my head to the heavens and prayed aloud, "Please, God, no storm."

Night fell without a storm developing. My prayers had been answered. I guess he had to throw a bone my way. As the stars peaked between the clouds I positioned myself from memory and as far as I could figure without instruments I was where I had estimated earlier. I ate a little more fish and drank a small amount of water, then I heard the familiar drone of aircraft flying north. Our B-29's were after the enemy again. "Give them hell, guys." I could not see them, but I knew they were up there, it was going to be a big raid, at least four or five hundred planes. With that many B-29's up there my outfit must have been among them. Did any of them think about me down here somewhere? Surely, they haven't forgotten me. Finally the last plane was out of my hearing range. Within thirty minutes they would be fighting for their lives and raining death and destruction down on the self appointed "Sons of Heaven."

How far could the fishing fleet be from me now? I felt they were of no concern, but there are probably plenty of fishing boats out this far looking for food to feed the people of Japan. The blockade and mining of Japanese waters was putting a squeeze on them. I felt bad about the civilians dying, but this war was of their making and they had to face the consequences for their leaders as we do of ours.

I hoped the absence of airplanes looking for me meant they knew where I was. We'd heard about the submarines doing such a great job out here, where were they? We'd been told they lurk close to the Japanese coast in search of prey and to pick up surviving aircrew members floating around in the sea. I remembered from the flimsey I'd been issued during briefing there was supposed to be a sub on station nearby, but it had to leave due to mechanical difficulties maybe that's the reason for the delay in picking me up, they must be coming for me. I knew the subs top speed was about 20 knots on the surface and less than half that submerged. I tried to think logically, but logic did not always hold true in wartime. My logic included the reason for the absence of aircraft was due to the fact that our people didn't want to tip their hand as to my location, yes, that had to be it. I would just have to be patient and make sure the enemy didn't spot me before our guys got here. I figured in my head how long it would take a submarine to get to me from the sub base in Guam and it made me feel better knowing there was still a chance they were on their way. Also, they could have been delayed if they got involved in some action. I convinced myself not to fret, my time would come if I kept the faith. I tried to think of other subjects to get my mind off of the seriousness of my position, but erasing it from my thoughts was easier said than done.

One thing I had learned from my ordeal, you had to maintain a good mental state and not let the adversities get to you, it was the key. Another item of importance was to rest as much as possible to keep up your strength. Eating helped also.

The sky was covered by a low overcast severely limiting visibility. There would be no rescue planes looking for me this day, I was sure. The clouds moved rapidly and soon there was no sky to be seen. The wind picked up as the sky became darker, I was in for a storm; the lightning could be seen some distance away. I could see the heavy rain falling from the clouds which caused the electrical disturbance. If the rain comes my way I can replenish my water supply. I'd been using my water sparingly, but it was necessary to collect more if possible. Water was always scarce even though you're surrounded by it. There was one thing in my favor, since I started eating fish. I needed less water, still a nice rain would help, providing the storm stays as it is.

I watched the storm, it seemed to come very close to my position, but stayed too far for me to reach. I had waited much of the day for the rain, but none fell on me. The sun never made an appearance either. It would be a dark night without the moon or stars to shed light.

My raft rocked back and forth as the water churned around it. It was so dark I could not see my hand in front of my face, it was frightening. It would be difficult to eat in this abyss. I had eaten the last of the peanut butter and now had only the remainder of my catch. Food was not my problem, water was. I would have to stick to my rationing and pray some rain came my way. I chewed a little fish and relaxed. The night finally passed.

The new day came to life as the old one had left. Again I saw the rain falling from the low-hung clouds and still none had reached me. It was like the storm had a center without rain and I was in the middle. The wind had increased with the coming of dawn and the white caps were slapping all around me. My raft seemed to move in all directions, but never closer to the falling rain. It seemed a real enigma, before last night all I wanted to do was escape any type storm now I prayed to have one of small magnitude, but it was not to be.

I tried to determine the direction of the storm. If there was no movement the storm was coming at you or moving directly away from you. In this case there was no motion, the storm was finally coming at me. I wasn't sure how long it would take to get here, but I wanted it to hurry before it changed direction in this squirrelly wind. I was fishing as I kept my eye on the rain and I caught two small odd looking fish. I cleaned them and started chewing on the white meat. Then my heart jumped a beat as the storm veered away from my position. It was so close I could feel the dampness. I paddled as hard as I could trying to find the rain without success. I was very fatigued. I sat back and looked at the clouds overhead, they seemed to drop even lower than before, I felt as if I could touch them, but I could wring no water from them.

I was cold, thirsty and disgusted. I felt my rescue was imminent prior to the low cloud cover of the past two days. Now, things didn't look so bright. The one thing that made my life less miserable was being dry, but it was a poor trade off for drinking water and clear skies.

My prayers were answered about mid-morning when I felt the first drops on my head. I quickly prepared for the rain I had waited so long for. The rain came down slowly at the start and I captured enough moisture to clean my cover and wash my face before the deluge hit me. My quick action was unnecessary. I filled all my containers and basked in the rain. I was wet from stem to stern and didn't complain. I drank water until I thought I would burst, but I drank slowly to prevent getting sick. The dehydrated feeling had vanished and my water facilities were replenished including my newly emptied peanut butter jar. The chance for a fresh water bath was so overpowering I removed my shoes pulled down my flying suit and washed as much of my body as possible. The water was cold, but refreshing.

The rain lasted for a few hours and then as quickly as it came it passed. I had lost track of time. I decided to get my routine chores accomplished. When I had finished all the necessary items I pulled out my fishing gear and relaxed as the sun broke through the clouds making long streaks of light. I believe they called it "Jacob's Ladder" if I recalled my bible studies.

I was encouraged by the turn of the weather and singing helped to keep my morale up. Night fell as the beautiful sunset gave way to the last streaks of light in the west and soon darkness commanded my world again. Stars came out one by one and the ocean had settled down to lazy rolls of water which gently pushed my small craft from one watery hill to the next. I studied the stars as they made their appearance in the black void above. I named every star I'd learned back in navigation school; it took my mind off my predicament.

The next morning exploded with a beautiful sunrise and a deep blue sky. My spirits were alive with expectation of a new day and a possible rescue. A few white puffy clouds dotted the sky making dark shadows beneath them on the deep blue surface. This was my eighth day at sea and I had survived all the ravages of nature. Nine nights alone in a three foot raft was probably no record, but if it weren't, it should have been, hopefully it wouldn't be any longer, heaven forbid.

Something didn't feel quite right that morning and I wasn't sure what it was. All of a sudden I became aware the sides of my raft were not firm and the water was lapping over. I pulled out the mouthpiece and began to reinflate it. I tried in vain to find the leak. I was sure I had one and it was enough to scare the crap right out of me. I moved each item in the raft and still couldn't locate it. It had to be on the outside of the raft so I carefully examined every inch with a moist hand until I saw the telltale bubbles coming from the under side. I quickly pulled in my floating glass balls for buoyancy and gathered up all my gear and made it fast, then with my repair kit in hand slid over the side of the raft. While in the water I carefully turned the raft upside down and found the leak. Apparently, the leak was caused by the sharks rubbing against the sides the other day. I patched the small hole and waited a few minutes to be sure the patch would hold. I turned the raft right side up and reentered wet as a drowned rat. I blew up the raft and was satisfied I'd repaired the leak and no air would escape. The sun dryed my clothing and I was glad my life support was once again in A-1 shape.

I fished as the morning became afternoon and dreamed of better times. I considered an alternative, maybe it would be more tolerable if the Japanese found me, anything would be better than being lost at sea forever. I thought of the stories which had reached us about the treatment of POW's from the undercover agents we had in Japan, they painted a very gloomy picture of life under the Japanese boot. The Japs did not abide by the articles of the Geneva convention. They treated all prisoners whether they be Allies or Japanese the same way, ruthlessly. I said out loud as my thoughts came back to the real world I'd rather take my chances on the open sea than as a Japanese POW. It was my duty to keep from being captured and if I was successful the POW thought was academic. I was sure if the Japanese knew I was down they would have found me by now. Only an accidental sighting by one of their ships or planes would bring them after me, I rationalized. On the other hand our forces knew I was out here and I had to assume they were looking for me.

My fishing line came taut; I had hooked a fish that felt too large for my tackle, but like all true fishermen I wasn't willing to let it get away. I was very curious about what I had on the other end, but was worried about the way it fought and pulled, the line was actually cutting my fingers. I wondered what the hell kind of a fish would take such a small hook and fight so damn hard. My competitive spirit had surfaced and I was going to fight it out until I either landed him or he broke my line. My raft was actually being pulled by the fish. I decided not to try and pull him to the surface, I just held on. I theorized the fish would either pull loose or it would become so exhausted I could handle him. The struggle continued for some minutes then the line went limp and I thought the battle was over. I was wrong. When I pulled the line in rapidly the fish responded with a hefty pull, I thought for a second I was going to be pulled into the water. He'd given his best effort, but

I knew I had him. I slowly pulled the line into the boat with my sore hands. I could now see the fish below the surface and to my surprise it looked like a small tuna. How I'd love a nice tuna sandwich! But forget it, this baby was out of my league, the fish broached the water's surface and spit the hook out and the line went slack. In a flash he was gone. He knew he'd been in a fight, but there would've been no way I could have landed such a fish without destroying my life raft. Even though I didn't get my fish I felt exhilaration from the struggle, it had made me forget all the miserable thoughts I'd had previously. Actually I had plenty of food for the time being. I settled down to try and catch a fish more my size. The sun felt good after the days of cold and wind and I basked in the warmth and for a short while forgot my troubles.

I kept searching the horizon from time to time without success. It was like I expected some large ship to come into view and find me. It was very difficult to keep my mind off the possible rescue. It was my whole life now. My thoughts kept returning to the same thing; someone should have found me before now.

The ocean was as calm as I had seen it since I disembarked from *Here's Hopin*. It was a good time to take off my boots and let my feet air out and to dry my socks. I removed them and then I dropped my line over the side; this time I was careful to keep the lure shallow I didn't want a repeat performance with a large fish. The small weight made a ripple on the smooth surface as it hit the water and I settled back to wait. I dozed in the warmth of the sun and was at peace, when. . . .

The calm sea erupted like a volcano and the following tidal wave hit my small boat and scared the shit out of me. I tried in vain to catch my pair of boots as they rose as if in slow motion and fell into the sea. I heard the terrifying explosion behind me and turned to see what monster of the sea was about to swallow me as the wave hit with its full fury and tossed me into the water. I struggled back to the surface half afraid to look at my tormentor. I held the side of my raft as I snuck a peek around the raft. I did not see what I'd expected.

It was a monster all right, but not a live one. It was huge and bore no markings that I could see. The submarine had surfaced behind me without the slightest hint and had popped to the surface, causing the uncharacteristic wave. I couldn't tell immediately who owned this monster, but within seconds men were

322

climbing from hatches and it was easy to see their faces were friendly. I cried as I waited for the small dinghy to reach me. I was soon to be aboard one of the United States Navy's fleet submarines.

I pulled myself aboard my raft and sat and watched as men ran on the deck of the huge vessel. A line was tossed to me and I held it tight as I was pulled to the side of the submarine by my saviours.

37.

My small raft was dwarfed by the submarine. I had always thought of a submarine as small, I was wrong, it was enormous, but best of all it finally afforded me with a place to stand erect. It had been over a week since I'd been able to stand and walk.

I was assisted to the deck by two young seaman who helped me stand. It was a good thing because my legs were like rubber. As I took my first step I wondered if I could walk unassisted, I wasn't given the opportunity.

I must have been a sight to behold, unshaven and shoeless. It made little difference to any of the men around me, they were happy and making quite a fuss over me. I was among real people, and Americans to boot. I had tears in my eyes and found I could not control my emotions.

"Welcome aboard, Lieutenant Lea," came a voice from the bridge.

I looked to see where it had came from, it was the captain who had called my name. I was bewildered as I raised my arm to salute. I asked myself, "How did he know my name?" I almost fell on my ass as I did my best to stand at attention. A tall lean petty officer first class took me by the arm and we headed for the hatch. I looked back at the two men who were pulling my raft aboard.

"Clear the deck, we're in enemy waters and I don't want to be spotted," called the captain with his megaphone to his lips.

As I was helped up the ladder to the bridge I was met by the skipper, a handsome dark haired man with gold oak leafs on his open neck shirt. Lieutenant Commander Mike Watson extended his hand and said, "Welcome aboard *Seabat,* we're sorry we're late. You must lose no time getting below, there are reports of enemy surface vessels in the near vicinity, we don't want to be caught with our drawers down."

I was getting some feeling back in my legs as I descended the

324

ladder with the help of two or three extra men. My legs felt as if they were asleep and had a strange tingling feeling as I stepped onto the deck of the conning tower. I heard the slam of the hatch above as the lookouts and the captain slid down the ladder behind me.

All around me men stopped momentarily to look up and wave as they continued their important part of the job of getting the submarine below the surface.

I watched for a few seconds in awe as the team within the control room worked without friction. I felt the deck below me slant as the submarine headed down. The klaxon horn had made me jump when it went off, but no one else was affected by its wail.

I was assisted by the pharmacist mate to a cubicle some distance from the control room. It was the cabin of the boat's executive officer. Just as we arrived we were met by the XO who welcomed me to his bunk.

"I'll have a cot set up next to the bunk. You'll sleep in my bunk temporarily," said the lieutenant.

"Sir, I'll sleep on the cot, I don't want to take your bed," I answered.

"I don't want to pull rank, but you will sleep in the bunk," he said with a smile.

"Lieutenant, how did you find me?"

"We knew right where you'd be. We had plotted your expected route since your entry into the raft and after a little plotting and checking the weather I was able to come right to you."

"If you don't mind me saying so, you scared the living shit out of me when you surfaced, the noise was beyond my comprehension," I said as I sat on the built-in bunk along the bulkhead.

"We're all happy you made it through the storm. I have to get back to work, we'll talk some more later," the XO turned to leave and I called.

"One fast question, please. How did you fellows know my name?"

"Easy, they told us before we left Guam." He walked out before I could say another word. The Doc as he was referred to as we made our way to the cabin helped me undress and then tucked me in.

"I'll bring you some food and look you over in a few minutes, but for now relax," said Doc as he too departed.

I was alone, but not really alone. The last thing I remembered was looking up at the ceiling as I felt the comfort of the clean sheets, but I still felt the rocking as if I were still on the raft, I hoped the feeling would go away soon. I was asleep within seconds.

It was strangely quiet as I woke from a sound sleep. I wasn't sure how long I'd slept or where I was. It took a few seconds to remember I was safe from the ravages of the open sea. I felt good as I opened my eyes and saw the Doc standing next to me. "Hi Doc, I guess I fell asleep, sorry."

"I was glad you did, you'll feel better now," he said as he pulled a tray next to the bunk. "Drink some of this soup slowly, it'll help."

I saw the soup with crackers and a hot cup of coffee on the tray, but I was more thirsty for cool water than anything. Doc obliged and I drank the water as slowly as I could.

"When you finish I'd like to give you a short physical examination to see how you held up after all that time out there."

I ate slowly and relished every bite. The soup was homemade and delicious, they had a good cook on this submarine. Soon I finished my food and the Doc asked me to sit up. He checked my blood pressure and heart. Looked down my throat and checked my ears. He made notations on an examination sheet. "Do you think you can stand, sir?"

"I think so." I swung my feet over the side of the bunk and with his assistance I stood before him naked as a J-Bird. He did a complete exam on me and then handed me underwear as well as a new set of khaki. I slipped on the T-shirt and skivvies and sat back on the bunk.

"It looks like you're fit as a fiddle. A little sunburned here and there and a little dehydrated and underweight, but nothing serious. I suggest you stay in the sack for a day or two until you get your strength back and then you'll be off the sick list as far as I'm concerned," said Doc as he picked up his clipboard and bag and left the cabin.

I called to him, "Doc, thanks, I sure feel great being with you fellows, I was awful lonely without anyone to talk to."

"I understand, we're glad we got to you before the Japs, they aren't pleasant captors, I understand."

I wasn't tired any longer and wanted to get out of bed and dress, but doctor's orders were to stay in bed and I'd abide by his edict. Soon the mess cook came into the cabin. "How was the soup, sir?"

"Just great, I could eat a bucket of it right now."

"I'll get you some more, Doc's says if you eat slowly you can have more."

"Great, I am hungry. I've been eating raw fish for some time and it sure doesn't compare with your food. I hope I never have to eat raw fish again."

The cook returned and brought with him a large bowl of soup and more salt crackers. "Is there anything else you would like, sir?"

"A glass of milk if you have it, thanks."

He rushed out and brought milk and a piece of chocolate cake as well. "Maybe you can get the cake down too. I'll bet it was hell out there all alone," he said seriously.

"It wasn't any fun, I'm sure glad you guys found me!"

"You'll have to tell us all about it when you're up to it. For now I'll leave, and I'll be back in a little while to pick up the dishes," said the cook with a big grin.

I finished my meal and laid back again. I had the feeling of flying except it was smoother. I could barely feel the vibrations of the motors as we moved under the surface.

The small ships clock on the bulkhead over the desk rang out a series of bells. The clock had an inscription which described the appreciation of the last skipper to Lieutenant Tom Webster, a valued comrade. In my groggy state I forgot to introduce myself to the Exec and he to me, but what the hell it's only a formality. The face of the clock presented no problem for me, it was the bells which I knew nothing of. It was 1800 hours east longitude time. I could still feel the motion, but much less than before I had fallen asleep.

Sub duty looked like good duty to me. If I hadn't been a flyer this would be where I think I would have liked to serve. I was anxious to look around the boat. I remember reading about how some people couldn't handle the claustrophobia, but it wasn't too different than being confined in small area aboard a plane. I also remember reading from the reports that submarines usually stay on a war cruise two months or more. I wondered if I would stay with them and if so would they let me help out with the running of this man of war! I was soon to know the answer as the skipper and his exec entered the small cabin.

"How are you getting along, Lieutenant Lea?" asked the captain.

"Fine, sir, I've been fed and got a couple of naps in, now I'm raring to go."

"Not too fast," said the exec. Then he said, "By the way, my name is Webster, Tom Webster, I didn't have time to introduce myself before."

"You already know my name. I'm happy to meet you both. Sir, I hope I can help while I'm aboard."

"Don't worry about that, no one goes for free on a submarine if he's able-bodied, and I'm short one officer anyway," answered the skipper.

"I'm ready now. I feel fine."

"Doc tells me you should stay in bed, at least for today. Tomorrow will be soon enough. We'll start you off on a cook's tour so you'll know where everything is on the boat then we'll talk about some kind of a training schedule, okay?"

"Sounds fine to me. Captain, I'm grateful to you for fishing me out of the drink, but as I told Lieutenant Webster you may have wet my pants, I'm not sure because your wake threw me into the sea. I thought some sea serpent was going to have me for a meal."

"We got to you as fast as possible and we're really glad you were still around. I'll look in on you later, Lea," said the skipper as he and his exec departed.

My second day on the sub found me rested and feeling fine. I slid out of the bunk and headed for the shower. After cleaning up and shaving I dressed. As I looked into the mirror I thought, the uniform makes the man. I looked like any other Navy lieutenant (jg). I was just ready to leave the room under my own power when Doc knocked and came through the curtain.

"How are you feeling Mr. Lea?"

"I feel like a new man, in fact I look like a new man. My beard made me feel and look crummy. I'm so hungry I could eat the south end of a jackass going north."

He laughed and then said, "The cooks have prepared something special for you. We can go to the wardroom and talk a bit more," said Doc as he led the way.

We entered the ward room which was a short distance down the passageway. All the others had eaten and were at their duty stations, we had the small room to ourselves. The cook appeared, "I have a steak ready, how do you like it," he asked.

"Steak! You must be kidding. This is too good to be true. Medium will do just fine, thanks."

"No sweat, Mr. Lea. Have a cup of coffee and I'll be back in a few minutes."

"By the way my name is Johnny. I forgot to introduce myself yesterday."

"Sir, my name is Dooley," he smiled, turned and left.

"Mr. Lea, Dooley is the best damn cook in the Navy, but on this boat it's different from the Air Corps, we don't address officers by their first names. It's okay for an officer to call an enlisted man by his first or last name, but it's a no-no for us. Most of the officers are called by their first name by the old man or the XO, but that's where it stops."

"Thanks for the information, I should have asked, I guess."

"No sweat Mr. Lea, we understand and appreciate your presence."

We drank the dark coffee and talked mostly about what had happened to both of us. Doc was a couple of years older than me and had been in the Navy for a year before Pearl Harbor. Soon the curtain parted and Dooley entered the wardroom with a huge steak and french fried potatoes. "I heard you submariners ate good, but this goes beyond my wildest dreams." Dooley smiled as he beat a hasty retreat from the room.

I dug in with both hands, but before I was half finished I was full. I tried to finish the steak and two potatoes, but couldn't stuff another bite in.

Dooley reentered the wardroom and looked at my plate with a frown. "Didn't you like it, Mr. Lea?" he asked with a pained expression.

"I loved it, but I can't hold another bite."

"Are you sure? I have ice cream for dessert."

"Maybe, I could squeeze a scoop down. I would like to keep this piece of meat and snack on it later, is that okay?"

"Sure, sir, I'll put it in the refer for you."

I could see how pleased Dooley was with my raving about his cooking. It made him happy to know someone appreciated him and from that minute on he always went out of his way to please me.

The skipper came into the wardroom as Doc was telling me not to overdo anything for a day or two.

"Good to see you up and around, Johnny. Are you ready for the tour?"

"Yes sir."

"Okay, let's get started." We headed for the conning tower to watch the action. The crew was making ready to surface.

"Lieutenant Lea, this is Mr. Young, Lieutenant to you. He is the diving officer responsible for the boat getting to the proper depth and also for making sure all goes well to surface."

There was a sailor who was always at the skipper's side when he was in the control room. He wore a headset and was called the talker. His duty was to relay orders to and from the captain to the rest of the boat.

"Bring her to sixty feet," was the order. Sixty feet was the depth at which the periscope could see on the surface. The captain's orders were transmitted to the rest of the crew and the diving officer was then in charge of attaining the proper depth.

"Up five degrees on the bubble," ordered the diving officer.

The inclinometer indicated up and the boat started its rapid climb from 150 feet. "Ease your bubble," he said as he approached the desired depth.

The skipper crouched at the periscope and ordered, "Up scope." The silver shaft rose and he rose with it, all the time he had his eye on the eye piece and arms drooped over the training handles. The captain made a rapid sweep of 360 degrees to be sure no danger lurked on the surface then called out his next command, "Down scope, surface."

The diving officer repeated the command and the boat raised to the surface. Poised in the conning tower was the officer of the deck and the lookouts. The hatch in the conning tower was opened and the men climbed the ladder to the bridge in record time.

As the submarine leveled at the surface the electric motor which had been its motivation was shut down as the four big diesels came on the line and now supplied the power. The skipper called his next order to use two of the diesels to recharge the batteries and continued his scan of the surface and sky. There were still two hours of daylight and the utmost caution had to be observed in waters so close to the enemy landmass. The lookouts were very competent and had a lot of experience. They were all business as they looked through their glasses ready to give the alarm in an instant.

After being on the surface for thirty minutes the captain was relieved by the deck officer. He briefed his replacement and then slid down the ladder to the conning tower. I'd been waiting and hoped for a breath of fresh air. The only fresh air I enjoyed came down the hatch. "Are you ready for your cooks tour of the boat?"

he asked as he met me.

"Yes sir."

"As you can see this is the hub of activity," he said as we walked into the control room. "Between the control room and the conning tower all decisions are made while submerged. On the surface the officer on watch or the captain makes decisions from the bridge. The officer on the bridge has two main problems to face. He must always be ready in an instant to give the order to dive when danger is imminent or be in charge when a surface attack is made."

"Captain, will I ever pull the bridge watch?" I asked knowing the answer would be no.

"No doubt you'll be standing watch both on the bridge and filling in as navigator, among other duties. I came out with a one officer vacancy and I traveled a long way to fill it," he said as he laughed. "A lot will depend on how you assimilate the information. You should be a lot of help with your experience."

"I would be most pleased to be considered a member of this crew, even though temporarily. I'll do my best to learn so I can be of some help, it beats the hell out of sitting on your ass."

"I might as well let you in on how submarines are run. No able-bodied man who has the skill to do any job sits on his ass, we can't afford that luxury. This is no different than other military organizations. The enlisted men expect leadership and we must provide it. If you have a problem don't be backward about asking one of the chiefs or someone who can help you with it. We're one big happy family, at least we are most of the time, and now you are one of us." The captain was a good guy and very serious when it came to running his submarine. I felt I was in good hands. Mike Watson had escorted me through every part of the fleet submarine from stem to stern. I could tell how proud he was of his command. It was easy to see the men felt the same way. During the tour the areas I knew I'd have to learn about were the torpedo rooms, battery rooms, engine room, and the command area. Later I'd see more of the bridge.

I was impressed with the knowledge of the average sailor as the skipper asked questions of them for my benefit. I knew I could make an immediate contribution as the navigator as well as help on the radar.

The tour ended and we headed back to the ward room. The exec was waiting for us with three cups of coffee poured. "What do you think of our cozy little ship?" asked Tom.

"To start with it is not all that small. A bit tight in spots, but it looks like everything has its place, I'm used to things being a bit cramped," I explained.

"Real good, John," said the skipper.

"Most people call me Johnny. Can I ask a few questions?"

"Shoot, we have some for you as well," answered Mike.

"I can always wait, sir. Please go ahead with your questions."

"We know there's a sizable fishing fleet in these waters. Did you see anything of them?" asked Tom.

"Did I! Christ, I ended up one night last week in the middle of a small fleet, and was caught between them and their nets. I was lucky to escape. Then the following day I was almost run down by another one. It was a good thing it was a bit foggy and the helmsman was not on the ball."

"Get him. He's already sounding like an old salt," said Tom as he chuckled.

"Can you recall how many boats there were in the fleet?" asked Mike.

"It was dark as hell, sir, but my best estimate was half a dozen."

"Did any of the fishing boats have fifty-gallon drums stacked toward the rear?" asked Mike.

"As a matter of fact, I did see some drums on at least one of the boats, I thought nothing of it. I supposed it was extra fuel."

"Hardly, they were most likely depth charges. How long would you estimate the length of the boats?"

"At least forty feet, maybe more."

"Were there any deck guns?"

"Not as far as I could tell, but come to think of it, I heard anti-aircraft fire from some boat when they picked up the rest of my crew. I'm sure of that. They must have been firing at the PBY. I'm inclined to think the fire came from one of the fishing boats or possibly an escort."

"Very good. Can you think of anything else?" asked Mike.

"Yes, there were Japanese aircraft searching the waters around me. I was real lucky not to be spotted. They were over my position for quite a spell. I assumed the PBY couldn't look for me because of all the enemy activity and maybe the shitty weather had something to do with it too."

"You were partly right, we were the first submarine to be leaving Guam for patrol and were given a special mission to pick you up. You were too close to the Jap coast to send in another plane or a surface boat. It was a shame there wasn't the air-sea sub in your area, but he broke down and all other fleet submarines were too far away or had other commitments to be of any help."

Mike asked a number of other questions and then said, "Would you please write down everything you've told us and think real hard, let us know if there's anything else you think is pertinent." Then he said, "What are your questions?"

"You answered them already, captain."

I sat at the table over a fresh cup of coffee and wrote word for word my whole experience as best I could recall. My memory was vague at points, but good enough. It was like a bad dream, days were hard to sort out, it all seemed to run together. I finished my task and headed for the conning tower where I found Tom working with a commputer called the TDC, short for, Torpedo Data Computer. It is a device for deriving a torpedos fire control solution from data on the targets course, speed and range. It is intergraded with data of the submarines course, speed, and the speed of the torpedo. The bridge supplies much of this information when operating on the surface and when submerged the same information is collected by use of the periscope and sonar.

"Hi Tom, how's it going?" I asked as I climbed the ladder and stood before him.

"Howdy, just screwing around with the computer, we may need it soon," he said as he turned around. Then asked, "Are you going on the bridge?"

"Sure, if I won't be in the way. I'd like to see the outside world without being in a damn one-man life raft."

"Don't blame you, I'll call the bridge and see how everything is going and ask permission for you to go on deck."

"Captain, request permission for Mr. Lea to come on the bridge."

"Permission granted," the captain called back.

As I got to the top of the ladder I could see there was little left of the daylight. The sunset was beautiful and the fresh air felt wonderful as it hit my face. It was exhilarating and I was relieved to be out of my raft and safely aboard this ship with new friends and a new way of life. As I stood on the bridge I thought to myself how ironic this was, I never thought I'd end up fighting the war in a submarine.

"It's a beautiful evening, sir," I said as I scanned the surrounding smooth sea.

"It sure is with a calm sea. Can you hear the aircraft engines?" asked Mike without taking the glasses from his eyes. "At first I thought we were in trouble and then I realized it was a bomber formation headed toward Japan. Would you like to take a look?"

"Yes sir, it might even be my wing."

He pulled the strap from around his neck and handed me the glasses. "Look over there and you'll see them."

I brought the lenses to my eyes and could see the stream of B-29's headed north.

"Do you miss flying?" asked the skipper.

"Yes sir, but I don't miss being shot at," I answer honestly.

"We can't take much time to look at our planes. What we must be careful about is the enemy planes, ships and even submarines," he said as I handed him back his binoculars.

"I guess we'd be sitting ducks if they caught us out in the open on the surface."

"You're right! This is going to be a new way for you to fight the big war. First flying over and now fighting under."

He was right, I thought, as I looked toward the B-29's unaided by the binoculars. Over and under.

38.

I woke rested and refreshed, but still felt the motion of the sea as if I were still on the raft. The sensation was odd, it made my legs feel a bit rubbery. I shaved and showered then put my new uniform on which had been laid out. I heard a knock, "Come."

"Mr. Lea, how are you this morning," asked Doc.

"Like a new man except for the sensation of riding the waves. I can't wait for Dooley's breakfast, I know it will be great."

"Let me have a fast look and then you can get your chow, sir."

He gave me a quick checkup and said, "You're fit for duty, sir."

"My only problem is the sunburn, but it's no big deal."

"Here's some salve use it as required. Now, I have to get to sick call. See you later, Mr. Lea."

"Thanks a lot for all your help and courtesy. You're all great guys in my book. This crew is like one big happy family. You all work so well together."

"We have our moments and occasionally there's an argument. As you say we are a family and all families have their disagreements, but for the most part there's little friction," he said philosophically.

I'd finished dressing as he talked and we both left the small cabin together. I stepped into the wardroom and Doc headed for sick call. There was no one there when I entered. I poured myself a cup of coffee and thought of my two brothers. I wondered how they were doing. My daydream was disturbed by the noise behind me; it was Dooley.

"Good morning, Mr. Lea," he said with a big smile on his face. He was a very pleasant fellow, always making me feel at home. It is always a good idea to have the cook as a friend.

"Good morning Dooley I hope I'm not causing you a lot of extra work coming in late."

"Not at all sir, you're a VIP on this boat and I aim to treat you like one."

"Please, I'm not a VIP just an airdale as one of your guys put it and mighty glad to be here, but I hope to help out in some way."

"What will you have, sir?"

"What ever you have, don't go to a lot of trouble."

"No trouble, I like to fix good food and especially for someone who enjoys it."

"Believe me, I'm one of those who enjoys your food. I've never tasted better in the four years I've been in the service."

He smiled and then blushed. "Thanks sir, I appreciate your compliment, I try. I hope when the war is over to work as a chef in a big restaurant."

"You won't have any trouble getting a good job with your talent. Could I have bacon and eggs?"

"Coming right up," he said as he rushed out of the room to prepare the food. I had only finished a half cup of coffee and Dooley was back with a plate full of eggs, bacon and potatoes. The toast smelled so good I could hardly wait to dig in. "That should hold you until lunch, sir."

"My God man, there's enough food on this plate to feed half the crew. I'll try and finish them off, I know the rule on this submarine about no waste."

He chuckled as he started to go back to his galley, "I'll get some meat on your bones."

"I hope you don't get me too fat."

The food was as good as it looked and I had little trouble putting it all away. I felt much stronger after polishing off the platter of eggs and ready to tackle my new assignment. I hated the idea of being a student again, but I was dedicated to learning as much as possible, and wanted to do my part as a crew member even if it was temporary.

I headed for the control room full of anticipation. I met Tom who was in charge of the boat at the time. "Now that you're fit you can move out of my bunk. I'm glad you heal fast. I told you as long as you were on the sick list you had my bunk, remember?"

"I sure do!"

"You can stay in my quarters on the cot if you'd like."

"Thank you sir but I'd like to move in with the other officers if that's okay with you."

"Why the rush? I was only kidding you. You're welcome to use my bunk as long as you like."

"Thanks again, but it makes it a bit cramped for you, and

anyway you're a big wheel on this boat and you know the old saying, rank has its privileges."

"I thought I could impress you with how the Navy treats its guests."

"You have. I understand there's an extra bunk in the officers quarters because you're short one officer. Can I use his area?"

"Sure, Johnny, but you're welcome to stay with me for a while, in fact it would give me a chance to pump some extra poop into you then you can move, okay?"

"Fine sir,"

"Call me Tom," he said as he ushered me to the periscope. "As you can see we're at periscope depth, which is sixty feet. This allows us to observe the surface, our only contact with the outside world except for sonar and radar. We picked up some high speed propellers a couple hours ago and came up for a look after being down to 200 feet until the danger was no longer present. You probably didn't know we were being stalked and were rigged for silent running. We were lucky no enemy cans were dropped, if they had you'd have known it, believe me. We'll stay submerged until dark since we're so close to the coast of Japan. We've been heading to our newly assigned area and are now off the southern island of Kyushu. We'll pass to the south of Kyushu and enter the South China Sea, our area of patrol." Tom was pointing out on his chart our exact location and where we'd be when we surfaced. "Our job is to intercept and destroy any shipping which comes our way. We expect most of the activity will come from the south heading for Yawata, Sasebo and Fukuoka. There's still a lot of shipping coming from Formosa and Southeast Asia. Our job is to disrupt the flow of materials and deny the enemy raw materials for his war effort. We are one of a number of submarines patroling the large area."

"It's like a blockade, right?"

"That's right, we're trying to starve them out. Anyway, we operate independently from the other subs unless ordered otherwise."

We both looked at the map which was spread out on the table. "I know this area pretty well, but it might be a different situation from down here. Your maps are different than the ones I use up in the sky, but Japan doesn't look any different. It wasn't too long ago I was on a bomb mission to Yawata, in fact, I've been there twice, once from Tinian and earlier from China. They gave us a bad time, but we kicked them around pretty damn good."

"Our big problem is to know where we are at all times because we can't always see where we're going, I guess its similar to what you have to deal with in bad weather. There are so many damn shoals in this area it's a crap shoot at times. If you goof and get hung up on a shoal it could spell doom," explained Tom.

"Navigation should be no problem operating at this speed. In the air you have to hurry or you'll be far from where you figured your last position to be. I can see the problem down here is currents, and in the air it's the wind."

"In any event, we're not worried about your navigation ability. Let's get into the control room and start from there. These gauges are most important to you," he pointed to a number of different dials and explained in detail their uses. I took notes for future study. Everything seemed to be straight forward. I asked many questions as he continued with the orientation. He was very patient, I could see he had a lot of experience with the equipment besides being an instructor. Tom was thought highly of in submarine circles. I was lucky he could spend so much time with me.

"Now, I want to show you the TDC. You already know its function, but you must know how to use the information given and get the information to the captain. He will plan his attack on information given, so accuracy is very important. You generally don't get a second chance after you fire your torpedos. There are usually Destroyer's up there protecting your target and the DD's are our most dangerous enemy. You'll get the targets course, speed and range as well as the speed of our torpedo and the data on the submarines course and speed. You spin the computer and out comes the information used to set up the launch of the torpedo. The information is supplied from a number of sources, the skipper, sonar, and/or radar. Some of the information can come from the bridge via the TBT, short for Target Bearing Transmitter. The talker will give you most of the information as he receives it. This is how you solve the problem," he set up dummy information and I input it into the computer; it was simple. He was delighted with my progress. After all, computers were part of my knowledge. It used to be said that the navigator's hand computer could do anything your wife could do except cook.

I studied hard and got a lot of information from a number of people all interested in helping me learn. I spent my off-duty hours reading technical orders and looking over different schematics and plans which helped me get a feel for the layout of the vessel.

We'd been cruising for three days, patrolling on the surface at night and submerging much of the day without making a contact. I thought the Japanese had quit shipping, but I knew it was impossible since it took 3,000,000 tons to keep the civilians alive to say nothing of the war machine.

My thought on the lack of shipping came to a halt when the sonar operator called the control room to report two, possibly three high speed surface vessels were heading toward us. "Bearing 055, range eight oh-oh-oh," called the talker as he relayed the information to the skipper. The captain swung the periscope around to meet the challenge.

"They look like tuna boats," he said puzzled. He knew they were the new high speed renovated fishing boats being used as sub-chasers. He could see the deck gun and depth charges on their aft decks as they got closer. It was useless to try and outmaneuver them; they were too fast and could dodge our torpedos with their maneuverability. One thing in our favor was that they were lightly armored; anything would sink them.

"Pull the plug," he ordered and without wasted motion the men at the controls did their jobs and the sub nosed over toward deep water. Tom was studying the charts to be sure we had enough depth below when the captain barked out his next order. "Bring her to two hundred and rig for silent running." The alarm klaxon made its awful noise and people were rushing to battle stations.

The electric motors were at full speed as we quickly descended through 150 feet heading for 200 feet. I was dismayed as I watched. I thought we'd stand and fight instead of hiding down here where we could do nothing. We leveled at 200 feet. No sound could be emitted, including talk or coughs. When they said silent running, that's exactly what they meant. I knew there was something I could do to help, but wasn't sure what it was. Sonar reported the boats directly over us and slowing down. Then it came, the first blasts from the string of depth charges rocked the Pigboat with ferocity. I must have looked dazed or scared.

"You really never get used to it, Johnny, so we won't laugh if you piss in your pants," said Tom in a whisper.

"It's not a hell of a lot different than flak bursts when they explode near your plane. What I don't understand is why we didn't take those yellow devils on by surfacing and shooting the hell out of those flimsey fishing boats, we have them out gunned."

"True, however, those fast patrol boats work real close with their Air Force and as soon as they make contact they radio back and we have a swarm of planes to fight off. On the surface we're no match for aircraft. Also, some of their patrol boats are fitted with torpedo tubes. There is one plus, those bastards up there can do themselves in if they slow down to drop their depth charges, they could become their own victims. We can keep our sonar working because they have to move so fast they can't hear too well. Let's hope they get tired of trying to find us, then we can go up and look over the situation. I have to get back to work, come along and keep your eyes open, you'll learn plenty."

We passed next to the captain as he stood next to the periscope shaft. He turned and said to Tom, "Let's get under way and try to slip away, as long as they're dropping those cans they can't hear us."

"Good idea, skipper," answered the exec.

"All ahead full," ordered the captain. The order was relayed by the talker and we seemed to jump ahead.

We could hear the depth charges getting farther away by the minute. The enemy had lost their quarry, we'd pulled the slip on them and we felt good about it.

"Come left to 270 and bring her up to periscope depth," was the skipper's next order. The boat slanted up and I watched the depth gauge as we rose rapidly. I studied how the tactics were applied for each action. I was impressed with the skill everyone displayed. I hoped I could become a useful member in the near future.

"Up scope," came the next order. The shining cylinder slid upward and halted as the eyepiece reached shoulder height. Eagerly the captain seized the control handles, slapped them to the horizontal position and walked the periscope toward the last reported bearing of the enemy boats. He seemed puzzled as he peered through the eyepiece. He returned the control handles to their vertical position alongside the periscope. It slid below on his briefly spoken, "Down scope."

"What have you got, captain?" asked Tom.

"Nothing, they're not to be seen and there's no place to hide." He turned and said to the talker, "Ask sonar if he hears anything."

The answer came back without hesitation, "No propeller noise, sir."

"Surface," he ordered. The boat began to rise immediately. At full speed Seabat broke the surface and shifted to diesel power without delay. As soon as the boat was on the surface the quartermaster had the hatch open and Mike and three scanners were on deck in a flash. Mike was so fast that he was dripping wet as the sea water poured from the open hatch.

I asked and received permission to come on to the bridge. I was delighted to feel the fresh air as we moved ahead into the darkening light. "Well, Johnny, how do you feel about submarines now?" asked the captain without removing the binoculars from his eyes.

"It was kind of hairy especially since I didn't have a specific job to keep me busy. When I flew combat I always kept busy. That way I was able to keep my anxiety under control. I never did like or got used to being shot at," I said making a joke of it.

The captain laughed and so did I. The night was clear and warm with a cooling breeze. It amazed me how just a few minutes earlier I felt a little uneasy and now I felt as though I hadn't a care in the world.

* * *

"I hope to hell that submarine commander gets to Johnny ASAP. You know I talked to him just before he left on their war patrol from Guam. He seemed like a good guy," remarked Bart as he Jim and Rich headed down the coral road toward their tent. They had just walked out of briefing on the mission for that night.

"What gets to me is how our crew got so chewed up on our thirty-third mission. Now four of our crew are gone and we still need two missions to finish our tour," said Jim as he kicked lose a piece of coral from the roadbed.

"I'd never leave here even if we finished our missions until we get Johnny back. I owe him that much," answered Bart seriously.

"Why don't we go down to the club and talk it over with a beer in our hands," suggested Rich.

"Not a bad idea," answered Bart as they passed by the tent and headed toward the club.

"Maybe we should go down to the flight line and watch the mission depart after a beer," suggested Rich.

"You talk like a man with a paper ass. Let's go into the club and get drunk; maybe everything will look better then," said Bart as they walked to the bar.

They found a group of other officers who were for a variety of reasons not flying. It was a very quiet group, unlike the usual hell raising bunch who generally celebrated the event of standing down on a mission.

Later the quiet of the night was disturbed as the countless engines came to life. The laboring sound of the takeoff followed then it was quiet again as the big planes disappeared into the darkness of the northern sky.

The group, although quiet, was not for Bart, he wanted to be alone. They found a small round table in a corner and settled down to drink and talk. The conversation kept coming back to the fateful night of their last mission and how after a perfect landing everything seemed to go wrong.

"Is this a private wake or can anyone join in," said Reilly as he and Dave Lewis stood next to the table.

"What are you doing here?" asked Bart.

"Airplane broke; we aborted our takeoff," answered Reilly.

"Sure, pull up a chair we're just shooting the breeze and having a few drinks."

"We were talking about how things went to hell when we lost Johnny the night we ditched. We're praying he's still alive and well. If that sub gets to him before something bad happens he might be okay. I hope to hear soon whether or not they found him," said Bart. He waved his hand for a waiter as the two joined them.

It was then two memorable events occurred. A corporal from group headquarters came into the club and went to the bar and asked a question. The bartender pointed toward their table and the corporal headed to it.

"Sir, are you Captain Ellis?"

"Yes I am, what can I do for you corporal?"

"Sir, I was just sent over here from group to inform you a message was received from COMSUBPAC, Guam. It stated that Lieutenant Lea has been rescued by a submarine and he is in good shape."

Bart listened for a split second then reacted violently as he sprang to his feet sending the round table spiralling across the floor with all the drinks flying. As he jumped into the air he let out a wild yell which startled everyone in the club. "The drinks are on me, so drink up. We just received the greatest news, our navigator has been picked up by a submarine and is okay."

Everyone in the club recovered and started clapping followed by a rush to the bar. The club had come alive and the noise was mounting, things were back to normal. The corporal was dumbfounded at what was taking place.

"Sir, if that makes you happy maybe you'd like to hear the rest of the good news."

"What could be better than this?" asked Bart.

"Sir, we got a message right after this one from Guam stating the war in Europe had come to an end."

"Sit down, corporal. By the way what is your name?"

"Adams, sir."

"Your first name?"

"Oh, Lou, sir."

"Lou, sit down and have a drink with us," said Bart.

"Oh, no sir, I couldn't. I would catch hell if anyone reported I was drinking at the officers club."

"Like hell, I'll call your boss, who is he?"

"Major Bell, sir."

"Get Lou a drink, I'm going to the phone and tell Bell we detained Corporal Adams." Bart returned in a few minutes and said, "All is okay."

Fresh drinks had been delivered and a toast was in order. Bart rose, as did the others and he raised his glass in front of him and said in a voice heard throughout the bar, "Here's to the Navy's Submarine Service and to the ending of the war in Europe."

Everyone in the club was on his feet with a drink and saying, "Here, here."

Corporal Adams finished his drink, wiped his mouth and stood, "Thank you for inviting me," he said, then fled.

Dave was very quiet and deep in thought with tears in his eyes, "Thank God. He answered my prayers, Johnny is alive and well. I can't wait to see my buddy."

The party was in full swing as more and more people crowded in to the bar to take part in the celebration. All the wheels from wing and group made an appearance.

"Maybe Washington will pay more attention to the war out here now," said one of the staff officers.

"Don't bet on it, we're going to have to finish this thing without the help of the people in Europe," said the wing commander.

"I sure am glad Johnny's off that damn ocean. He was out there by himself for over a week in the worst storm of the year. Christ, we were in a big boat only for a few hours and we were scared shitless, my hat is off to him," said Rich soberly.

Bart stood again and demanded the floor. "Gentlemen," he yelled as everyone turned to see what the commotion was. "I want all you people who just came in to drink a toast with me." Without waiting to see the reaction he said in a loud voice. "A toast to two great events, the war ending in Europe and the rescue of our fine navigator."

The commanding general turned and said, "Here, here," and drained his drink.

A staff officer said quietly, "You would think finding his navigator was more important than the war ending in Europe."

Everyone at the small table sat down and the party had a different flavor. It appeared they'd all had a very heavy burden removed from their backs. Now they could smile again and not feel guilty for leaving their friend all alone in the wild Pacific Ocean.

39.

Seabat cruised its assigned area of patrol for two days and found no quarry. The crew was getting restless, but discipline never faltered, patience was a virtue in this business.

Training was very demanding and there was much to remember. It was difficult to sort out what I was supposed to do. After all, the crew was professionally trained and I was trying to catch up with only books and spasmodic instruction. Tom was my best source of information and was never impatient with questions. I felt actual hands on training was helping me more than any other effort.

The lull in combat operations worked to an advantage, as time passed I gained knowledge and understanding. I wanted to help the people who had saved my life and be an asset to the crew by doing my share, my navigation training had already paid part of my bill. The big problem was getting used to the changes in speed and procedures. The Navy lingo was coming easier and in the words of Tom I was becoming "an old salt."

My duties as I understood them would be to assist Tom. I would have to navigate and operate the TDC. I worked hard with false data to become familiar with the computer and after much work and instruction I was feeling more comfortable about using it. I actually felt I could operate under combat conditions and was looking forward to testing my knowledge.

I realized as time passed that the crew was accepting me as one of them instead of as an "airdale" they'd plucked from the sea. I heard no complaints about my work and I felt much more confident. I kept asking questions from people within the different sections; their answers helped put all the pieces together and gave me an opportunity to share their knowledge.

At 1800, 9 June 1945 the officers of the boat were being served dinner in the wardroom. As was the custom, the captain sat at the head of the table and as usual Dooley had prepared a fine meal. Mike laid his eating utensils down and spoke, "Gentlemen, our newest officer will pull the morning watch on the bridge. I can understand his apprehension and I would like to see you all lend any assistance necessary. I think Mr. Lea has done an exceptional job considering he has been with us for just over a week. At times I forget he's not a Naval officer, but I guess if the situation was turned around we'd hopefully be of some use to an aircrew. Good luck, Johnny." There was a short applause which embarrassed me. I was speechless.

My first watch commenced at 0600. I reported to relieve the officer of the deck. I was lucky. Ensign Frank Wayne was assigned to help me in case I got into something I couldn't handle and to answer any questions I might have. Frank was a bright young fellow who came from a long line of seagoing men. His home was in New Bedford and his accent left no doubt that he was from New England. His family went back many generations in the small ocean community so well known for its Yankee sailors. He was a natural sailor and understood the sea. Frank was on his first combat cruise since his graduation from the submarine school at New London, but from the way he acted, and reacted, you'd think he had been aboard a submarine all his life. We kept the vigil in the foggy cool morning and had an opportunity to get better acquainted.

"Most people don't understand what a submarine is. A submarine is a surface vessal capable of submerging. It has to frequently return to the surface for fresh air and to charge the batteries for the motors which propel it while submerged," he explained.

I'd never heard it stated in that way, but it made sense. Most people would never think of a sub as a surface vessel. The fog hung close and visibility was severely limited. We received reports from radar, no contacts had been established.

"I hate this fog. I can't see a thing," I said.

"If we can't see them they can't see us. Don't worry, radar and sonar will let you know if they spot or hear anything, then you can take appropriate action. It doesn't mean we can relax our vigil, it means we must be more on the ball. Remember the responsibility of the boat is in your hands. Never take this post lightly."

I was about to tell him he needn't worry when I was interrupted by a call from sonar. "Sir, propeller noises approaching from the southwest at approximately eight miles."

It was up to me to make an assessment and take the necessary action. "Ask sonar if they are fast or slow moving."

"Aye, aye, sir." answered the talker. Then without wasting time reported, "Sonar reports the targets are moving at eight knots and from all indications there are two ships, sir."

"Clear the bridge. Dive, dive," I ordered. The lookouts followed by Ensign Wayne hit the conning tower ladder so fast I was amazed. I followed on their heels. The hatch slammed over my head as I descended to the deck. The sub was sliding under the surface as I met Mike who was waiting to be briefed.

"What do you have, Mr. Lea.?"

"Two slow moving ships, approximately eight miles, at eight knots bearing 045, sir."

"Good work, maybe we can get in some licks finally. Hold at periscope depth. Up scope," he ordered. "Foggy as hell up there, isn't it?"

"Yes sir, the report came from sonar and radar. It's been confirmed." He swung the boat around to meet the challenge, but was limited by the fog. The fog was lifting slowly.

"Sir," said the talker.

"Go ahead."

"Targets bearing 045, 8 knots 6 miles and now there are three ships identified and coming straight at us, sir."

"Target five miles and closing," came the next report.

"If the fog lifts a little we can make a reasonable attack. I would much prefer a visual attack, but we'll take anything we can get. The targets will be at point blank range soon." reported the captain, he kept his eye glued to the periscope eyepiece. "Let's go to general quarters."

"Man battle stations, torpedo," rang out the command.

The Klaxon signaled the voice command and men ran to their battle stations eagerly awaiting their next order. I stood close to Tom awaiting instructions.

I felt the exhilaration of going into battle, I trembled with excitement. As I waited for further instructions I wondered if I did the right thing by diving. It may have been better to close on the target on the surface, but I had to make the decision and no one second-guessed me. Then I remembered the captain telling me, "good work." He was a sincere man and when he told a person he did good, he meant it. I felt proud of myself, I was actually involved with combat operations of a United States ship.

"Sonar reports, target changing course to 025, range one, five, oh, oh."

347

"Come right to 345 and stand by."

"Forward torpedo room ready . . . Aft torpedo room ready . . . Maneuvering ready . . . " Came the stream of reports from each operational area of the ship.

"Load all tubes fore and aft," ordered the captain.

Because of the limited visibility it was not necessary to bring the periscope down during the set-up stage of the attack. The skipper was sure no one on the surface could spot our periscope wake as it cut the water on the surface in the murk.

The reports from sonar and radar kept coming in and the target was now only 5,000 yards away and still maintaining the same course and speed. It was then the fog started to lift and the captain said, "Range, mark. Bearing, mark."

"One, one, double oh. Zero, four, five."

Tom was at the TDC as I stood by. He was spinning the TDC each time new information was supplied. He passed the gyro settings to the torpedo rooms.

"Come right to 360," ordered the skipper. The boat swung easily in answer to the rudder bringing the bow of the sub to a point ahead of the convoy.

"Steady on 360," came the response from the helmsman.

The captain could clearly see the Maru of 8,000 tons being escorted by a destroyer. Another ship was on the far side of our position and unidentified as yet. The destroyer swung around to the port side of the Maru leaving it exposed. The last readings were fed into the TDC and the calculations passed on to the forward torpedo room.

"Down scope . . . fire one, fire two." The commands came in rapid succession. Firing the two torpedoes so close together indicated he felt certain of his target. "Take her to 100 feet, come around to 180 and all ahead full."

I thought he would keep his periscope up and watch the hits as the two torpedos raced toward their target, but I was wrong. The captains eyes were glued on his stop watch as the seconds ticked off. Everyone had sweat on their foreheads, including me. Silence gripped the conning tower and was broken only by the whine of the electric motors as they carried us to comparative safety. Then, through the hull we heard the sound of a muffled roar.

"Sound reports, heavy explosion," reported the talker. A second explosion sounded before he could make his full report. Two torpedos, two hits. Mike was proud of his marksmanship, it was his

348

first torpedo launch since becoming captain of his own ship.

"High speed propellers bearing two, four, zero." came the report from sonar.

"Tell him to keep the bearings coming."

"High speed propellers now bearing two, four, five."

Mike smiled, he knew the enemy destroyer was racing to the position from which he had fired the fish.

"Propeller noises slowing, sir."

"Rig for silent running," ordered the skipper. "Speed two knots."

The slowing of the enemy ship indicated they were listening for any noise which would give our position away. Sounds could be picked up by the hydrophones.

Seabat crept silently toward deeper water. Occasionally the sound gear would register high speed propeller noises in short spurts as the enemy craft explored different areas. It was a cat and mouse game. After a period of thirty minutes without surface noises Mike decided to have a look. "Bring her up to 60 feet." The sub nosed up and as we reached the desired level he ordered, "Up scope."

The fog had lifted and at a distance of four miles the tanker and the patrol boats were plainly visible. The destroyer was on the opposite side evacuating the crew when all of a sudden the fire that was burning slowly, flamed up. An explosion seemed to lift the ship out of the water in a wrenching manner. Another more violent explosion occurred. It was plain to see the ship was sinking.

We were lucky to observe the sinking, often even though you were sure of a sinking, without confirmation you received no credit. Only a possible. The tanker was settling by the stern as another more violent explosion occurred. It took but seconds for the ship to slip to the depths. We had denied the enemy a large quantity of oil they needed so desperately to keep their war machine running.

Lieutenant Commander Michael Watson had sunk his first ship and he was proud of his ship and crew. He now considered going after the destroyer, but gave up the idea because of the number of enemy patrol boats in the area. He silently left the area to look for more prey.

I felt elation too, I had in some small way helped to sink an enemy ship, I was on my way to becoming an accepted member of this crew.

40.

On-the-job-training continued with each passing day, making me more a Naval than on Air Force officer. I'd put flying on the back burner.

Three days passed since the sinking of the Maru tanker and dullness had set in again. On one occasion yesterday we had to hug the bottom to escape detection by Jap patrol boats unworthy of doing battle with.

We surfaced just after dark and were using two of the four diesel engines for charging batteries. The sea was calm and it looked like a nice night ahead when the talker broke the silence with a message from sonar. "Sonar reports a rain squall ahead, sir."

Visibility dropped to 300 yards when radar reported a number of surface ships stationary and dead ahead, one mile.

"Must be a fishing fleet," called Tom through the hatch to the bridge.

"Clear the bridge," came Mike's first command and as the lookouts scrambled down the conning tower ladder. "Dive, dive," was the second command as he slid down the ladder. "Bring her to periscope depth. We can't take a chance of them seeing us, they probably have radios."

We passed beneath the fleet of fishing boats unnoticed. I wondered what they'd think if they knew their enemy was a few feet below them in the dark water.

"Up scope," ordered Mike. The silver cylinder rose, and as it did Mike came with it waiting for the periscope to break the surface. After a careful search, he ordered, "Down scope, surface."

Seabat rose swiftly out of the dark water and rode freely on the surface as the diesels kicked in. Things returned to normal as we continued on our search of quarry.

Later that evening the silence was broken, "Contact, heading 210 degrees, range two, oh, oh, double, oh."

"Battle stations, torpedo," responded Mike. The faint light which had shown through the rain barrier disappeared.

"Contact, now bearing 205, range one, eight, oh, double, oh."

Mike didn't need to wait for the tracking party's report, he knew he was in a good position for an approach to what ever was out there. *Seabat* was in position off the starboard bow.

"Large group, six ships I make it," reported radar.

"Target, speed fourteen knots, course zero, two-five." reported Lieutenant Moyers from the plotting board.

"Flank speed," Mike ordered. "Come right 270."

The new speed would assure that *Seabat* kept ahead of the approaching enemy ships and close enough to their track for a submerged attack.

One of the forward lookouts shouted, "Target in sight, sir. Four tankers and two destroyers."

The report automatically brought Mike's binoculars around to the sighting. He confirmed the report, the lookout had made no mistake. The four tankers were deep in the water and in line with the destroyers on the flanks of the lead ship. The rain stopped suddenly and the outline of the nearest destroyer showed up clearly silhouetted against the moonlight as the clouds parted. The range was eight miles.

The lookouts responded and in seconds the only member of the ship's company on the bridge was the captain. The open area between clouds which had illuminated the convoy now showed they were heading toward us. The broken cumulus clouds above were being pushed at 25 knots, making alternate moonlight and utter darkness. Mike fought the urge to submerge to lessen detection, but it would mean a loss of speed which might allow the convoy to continue at maximum speed as the range closed by the minute. Our luck ran out as the brilliant moonlight flooded the *Seabat* and brought prompt response from the nearest destroyer. He swept around in a high speed turn while putting down a heavy cloud of smoke to hide the convoy as he waited for the submarine.

"Come right to 360," Mike shouted as he slid down the ladder to the conning tower. The quartermaster slammed the hatch behind him. He figured the destroyer would not pursue and leave the flank of the tankers exposed to the attack of a possible second submarine. He was wrong. The Jap skipper promptly demonstrated he was more interested in sinking the known target than waiting for a submarine which might or might not be there. With the diesels at 100 percent power *Seabat* left a broad wake streaming astern and the destroyer knifed through the trail of foam closing range with a speed advantage of ten knots.

Mike casually called, "Up scope," and trained it astern. "We'll let him gain until he starts shooting," explained Mike. "Then, we'll see what can be done with him."

The long chase gave Mike ample time to figure the destroyers speed at 28 knots. There was no doubt of his course, he followed right down *Seabat's* wake.

"Range nine, oh, double, oh," reported radar. It checked with the stadimeter in the periscope.

"This guy looks like he's going to rear-end us," said Mike with a grin.

Moyers was at the TDC cranking in range and bearing data, changing information constantly as it was received. The training and precision of the tracking party was apparent as everything was accomplished with speed and efficency.

"He's nuts for not firing his forward gun," said Mike as he kept a watchful eye on his pursuer. "He's buying himself a pack of trouble."

Most people would think it crazy to let a destroyer move within a few thousand yards while still on the surface, but that kind of thinking had been the reason the Japanese were running out of ships.

"Range, seven, five, oh, oh," reported radar.

"That's close enough for our purposes. Take her down to sixty feet. All ahead one-third, come right to 270."

The submarine slid under the surface smoothly, shifting easily to electric power and steadied exactly on course at sixty feet in a matter of seconds.

"Set torpedo's for six feet," ordered the captain.

Above, the destroyer raced along on a set course down the wake. Mike pictured in his mind the Japanese looking for the submarine that suddenly wasn't there any longer.

"Angle on the bow, port thirty . . . range mark, bearing mark."

"Set." Came the response.

"Fire one . . . fire two . . . Fire three."

The dead silence which followed the launching of the missiles settled over the conning tower and the control room. Tom studied the sweep of his stop watch hand counting off the calculated time to the target. Mike kept his eye to the periscope. He could see the wake of one of the torpedos foaming on the mooning sea. The Japanese captain probably saw it too, but at a range of 1150 yards there was nothing he could do about it. The first torpedo missed, however the second and the third tore the destroyer to pieces. We could hear and feel the shock wave as it hit Seabat. We knew the result without seeing it. A second explosion announced the destruction of their ammunition and fuel.

"Surface," ordered Mike. "Fire control party to the bridge."

The stern of the destroyer had risen to a vertical angle just as the group emerged on deck. As the destroyer sunk, great white plumes of water shot upward from the depth charges which were intended for us, it helped crush her hull.

Mike had invited the fire party to see the results of their calculations, it was a habit formed by many of the submarine commanders of the day. In the darkness the destroyer took its final plunge. The flickering light of the marker buoy bobbed in the waves. Mike maneuvered slowly toward it and looked for survivors, none were to be seen. It was all over in a matter of minutes.

"All ahead full," ordered Mike. "Come right to 250." The fire party had descended to their assigned locations and awaited their next order. Seabat was off in pursuit of the fleeing convoy, now short one destroyer. The convoy had raced at flank speed to gain the safety of the nearest port, but we would over take them before they could get there.

"Target range nine, seven, five, double, oh. Bearing zero, two, five."

We were off and running in hot pursuit of the convoy. Now it was our turn to follow in the wake. It was to take us the better part of an hour to be in position for the attack. The captain wanted to sink at least one more enemy ship. It didn't matter which. We preceded at flank speed and after a long chase we closed on the rear tanker. Radar picked up another target coming fast from the northeast. Mike knew it meant another destroyer was closing in on him.

"Set torpedo's for twelve feet. Come left to 345. Fire one . . . Fire two . . . Fire three . . . Fire four. Down scope. Dive, dive. Come further left to 180," ordered the skipper in quick but clear language. He could not wait to see what damage his torpedos would inflict, for now we were the hunted.

It was necessary to go deep and fast to try to avoid the new menace from above. We were headed for 250 feet. As we descended we felt the concussion of the explosion. We were buffeted which indicated we'd hit the tanker.

"Sir we heard three explosions and now we can hear the Maru breaking up," called sonar. The tanker was breaking up in small pieces. There was no doubt we had destroyed not only a fighting vessel but also one quarter of the oil the convoy was carrying.

Captain Watson had sunk three ships in a short period of time. If we survived to tell the story it would suit me.

We leveled at 250 feet as sonar reported high speed propellers approaching. I was apprehensive, not knowing what to expect, but the others aboard knew what was coming. The enemy unleashed a depth charge attack and he was pretty sure of where his target was. I heard the first string of depth charges exploding. Apparently the destroyer had lost contact, his depth charges were going off some distance away and doing us no harm. I asked Tom, "Why's the destroyer so far off?"

He answered, "Probably the thermal layer. At depths there's a thermal layer which reduces the quality and effectiveness of sound gear."

We had rigged for silent running and headed south as Tom and I looked over the depth charts. It was a slow way to travel, but a safe way.

The destroyer, after two more far off attacks gave up and no more sound was heard from the enemy screws or bombs.

After we were sure there were no more enemy ships above we headed for the surface once again.

Mike said he wanted to try and contact COMSUBPAC to give his second report. The special mission of Mike's first combat patrol had been accomplished successfully and I was living proof of it. That I was no longer "missing in action" was the subject of his first report.

It was just after midnight as we got underway on the surface. It was quite peaceful as the boat glided along the smooth sea in the moonlight. The luminescent bubbles followed *Seabat* as the wake widened behind. Only a passing cloud disturbed the bright display of stars. The men of *Seabat* had been relieved from general quarters and a feeling of relaxation and relief was apparent. Only the men on watch were to suffer the letdown of returning to the routine of sailing this warship.

Before Mike turned in he wrote a message and handed it to the radio operator for immediate coding and transmission to COM-

SUBPAC. The message contained the strike report as well as the status of the enemy convoy and their location and presumed destination. We knew the report would be picked up by other submarines operating in these waters and an interception of the convoy might be made.

The routine of patrol went on for a number of days without enemy contact. The respite allowed me to learn more and I was feeling at ease with the procedures, I was definitely gaining confidence.

The aerial attacks by the B-29's of the Japanese mainland continued at an accelerated pace. Often we viewed the fires burning on shore from our vantage point at sea. The glow was eerie as the fires burned out of control. It was a frightening sight.

When I saw the attacks I thought of my friends back on Tinian and wondered how they were making out. I wanted to know if Bart and the others had continued to fly! It's possible they were finished with their tour and on their way home, but I was sure Bart would never leave until I got back. Dave by now should be a seasoned veteran. I hoped to find all of them on Tinian when I returned.

My thoughts often were of Kimberly. I fought to remember how beautiful she was and how she had made my visit to Australia one of beauty and pleasure. I wished I had a picture of her, but no such luck. The picture she'd sent me after I returned from Australia was with my personal effects on Tinian, unless they'd sent them home. The policy of never carrying personal effects on missions was sound. If the enemy captures you with pictures or letters they can use it for propaganda. Only name, rank and serial numbers were to be given if captured. However, even those strict rules were being relaxed somewhat.

We had been sailing in a southerly direction hoping contact could be made with enemy shipping. It was becoming more apparent how many ships the enemy had lost to the silent service. Still, they were getting some supplies through and we had to shut them off.

By the evening of 21 June we had sailed the length of the Ryukyu Islands, north of Okinawa looking for prey when all at once the watch officer announced: "Challenge to starboard."

The captain was next on his way up the ladder like a shot out of a cannon. He stood on the bridge with his glasses trained in the direction of the challenge. Mike could see the blinker and read the signal as it was delivered.

"Have the signalman report to the bridge," he called down the conning tower hatch.

The signalman was at the captain's side within seconds with his signaling device which looked like an overgrown shotgun. The barrel could be aimed as a gun and had a very narrow beam. It would be difficult for any other ship to see the signals unless they were in line with the barrel.

"Send him our identification," ordered Mike as he watched the signal from the other ship.

After receiving the message a thanks and good hunting was exchanged and soon the area was in darkness once again.

"Ease to port," he ordered, we continued on our patrol as did our sister submarine.

Our batteries were fully charged, but we continued on two engines to conserve fuel.

"Another step closer to Japan," said Mike as he read the message. "Both Okinawa and the Philippines are now ours. The only thing left is Japan proper. I hate to think of the casualties we'll sustain if we have to invade Japan," he announced to anyone in hearing distance.

I turned to the captain and said, "Captain, during a briefing back on Tinian we were told the estimates of casualties of a land invasion of Japan is 1,000,000 men."

Our course was now taking us north in the East China Sea approximately midway between mainland China and the Ryukyu's. It was peaceful, the sea was flat and almost smooth. I remembered how seldom I'd experienced such conditions when I was floating around in my tiny raft. It didn't seem fair, ever since I came aboard the weather had been good, there is no justice, I said to myself.

July started with action. The evening of the first had turned to blackness. The darkness was so complete you could hardly see the three lookouts a short distance away. The wake of *Seabat* was a beautiful shade of blue as the luminescent bubbles followed. Mike searched the surface constantly as did his lookouts. All at once he saw something. There was a hint of light just below the horizon. He had to look away to pick it up with the more sensitive portion of his eye. Then all at once he heard, "Radar contact, bearing two, five, five." The voice had broken the silence like an explosion coming from the conning tower hatch below the bridge.

Mike swung his glasses around in the direction of the reported target, then waited for the next report. "Range one, one, seven, five, oh."

The target was less than six nautical miles away. Bill Moyers was at the captain's side. As officer of the deck he too was scanning the direction of the reported target.

"Can you make it out, Bill?" asked the captain.

"Not yet, sir, but I know it's out there, I can feel it in my bones," answered the torpedo-gunnery officer. "Wait, sir, there's something at about fifteen degrees to starboard."

"You had better get to the TDC, Bill. We'll start working into position," said Mike.

"Permission to sound battle stations, sir," asked Bill as he headed for the hatch.

"Wait, I don't want the crew alerted as yet and I don't want to attack by radar unless I have no other choice. I would rather wait until I can pick them up on the scope."

Bill descended the ladder and found me at the TDC. "How's it going?" he asked

"Not bad, I'm anxious to handle one by myself, but I wouldn't mind you looking over my shoulder to make sure I don't goof up."

Mike was proud of his crew and as he glanced over at the lookouts each searching his own area of assignment instead of all looking in the direction of the target, he knew they could be counted on to sound the alarm if an enemy slipped in during the excitement. The lookouts knew their jobs and would not relax their vigilance for a second.

"Bearing two, two, two . . . Range, one, two, two, oh, oh," reported the radar operator.

Mike could tell from the trend of the reports his target was pulling away from *Seabat* to the north. He knew he had a speed advantage which would allow him to maneuver for a favorable position.

"Come right to 240," he yelled down the hatch. The message was repeated and the helmsman made the change rapidly and correctly.

"Target, course oh, oh, five . . . speed, one, four. . . ." Tom called to the bridge.

Mike felt things were going well, he still hadn't ordered battle stations, but word had spread throughout the boat and most of the men were already at or near their action stations knowing any second the word would come.

"Come right to 005," ordered the skipper. He was paralleling the enemy. With his speed advantage he would be ten miles ahead of his target before dawn. He planned a submerged attack. The sub vibrated as it heeled over answering the rudder and the phosphorescence fanned out broadly aft as the wake lengthened with the increase of speed.

Tom climbed the ladder to the bridge to talk to Mike. "The radar picture is very interesting, there are seven pips on the scope. Judging from their disposition it looks like six ships screening for a seventh."

"Sounds like a carrier. I've had dreams about sinking a carrier. What a break!"

"I don't think it's a carrier flotilla, the pips aren't large enough and they're not traveling fast enough. A carrier would be traveling faster than fourteen knots," explained the executive officer.

"You're right. I guess it was just wishful thinking. It must be an important mission for seven ships, however. I think I'll wait until we have a visual before we set up for an attack."

"Good idea, captain."

Radar plots kept coming in as we awaited daylight. It was obvious the enemy was unaware of our presence as we maneuvered to within two miles.

Mike consulted the chart and could see we were pulling ahead of the convoy. He had left the bridge in the capable hands of his XO. The captain had little trouble adjusting to the dim red lights of the operational area. As we paralleled the course of the seven ships Mike became anxious, but knew he had to be patient. Mike headed for the conning tower ladder and climbed to the bridge. After he looked the situation over he decided it was time. He called down the conning tower hatch and ordered, "battle stations, torpedo." The alarm horn sounded throughout the submarine and people jumped to action. "Clear the bridge." The usual procedure was followed.

"Dive, dive," was his order and again the klaxon rang out. The air whistled out of the vents as the water entered the ballast tanks. The boat was already on its way beneath the surface as the captain approached the periscope. *Seabat* settled into the depths with ease as the thunderous diesels were silenced. The whine of the electric motors became its sole source of locomotion.

The submarine approached periscope depth, the engineering

officer could be heard saying, "Ease your bubble." *Seabat* leveled at sixty feet according to the depth meter.

"Up scope," the skipper ordered. The periscope slid quietly and smoothly to the fully extended position. Mike reached for the directional control handles, slapped them to the horizontal position and "walked" the periscope toward the last reported bearing of the enemy convoy.

"I'll be damned! This is a tough one to figure!" he said as his forehead wrinkled.

"What is it, captain?" asked Tom.

"Five destroyers, a cruiser and one Maru. The Maru is deep in the water, really loaded," he said. "Take a look, Tom."

"Why the hell would there be six escort ships to one Maru?"

"That's what I'd like to know," answered Mike quizzically.

"Mighty unusual."

Tom slapped the directional handles to the vertical position and ordered, "down scope."

"I wonder where they came from and how they were missed by all our other subs? It must be important cargo to rate all that protection. I think we should go for the Maru first. If they consider it so important it must be a prize to sink. I still wish it were a carrier, but hell a cruiser would be a nice prize."

"We'll set up for the Maru, then hit the cruiser, time permitting, right?" asked Tom.

"Right. I want to take them down the groove. As soon as they get to a comfortable range, say, 600 yards and forty-five degrees angle on the bow, we'll let them have it."

The talker relayed a message from sonar, "Sound reports numerous propeller noises, bearing two, three, five, sir."

"Keep the bearings coming," called the captain. Then he turned to me as I manned the TDC and said, "How's the setup, Mr. Lea?"

"Fine, sir, the convoy is slowing down," I answered.

"Sound reports propellers steady on two, three, five, sir."

"Up scope. Bearing, mark . . . range, mark . . . set torpedo's for twelve feet," came the succession of orders.

"Forward torpedo room, ready."

"Aft torpedo room, ready."

"Maneuvering ready."

After hearing the three responses the captain ordered, "Fire one . . . fire two . . . fire three . . . fire four . . . fire five . . . fire six . . . down scope. Take her down to one, five, oh. All ahead full," he ordered as the last missile was launched. "Come right to one, eight, zero."

The exec stood by his side with his stopwatch running. It was difficult to tell how many explosions were heard and felt. It seemed they continued unabated. It was unnecessary to get the report from sound; everyone felt the shock waves and heard the muffled roars.

Mike was about to rig for silent running when sound reported, "Heavy rain squall has hit the area above."

"Good. Bring her up to sixty feet. Let's have a look at our work. There should be a lot of confusion up there, right now."

The inclinometer and depth gauges indicated the rapid rise to sixty feet.

"Level your bubble," again was heard in the quiet of the control room.

"Up scope," Mike ordered. He was quickly on the periscope eager to see what had transpired on the surface. It appeared, as he peered threw the heavy rain, three ships had been hit, but it was difficult to see with the heavy rain.

"Aft torpedo room, this will be your shot." The forward torpedo room had not completed the reloading of its tubes. Mike figured a shot from the aft torpedo room would also give him a start on his escape. The captain received the last bearing and range information and we were ready to go.

"Fire one . . . fire two . . . fire three . . . fire four. . . ."

Then came the report of high speed propellers and we knew we were in for it.

"Emergency, 200 feet," he ordered as the ship nosed over in a steep descent to the depths below.

As we dove for cover we heard the explosions from the torpedos hitting their mark. Now we had to try to either get away or hide on the bottom.

One of the enemy destroyers had decoyed us and we were in for a depth charge attack. He had a pretty good bearing on us, too!

"Rig for silent running and come left to 360," was the skippers next order. We leveled at 200 feet in total silence. The destroyer was right down our throats and we were going to catch hell because we were so close when we launched our last torpedos. I was sure they could hear my heart beating on the surface.

"One destroyer hung back," he explained to the puzzled XO. "I didn't see him in the rain. I guess I expected them all to be

360

helping the sinking ships," said Mike with a frown.

"Captain, I'd give anything to see what the hell is going on up stairs," said Tom disappointedly.

It was at that instant the first string of depth charges started going off all around us. We could only travel at two knots when rigged for silent running; we'd need a hell of a lot of luck to escape the onslaught from above. Apparently we'd done a good job or there would have been more than one destroyer after us; the others were obviously busy evacuating the sinking ships. Our big hope was the rain squall; it could hinder the hearing of our tor-mentor.

The third charge in the first salvo had caused damage up for-ward. It was a frightful experience to say the least. It was even more terrifying than flak bursts; it felt as though the pressure of the water held you. In the air a miss generally rocked you, but down here it felt like it was pushing the sides of the submarine in and the noise was enough to make a guy pee in his pants.

The forward torpedo room reported a leak and were trying to control it without success, thus far. They also asked permission to start the pumps and were denied. Using the pumps would be tantamount to pointing an arrow directly at us. Bucket brigades were busy moving the water aft to balance the submarine. They had to control the leak; there'd be trouble if the water got to the battery room.

The depth charges continued unabated. Some of the cans were coming very close and others were going away. We had to play cat and mouse as long as it took to shake them.

I looked at the chart and knew we were in deep water. The skipper wanted to go deeper but had to wait until the forward torpedo room could shore up the leaking area.

The forward torpedo room was a mess; the problem was that we couldn't stay on an even keel due to the excess weight. Every available man was assigned to the bucket brigade as the engineers worked to halt the leak.

It was a calculated risk to go deeper, but the thermal barrier would help us escape. He called forward and asked how the work was coming and was told they had it under control.

"Let's take her down to three hundred." We dove deeper and as we descended I felt as if we were on an express elevator heading down and there was no first floor. We were in very deep water. I prayed we wouldn't go any deeper than 300 feet.

The depth charges continued; most were some distance away. None were getting to our depth. If we could stay here without getting crushed by the pressure being exerted on the hull we had it made.

Thirty more minutes went by before the depth charges ceased. The tenseness vanished from many of the crew's faces. The question was, would we be able to rise with all the additional weight from the flooding? I didn't want to ask the question, I just waited like the others. We kept sweating it out awaiting the next order.

"Sound reports, sir, he can hear at least one ship breaking up and the high speed propellers are out of range." That was damn good news to all of us.

The captain waited patiently for another hour before he finally said, "Take her up to periscope depth, let's have a look."

Tom had been at Mike's side from the minute we headed down. I could see them both brace as the submarine started to rise. It lifted gently and slowly. Mike then gave the order to start the pumps. We had to exit some of the water which was flooding the forward torpedo room. Getting the water out was important for two reasons, making the boat lighter and not letting the water enter the battery room which could cause lethal toxic fumes. We were lucky; the water was under control.

As we leveled at sixty feet, the scope was ordered up and Mike walked it through the full arc to be sure no more destroyers were lying in wait. What he saw was mass confusion. The destroyers were picking up survivors. He could see many enemy sailors in the water holding on to flotsam and jetsam. Some were in rafts and small boats, it was a mess as the captain put it. The cruiser, a destroyer and the Maru were not to be seen. Mike invited Tom to take a look and all we heard from him was a low whistle.

The skipper decided we were in no condition to continue the attack. We were down to six torpedos and we had to get to the surface in order make repairs to the forward plates.

I would have liked to send the other six torpedos into the rescue ships, but he was the boss and we headed away from the ghastly scene.

"If we had had another submarine with us we could have finished the whole convoy off," commented Tom.

"True, and maybe we could go in there and get another ship, but I don't think it's advisable. We could lose the *Seabat* and all hands easily. Perhaps tonight we can get a message off and someone can take care of the rest of them," said Mike. "We did our job and I think everyone on this boat can be proud."

"Set course for Okinawa Tom, let's go get fixed and fill up. Scope down." *Seabat* was on her way to a friendly port. The rain continued very heavy and the skipper ordered his ship to the surface. The bridge was cold and wet, but you heard no complaint from the lookouts or the officer of the deck.

"Sir, a heading of 165 should do it," I said to Tom.

He paused, scanned the readings and said, "Let's get the hell out of here."

It was not until after the war that confirmation was made of two sinkings. The cruiser and the *Maru* had gone down, the third ship had its bow blown off and was able to get away from the scene. However the destroyer never made it to port, another U.S. submarine sent it to the bottom that same afternoon.

41.

Seabat docked the morning of Independence Day, 1945. No special celebration was noticed. It was just another day in the war. Waiting was the sub-tender and an oiler. Repairs to the hull were the first order of business after which we would take on fuel and supplies. We had a long shopping list to fill and they were eager to accommodate us. First there was the red tape of checking what stores we were requistioned and then waiting for the official approval. After that was accomplished the tender was loaded with all the essentials required of a fleet submarine.

Most of the crew were granted a short liberty and wasted little time getting on the beach. As for me it was comforting to set feet on terra firma; it had been a while. I just wanted to walk on firm ground for a bit then I'd be ready to go back to sea.

The American fleet had taken a pounding from the Kamikaze attacks. I felt sure this type attack would be the norm for the rest of the war, especially if the fleet moved into Japanese waters.

As I left the *Seabat* and walked across the gangway, Mike followed me. On the dock he stepped into a waiting jeep and drove off to make his report to the admiral.

Mike returned two hours later as most of us sat on the dock and soaked up the warm sunshine. I could see the smile on his face as he stepped from the jeep; he seemed to be walking on cloud nine.

"Hi, captain, how did everything go at the head shed?" I asked.

"Just great. The admiral was very happy with the events of the past few weeks starting with fishing you out of the drink. In fact we had a long conversation about you. He wanted me to leave you here before we continued the patrol. I told him I would ask you what your desires were. If you elect to stay here they'll get you back to Tinian as soon as transportation is available, it may take awhile. Think it over and let me know as soon as possible and I'll report your decision."

"I don't need to think it over. I'd like to finish out the patrol. I'm just getting used to the submarine and they can do without me back on Tinian, I'm sure. Will the Navy have to tell my unit I decided to stay?"

"Not really, the Air Force knows you're with us, but they would have no way of knowing we stopped off here. And, by the way, I took the liberty of telling the admiral you would stay with us. I figured if you didn't want to stay aboard it would be easy to drop you off."

"Holy cow, you got promoted! Congratulations."

"Thanks, you helped me get it. You have contributed greatly to the crew and have made the shortage of one officer unfelt. I'm not the only one who got promoted, Tom made the grade too."

"Does he know it yet?"

"No. I plan to call the crew together and make the announcement."

"What happens now? I know you don't find too many full commanders in command of fleet submarines!"

"True, but since we are halfway through the patrol and I haven't been reassigned I'll remain in command until we return to Guam."

"Tom really deserves his own command. Will he get it?"

"That's the plan. I too hope to stay active with the sub service."

"Tom has really helped me, just knowing he was my exec made it so much easier. He knows his stuff and will make a damn good skipper."

"I think he's really a great teacher. He's one of the main reasons I want to stay with you, after all if I do good he should get the credit."

"I'm planning a promotion party at the Navy club tonight and I'm buying all the beer the crew can drink at their club."

I followed Mike aboard, after saluting the officer of the deck and the ensign I waited to see Lieutenant Bill Moyer's face when he saw those shining silver oak leafs on Mike's collar. As we passed him he called out. "Hold it, sir. Do I see what I think I see?"

"You sure do."

"Congratulations, Commander, no one deserves the promotion more than you."

"Thanks, we have another surprise. Our exec is now a lieutenant commander, we'll do a little celebrating tonight at the officers' club."

"Aye, aye, sir."

We went below and the news of the promotions spread throughout the ship like wildfire. There was so much commotion Tom stepped into the companionway with a puzzled look, then he went to Mike's cabin to find out why there was so much noise aboard the boat.

"Mike, I'm really happy for you, you deserve it," said Tom unselfishly.

Mike said thanks. "I have some other news, your promotion came through, too."

"You gotta be kidding!"

"Straight scoop, in fact come over here and I'll do the honors myself." Tom stepped forward with a smile equaled only by the cat after he ate the canary. Mike pinned on the new gold oak leafs and shook Tom's hand.

"Before you know it you will be wearing scrambled eggs on your hat too, Tom," I said.

The party was a great success and Mike and Tom were as high as kites, and not on booze, at least not yet. We had to leave Ensign Davis aboard *Seabat*. I volunteered to relieve him so he could enjoy some of the festivities.

The next afternoon on the tide *Seabat* slipped out of the harbor repaired and loaded with torpedos and other supplies. The honor of taking the con went to our new lieutenant commander. He looked so proud as he manned the bridge. It had been mutually agreed that even though Mike was officially in command, Tom would act as captain and run the submarine for the rest of the patrol.

We cleared the harbor and stayed on the surface for an hour before the order to crash dive was received. We went down to periscope depth to avoid detection by friend or foe. It turned out to be a test. It took but nine seconds for us to get the ship below the surface, many such drills had perfected the procedure.

Our shakedown proved the repairs to the forward part of the boat were sound, we were as good as new as Tom put it. "I like keeping the ocean on the outside," he said with a short laugh.

Tom loved to play cribbage, he proceeded to teach me the game and I beat the hell out of him, but he was a good sport and I didn't rub it in. That was one of the few times I'd beat him for the rest of the cruise. He was amazed I learned so fast and I told him all it takes is card sense.

Night fell and we resurfaced and traveled at fourteen knots. Tom was on the bridge and Mike was relaxing in his quarters. He had only been resting for a few minutes when the messenger from the radio shack knocked on the bulkhead outside of Mike's cabin.

"Sir, I have a message from COMSUBPAC, we have just decoded it," the sailor stepped back and waited for some response.

Mike opened the envelope and read the message and then dismissed the sailor by saying, "no answer required."

The sailor said, "Aye, aye, sir," turned and left silently.

Tom had in the meantime descended to the control room leaving the bridge to the duty officer. He looked over my shoulder as I finished computing our position.

"Tom, do you have a good fix on our position?" asked Mike.

"Yes, sir. Mr. Lea just finished plotting it, we're right here," he pointed to a small triangle indicating *Seabat's* position for the time indicated.

"Good. We'll have to plot a new course." He handed the message to Tom, we both read it.

The message directed us to proceed to a set of coordinates which when plotted was a spot south of Kyushu and north of the island of Tanega Shima, in the straights of Osumi.

"That's a narrow stretch of water with plenty of small islands, captain," I said.

He looked me in the eye and said, "If it was an order to enter Tokyo harbor that's where we'd go. I want to be there before daybreak. Can you work me up a good ETA?"

"Sure thing, captain." It took but a minute for me to hand him the information he wanted. Our speed was upped to eighteen knots and we were on our new course to arrive at our new area of patrol ASAP.

"I'm going back to my quarters for a little rest. Let me know if you need me; otherwise, it's your ship," Mike turned without waiting for an acknowledgement and was gone.

Tom and I read the whole message after Mike retired. "Now I see why we were in such a hurry, we're on a special mission to pick up a downed B-29 crew," said Tom.

Apparently the crew didn't have time to get further out to sea, it reminded me of our ditching. "Going down in a confined area such as this means they were in real trouble," I added.

Tom climbed the ladder to the bridge and I followed him. The night was clear and *Seaboat* was cutting through the small swells like a knife cuts through butter.

Word spread around the boat of the rescue attempt. Everyone knew the danger of a rescue so close to land but no one expressed any doubt of our ability to make a successful rescue. As for Tom, it was full speed ahead. This was his chance to show his stuff.

After an all night speed contest we were in the area reported as the rescue spot. We found no trace of the crew or any debris. Radar searched the area without success. It was assumed the plane must have sunk and all the men with it, but knowing how well a B-29 floats, I had my doubts.

Mike had joined us on the bridge and he said, "Are we sure we are at the right place?"

"Yes, sir. I just rechecked the coordinates, 30-25N and 130-55E. I was thinking, sir, it may be possible the aerial navigator got confused and gave the wrong coordinates. Look here, this place looks a lot like where we are and it's about ten miles up the coast."

"You think they might be there?" asked Mike.

"Well, sir, if they had little time it is possible to make an error like this. I recommend we take a look," I said.

"I agree, it's getting light fast. Give the order to proceed to the new location at flank speed," ordered Tom.

Seabat responded to the new command and jumped like a motor boat at full speed. Tom had decided to stay on the surface as long as possible knowing we'd be in great danger. He knew if we didn't get there in a hell of a hurry the Jap's would.

We were doing twenty knots until Tom decided we had to submerge or risk detection and possible fire from shore batteries or worse, an air attack.

"Clear the bridge. Dive, dive," commanded Tom and all hands were below within seconds. "Take her down to periscope depth and give me all the speed you can."

We were making ten knots and closing on the new position at sixty feet. The diving officer had monitored the descent like a hawk. "Up scope," Tom ordered as Mike came to his side. It was different seeing Tom at the familiar position at the periscope, but I knew with his years of experience we lost nothing at the command level. Tom swung the periscope around in a complete circle to be sure we weren't being decoyed.

"Sir, the ETA is coming up fast, can you give a visual fix on a shore position?" I asked.

"Hold it, I think I see something dead ahead. Yes, it's a raft, there are men in it. Mark, range," ordered Tom.

The range was 2,000 yards. The sun hadn't risen as yet; however, it was light on the surface. This rescue could be a real crap shoot.

"Sir, there should be two rafts up there, maybe only part of the crew escaped," I said.

Tom maneuvered the submarine in close and then ordered, "Down scope, bring her up." The boat rose rapidly as the pumps pushed the sea water out of the ballast tanks and the boat came to the surface. "Battle stations, surface," came his next order. Men were running toward the hatches ready to spring to action. I was excited wondering which wing these guys were in. I secretly hoped it wasn't one from the 444th.

As I came to the bridge all the *Seabat's* crew were at battle stations and ready for anything. There were two rafts. Apparently one was hidden behind the other and Tom couldn't see it. I was happy as I tried counting the men in the rafts. There were five men in one raft and three in the other; some were wounded.

A line was tossed to the raft and both were pulled next to the submarine and the men were helped aboard. Both rafts were punctured and sunk. I tried to see if any of them looked familiar, none did and I was relieved. The lookouts were searching the surrounding sky and water when all at once a cry came from one of them, "Enemy aircraft, to the north."

We were in trouble, this was definitely not the place to try and fight off an enemy air attack. The sailors were told to rush to get the airmen below and the gun crews trained their guns toward the direction of attack. Two enemy fighters flying wing tip to wing tip swooped down to make a strafing run. There was no doubt they were Zeke's, more commonly known as Zero's. Their guns were blazing as they attacked. Our antiaircraft guns fired rapidly in defense. The stream of bullets ripped across the water and hit forward without any apparent damage. Our gunners were firing as fast as their guns would allow and doing a mighty fine job. I knew the enemy pilots thought they would have little opposition and were not prepared for what they got. However, the fighters were not discouraged by our fire, they made a sweeping turn and came back down to press the attack, I only hoped they had no bombs. The defensive fire was impressive but did not stop the next attack. They came down at a steeper angle and I could plainly see they had no bomb racks. The next strafing run found its mark, one of the men from the B-29 as well as a sailor assisting him were hit and killed, it was a horrible sight. I hoped we could get below the surface soon or bombers might arrive.

All the lookouts were on their way below as well as the gun crews when I noticed something coming from the north. It was but a speck, but coming like a flash. In seconds I saw what it was, a P-47, American. He dove down on the unsuspecting Jap fighters. They were so intent on their target they didn't hear or see him. Why the P-47 was alone puzzled me, I knew they always flew in formations and certainly never less than two. The eight fifties tore into the first Zero, he never knew what hit him as his plane exploded in a ball of fire. He turned to attack the second Zero, but from nowhere six more enemy fighters arrived on the scene and immediately started to attack the lone eagle. The American was an experienced pilot, there was no doubt. He turned to meet the attack and hit another Zeke just as his ammunition gave out. It was clearly a one-sided show. The enemy pilots knew he was going to crash, he turned his fighter toward our position and bailed out. I prayed his chute would open, it did and he plunged into the sea close to us. We were in trouble but Tom refused to leave the fighter pilot on the open sea to be captured or killed. He had saved our necks, at least for the time being. We owed him our assistance.

The enemy maneuvered for the attack, they knew they had no opposition. We prepared for the worst, then an odd thing happened. The remaining Zeke's instead of attacking the submarine turned away from us at top speed. I looked again toward the north and saw why they'd left so hurriedly, a flight of P-47's were bearing in on them. The Jap fighters dove to evade their attackers, but their maneuvers were in vain. The "Jugs" came down with guns blazing, it was a sight to behold. They cleared the sky of enemy planes, only two had escaped. The P-47's circled overhead until they were sure we had plucked their buddy out of the water and had him safely aboard, then they flew over our position at a low altitude wagged their wings in recognition and flew on to their base on Okinawa.

It seemed an eternity, but finally the familiar order rang out, "Clear the deck, clear the bridge." Men secured and ran for cover. All the lookouts cleared the bridge and I was following with Tom on my heels.

370

"Take her down, and give me flank speed. Set a course to the northeast." Tom knew every sub-chaser and destroyer would be looking for us and we had to get the hell out of this tight spot. "Mr. Lea, make sure of the depth in this area, I know there are shoals and I don't want to get hung up here," said Tom.

Everyone aboard was working hard to get everything accomplished. We now had to accommodate the seven remaining B-29 crewmen as well as the P-47 pilot. If this kept up we'd be awfully crowded.

"Sir, we are clear and we have all the depth you can use," I reported.

Tom's assessment was correct. The talker reported, "Sound reports two high speed propellers 12,000 yards approaching from the north."

"Take her down to 200 feet," ordered Tom.

We leveled at 200 feet and Tom gave the order, "Rig for silent running and let's hope they don't stop to listen." He knew below the surface we couldn't outrun the enemy, the next best thing is give him no target. The boat became as quiet as the proverbial church mouse. Mike and Tom both knew the enemy surface vessels had a fair fix on us and we were going to get some "cans" any second, but we hoped to fool them by heading northeast.

"High speed propellers slowing." Seconds after the report we heard and felt the first string of depth charges going off close by.

"Take her down to 250 feet."

The depth charges continued, but seemed to be coming from two different directions in a straight line. It looked grave, the cans were coming close, just above. "Let's go down to 300 feet," ordered Tom as Mike watched without interjecting any comments. Mike knew he would have handled the situation the same way.

This was it, 300 feet is the limit unless emergency measures were taken. No one was sure we could survive at this depth. We kept our fingers crossed.

The depth charges never ceased, however they were now far off the mark, probably due to the thermal layer. I wondered what our new visitors were thinking. Doc had his hands full, but he was damn good and we were sure he could handle the situation.

After thirty minutes at 300 feet the depth charges stopped. Tom took the boat up to 150 feet and we made for the open sea. Everyone aboard was happy to leave the deep water. The air got so heavy you felt fresh air would be worth anything. The more experienced sailors suffered less than the others.

Another hour passed then Tom took us up to periscope depth and found we were in the clear and away from immediate trouble. We'd come through another tough situation in good shape. He scanned the area. "Have a look captain to be sure I didn't miss anything," asked Tom.

Mike twisted his hat so the visor was to the rear and put his eye to the eyepiece of the scope and swung it around the entire 360 degrees, "Look's like we lost them, but we'd better be on our toes, they may come after us again."

I was relieved of duty and had an opportunity to visit the B-29 officers and found they were also from Tinian. They were from the 9th Bomb Group, 313th Bomb Wing who flew from North Field. The survivors included both pilots, flight engineer, CFC gunner, a scanner-gunner and tail gunner. The other scanner-gunner was killed on the deck with one of the sailors and the navigator, radar man and radio operator had lost their lives earlier.

They told me they'd been on a mine laying mission at the entrance of the Inland Sea, near Kure and Hiroshima. They'd been hit by antiaircraft fire then the fighter jumped them. They were trying to make it to Okinawa, but had lost so much fuel they had to ditch. I questioned them about their ditching position and was told the bombardier had worked the position. I then went to see the fighter pilot, a member of the 8th Fighter Wing based on Okinawa.

"Howdy, my name is Lea, Johnny Lea," I held out my hand.

"Mine's John Houston," he said with a twang. He told me he was from Houston, Texas. With a name like his he couldn't miss. He had graduated from Texas A&M before the war started and had gone into the flying business just after.

"I think you're going to bunk with me. Why were you flying alone? I thought you always flew in pairs."

"We were making ground sweeps when my wing man got hit by automatic weapons fire and went in. I was on my own when I saw the two Zeke's diving on you. I radioed the squadron leader of my action when I spotted the submarine picking up the men in the rafts. Those yellow little bastards would have never taken me if I hadn't run out of ammo and had a good engine. I took a hit on my last sweep just when my wing man blew up and half of my jugs were hanging out of the cowling."

This guy was either the bravest SOB, or the best damn fighter pilot in the Air Force. Whatever the case he saved us from certain disaster and that we wouldn't forget.

The skipper was making arrangements for a burial at sea after dark. It was a sad day for the ships company as well as the B-29 crew losing two men to the enemy fighter attack just when it looked like they were safe.

Tom made the decision to stay submerged until we were well away from land and it was totally dark. I returned to the control room to see how everything was going. Tom asked, "Would you like to take a look before I stow the periscope?"

"Sure thing, sir." I put my eye to the eyepiece and looked out at the sea splashing on the glass. We were still in sight of land and had not passed through the straits of Osumi. Looking through the periscope was like looking through the prisms of a sextant except you had a greater field of vision. For the next two hours we continued to sail beneath the sea and no suspicious noises were detected. After dark we cleared the straights of Osumi. Tom made another survey of the area and then ordered *Seabat* to the surface. Mike took the deck watch, I was sure he was bored watching another man do his job. We headed away from the area to await further instructions.

The burial service was held soon after the ship was on the surface and all hands had stood to. The two bodies had been sewed in canvas and weighted. The captain read the words and then both bodies were commended to the deep.

We made radio contact with COMSUBPAC as we monitored the assigned frequency. We were told to continue patroling along the coast to the northeast until further orders. When radio contact was again made our orders were to patrol off the southern coast of Honshu.

For the next two days we found no shipping worth a torpedo and avoided them. Mike commented, "The war must be winding down, we can't even find a target no matter where we go in the area."

The night of 12 July we received another message from COMSUBPAC, it was simple. We were told to continue patroling the new assigned area and be aware of a large bombing mission which would be conducted the night of 12-13 July. It was obvious most of the attacks by the 20th Air Force would be concentrated on Honshu and we were to act as lifesavers.

373

All the stops had been pulled, it was an all out effort to finish off the Japanese. General Carl Spaatz had been appointed commander of all Strategic Air Forces in the Pacific. He had stated, "Air conquest of Japan is to be attempted to make invasion of the home islands unnecessary."

It was easy to see if we were to avoid invasion we would have to make a maximum effort on all bomb missions. And to prove it there would be over 500 B-29's over Japan this night.

Aboard *Seabat* we doubled up on all the officers quarters except for the skipper's cabin and if we got more company he wouldn't be excluded. We had to eat in shifts to accommodate all the new faces in the officers' wardroom. The big problem would arise if we were to pick up another full crew or two. I wondered how long this cruise could last with all these extra passengers! The amazing thing was no one bitched about the cramped quarters except one of the enlisted aircrew members. I was fast to correct his problem through his senior officer.

It had become a joke on the boat about my assignment. All the Navy personnel knew I was an Army Air Force officer, but none of the Air Force types had any idea. At first I thought it fun to hide it, now I was finding it hard to explain why I didn't tell them earlier. I decided it was nothing to worry about and put it off. It was fun watching the faces of the Air Force people when I used obvious Air Force jargon. This was especially true of my roommate.

Captain Houston told me he'd decided on a military career before the war started and he hadn't changed his mind. I thought he was nuts, but I'd ended up doing the same thing. I tried to tell him who I really was but he never made it easy. I continued as Lieutenant (jg) Lea instead of 1st Lieutenant Lea. I came to like him even though I considered him stiff. He was a real hero and there was no doubt in my mind he would do it all over if he was given the chance.

When the time was right I told him who I was and for the first time he was pissed off. After a few minutes he said, "Why the hell didn't you tell me? I've been trying to explain the Air Force to you and you just let me do it."

"I'm sorry, it was a little game we had aboard the boat, but I decided I'd tell you since you're my roomy." I explained to him what had happened and how they trained me as a replacement for the missing officer. He was amazed and amused.

It was two hours after dark when the telltale sound of the B-29's with their powerful engines streamed overhead to their targets north of Tokyo. We had a terrific view from our vantage point fifty miles south of Honshu.

I estimated over a hundred aircraft had passed over our position in a short period of time. "Give 'em hell," I said under my breath. It took little time for the sky line to light up like a huge bonfire on the horizon. The low clouds made an eerie red glow that reflected off the clouds like a sunset in the middle of the night. It was an awesome sight, it looked much different from the surface than in the air. The big planes would soon be heading south toward Iwo Jima and the Mariana's. "Good luck guys," I said aloud.

We didn't have long to wait as the radio operator received a "Mayday" message from a B-29 in trouble. I was on duty at the plotting board and had the aircraft's position fixed on my chart and updated the information as I received it. The superfort was northeast of us. We turned toward the spot where we knew they'd cross the coast as they headed out to sea. The plan was to position the submarine as close to their track as possible. The plan was extremely well thought out and the B-29 crew was experienced. The plane's crew execution was like clockwork as was the submarine's. The B-29 flew directly overhead very low. Apparently setting up for their crash landing into the water. The lookouts on deck reported two engines were not running. It reminded me of the dreadful night when we ditched not too far from here.

Tom ordered *Seabat* to follow at flank speed. We were on a merry chase of the big plane and holding the same course. We estimated the plane would ditch within a few miles. It took little time for the sub to be making twenty knots in hot pursuit of the plane. It was probably the first time in history a submarine chased an aircraft and caught it!

The moon broke through the clouds lighting up the area and making the search for the plane easier. Radar spotted it on the ocean surface one mile ahead, we closed rapidly. As we got closer the lookouts spotted the plane low in the water and sinking slowly. I requested permission to come on the bridge and my request was granted. I scampered up the ladder anxious to see the plane to identify which wing it was from.

"There she is dead ahead," cried Tom as he pointed in the direction of the huge silver bird broken and setting lower in the

375

water.

We approached the plane on its port side and I still could not see the tail. I had to wait until we were abeam. We swung out to avoid the wing of the plane and I could now see the tail. It had a huge triangle with an "N" in the center. The plane was from my bomb group. We inched forward and all at once I saw the nose.

"My God, this plane is from my squadron!" I yelled at the top of my lungs.

"You've got to be kidding!" answered Mike who was at my side. Then he said, "Are you the only guys who ditch airplanes?" he said kiddingly.

"No sir, but we do it right."

Mike brought the boat up on the left wing and ordered, "All stop." We were sitting motionless in the water as the crew of the plane scrambled over the wings and entered rafts. I tried to count them and was sure there were eleven figures.

The two rafts were boarded and headed toward us and soon the sailors were hauling them aboard. I tried in vain to see if I knew any of them, it was too dark.

Tom gave the order to dive and we all slid down the ladder to the conning tower below. The chief of the boat closed the hatch from the bridge and we started to submerge. I was behind Mike as the men of the plane came down the passage way toward the wardroom. I was trying to see their faces as they filed by in the dim red light. I couldn't see the face of the first few men as Mike shook their hands. Then a tall fellow put out his hand and said, "Thank you captain, you guys are really on the ball."

I stood there motionless, unbelieving, it was impossible! There was only one voice like that, it was of all people, Bart Ellis. I stepped from behind Mike and blocked his way. He looked up in disbelief and we stood motionless for a second.

"Bart, you old son-of-a-bitch what the hell are you doing here?"

"I might ask you the same question."

We embraced. I was never happier to see anyone in my life. I could not believe my eyes, but it was true, Bart and I had finally got together again.

"Johnny, I have another surprise for you."

"Surprise!"

"Yeah, guess who was navigating that bucket out there?"

"I can't guess. Who?"

Then he stepped into view. "My God, is it possible?" I said

stunned by the events.

"It's me ya'all, your wayward sidekick."

I looked at Dave and tears jumped into my eyes. I was nearly at the point of breaking down and didn't care if I showed it. I was never happier to see two guys. It was like old home week.

"This was the only way I could run you down, sailor!" said Dave with his ususl drawl.

"Yeah, we had to catch up with you somehow," added Bart. As if ditching a B-29 off the Japanese coast was an everyday affair.

"You're getting to be a real ace for the Nips," I said with a chuckle.

"Yup, two for two," said Bart in a casual voice. I always knew he had ice water in his veins.

"You're going to run the 444th out of airplanes if you keep this up," I said sarcastically.

I knew some of the other crew members from the squadron, but not well.

"Is this a new crew you put together? Where are the guys from our old crew?" I asked.

"No, Dave and I were just filling in. They needed a lead crew and had to put us with these fellows," answered Bart.

"Look, you guys go in and get settled and I'll get with you as soon as I'm off watch, okay?"

They smiled and turned to follow their guide and I returned to the conning tower to await my relief. My watch ended a little early because Bill Moyers knew I was anxious to get with my old buddies. I appreciated it.

I found all the officers from Bart's plane in the wardroom having coffee. Dooley was a great host as usual. "Hi, are you guys still awake?"

"We're tough old soldiers, didn't ya'all know?" said Dave as he refilled his coffee cup.

"So, which do you like best by now, Navy or Air Force?" asked Bart.

"It's like this; this isn't the surface Navy, this is the sub service and they are as different as the Army and the Air Force. I've been treated with respect and they've taught me to be one of them. But, in answer to your question, I love to fly and miss it, however, if I had a second choice it would be right down here with these guys."

"Sounds like you're getting ready to re-up in the Navy," said

Bart.

"What happened to you guys last night?"

"We were up north of Tokyo at a place called Utsunomyia with 120 birds. Each wing had separate targets in the general area. We did great until just after we got rid of our bombs, then we caught a bad burst of flak and lost an engine. Johnny, it was a lot like what happened to us when we ditched except we didn't get hit by fighters. A guy could get killed up there!"

"Christ, he can get killed anywhere. We picked up the crew from the 313th and got hit by fighter and lost one airmen and a sailor on deck. We buried them at sea last night, real sad," I said.

We talked for another hour about what had happened after we parted and how I wanted to kill them for leaving me alone. They brought me up to date on the outside world and who was lost and who had finished their missions, etc. Bart had completed thirty-five missions as had Jim. Dave had finished twenty-one.

Mike came into the wardroom and informed us we were heading home. It was great news, but I was sad thinking about leaving my new friends. I was lucky though I had my old friends back. After our return Captain John Houston was recommended for the Medal of Honor. After much deliberation at the top level he was awarded the second highest award a man could earn, the Distinguished Service Cross. I personally thought he deserved more.

42.

Seabat headed toward Guam 1,500 miles to the south. As long as we were in open water and could cruise on the surface life aboard was reasonably comfortable.

Bart, Dave and I missed chow the next morning, but as usual Dooley took care of me. It was mid-morning when we finally hit the deck. I could smell the coffee as we approached the ward room. Up to this time it had been a nice smooth ride with only the crowding causing any annoyance.

"You guys were really lucky to ditch and come through it without a serious casualty," I said as we sat down in the ward room.

"I just used skill and cunning. My big worry was getting to the open sea; we were too low for bail out and I sure didn't want to become a POW this late in the war," answered Bart.

"No conceit in your family, you have it all," I retorted.

"As a matter of fact he did just fine. I hardly felt the landing," drawled Dave.

"That's because he's had so much practice," I added.

"You Navy guys wouldn't understand," said Bart.

"How is the air war going? Are we winning?" I asked.

"There's no doubt, we now go after a minimum of targets for each wing. Soon, they tell me, we'll be hitting targets by individual groups."

"You finished up your missions, why didn't you head for home?" I asked Bart.

"When I go back, we all go back. I don't know what the policy will be about you getting another mission. I feel it will be up to you," said Bart.

"Johnny, don't be a fool, go home as soon as you can," said Dave seriously.

"You've done more than your share. I hear you guys sunk a bunch of ships and had depth charges after you and even got strafed by the Nips. Why the hell do you need to do more?" asked

Bart.

"How are the other guys from our crew doing, Bart?"

"As you know John Wright was left on *Here's Hopin* and Roundy, Roy and Pops were sent home. With you missing we only had eight of the original crew left. We got fill-ins and flew some and were assigned odd jobs around squadron and group. It was a pain in the ass. It was never the same after we lost you. We had a big celebration after we heard you were safe. All the guys blamed themselves for getting separated from you that night, but it was my responsibility and I let you down," said Bart.

"Hell it was nobody's fault," I said.

"I tried to get the damn Navy pilot of the PBY to go back for you, but he was worried about Jap boats in the area and the wounded. He really pissed me off, but I couldn't do anything about it."

"Being half pissed off at you guys helped me to survive out there alone."

"That's all behind us now. Pops and Roy were sent to hospitals near their homes and Roundy was sent home. They'll probably be discharged as soon as they recover."

Dave broke in and said, "Let's talk about a different subject. I'm tired of talking about this stinking war. Let's take the tour of the submarine you offered us."

After the tour I had to get ready for my watch on the bridge. I told them they could come up when I took over, if they liked.

The night before we arrived at Guam we radioed our position to COMSUBPAC and gave them an accurate accounting of passengers. After the message was transmitted I laughed as I said, "Captain, I think you forgot to include me on the passenger list."

"No."

"How's that?"

"You were included with the boat's company."

"Does that mean I'm now in the Navy?"

"Until we return to port, you are."

"I want you to know, Tom, it's been a pleasure and a real education, most Army Air Force officers will never get a chance to act as a Naval officer aboard a submarine. It proves the services are not all that different and should be able to get along better. I really think more officers and top enlisted men should be exchanged on a tour basis.

"It's an interesting idea. Someday in the future I imagine it'll happen. Maybe we started something new."

The captain turned to Bart and said, "By the way, Ellis, I'm glad we picked you up. I remember talking to you before we left on patrol and how close you came to threatening me about picking up your navigator. Do you remember?"

"I was hoping you hadn't remembered, sir. It would've all been unnecessary if that damn PBY pilot hadn't run for home. To make it up to you captain, I'd like to throw a party in the Navy club the night we dock for all your officers and all the Air Force officers to show our appreciation to one hell of a good crew. We can also have a party for all the enlisted types," said Bart.

"Damn good idea," I said.

"How about letting all the Air Force officers pitch in and we'll do it up brown," added Dave.

I had the midnight watch and we planned the dinner and party with all the passenger officers until I went on watch. This would be my last watch aboard *Seabat* and I was sorry. I liked the activity aboard the sub and knew I'd miss it and the crew of this damn fine submarine.

During my duty tour I took some celestial observations and made the last calculation to take us to the Agana harbor on Guam. I could see the lights of Tinian and Saipan far to the southwest and I confirmed my celestial with radar and radio bearings. We only had 125 miles to go and my Navy tour would come to an end.

My ETA put us at the harbor entrance just before daylight, a good time. We didn't want to sail these waters on the surface during the day, some eager pilot or skipper of a ship might decide to shoot first and ask questions later and that would never do so close to home.

On the bridge I felt good with the slight cool breeze hitting me in the face. I looked around and saw all the lookouts alert and on the ball. I knew there was little for me to do on the bridge, but it was much more comfortable here than below. I recollected the contribution I'd made while aboard *Seabat* and felt proud that I'd earned my keep and had made so many good friends. Most of all I'd cemented relations between this command and the Twentieth Air Force.

The less appealing thing about returning to Tinian would be going back to living in tents, at least aboard ship you had a decent bed as long as you were afloat. The food was really what I would miss most. They don't have cooks like Dooley in an Army mess.

Of course, he didn't have to try to make dehydrated goat taste good.

My watch ended before dawn and I went to my quarters, laid back on my bunk and closed my eyes. I knew I could only rest for an hour or so because we were getting close to docking.

Excitement was at a fever pitch as we entered the harbor making for the sub base. All the officer passengers had gathered in the wardroom for the last minute planning of the party. I had breakfast as I listened, it was going to be a party to end all parties. One of the officers from the 313th said he thought he would kidnap Dooley and take him back to Tinian and in exchange the Navy could have a dozen cooks, he was worth more.

Mike had taken the con to bring *Seabat* in and he did it with skill and competence, it was just 0700 as we secured to the dock. Quarters were found for all the passengers until transportation could be arranged.

A C-54 was scheduled to make a trip to both fields on Tinian the following day at noon then on to Okinawa to drop off Captain Houston. That should give us a little time to get over the hangovers we were sure to have.

The quarters were more than adequate large quonset huts. I liked it on Guam, there were palm trees and a lot of foliage. On Tinian you saw fields of sugar cane and open ground, there were no palm trees.

The day passed rapidly and it was time to go to the club. I was issued the familiar Army khakis and was at once transformed from Lieutenant (jg) to First Lieutenant John Lea, it felt good, but sad. A room had been reserved at the spacious club for our dinner party and soon everyone was present. A small portable bar had been put in the room and the gang surrounded it like bees at a hive, they sounded like it too. Invited as guests were the commander of the sub base and part of his staff which lent a little credibility to our party.

During the day it had been announced that Commander Mike Watson was joining the staff of the admiral and Lieutenant Commander Tom Webster was named as the new skipper of *Seabat*. Another guest of the party was Tom's new exec, Lieutenant Ross Adamsley. Ross thought us all a little crazy and he was right.

After dinner the drinks flowed like water and one by one people were spinning in. Mike had made a short speech as his last official act as captain of *Seabat*. He heaped praise on all of us, but singled

382

out Tom and I. It may have angered some of the other Navy officers but they didn't show it. The party lasted until after midnight and there was not a sober man left. We had to be guided back to our quarters as this night of nights came to a soggy end.

One of the conversations which made me laugh was when John Houston told me he knew all the time I was an Air Force officer, I just laughed and told him he was full of shit, but good shit.

The next morning most of us slept in and nursed our headaches, but we knew we had to get our butts in gear, we were leaving soon and had to get some food in our stomachs. The Navy mess at the sub base was good, but it would never pass muster for Dooley's chow.

A gray bus hauled us all to the waiting plane on the ramp at the Navy air field. I didn't feel all that good, but my spirits rose when I saw the gray jeep pull up and Mike and Tom get out to wish us all well. Mike came to me and said, "Lieutenant Lea, I forgot to do this last night, but better late than never." He stepped up in front of me and pinned a set of submariner's dolphins on my chest, shook my hand and saluted. "This badge signifies you are a qualified submariner and I am proud to have sailed with you."

I was so delighted it was hard for me to contain myself. I was truly proud. "Sir, I thank you for this honor. I'll always cherish my memories of you and the officers and men of *Seabat* and I'll wear this badge with honor and distinction."

I shook hands with Mike and Tom as the others applauded. I turned and boarded the plane with a tear in my eye.

It was the last time I ever saw either of them. *Seabat* went down on its next war patrol two days before the end of the war. Mike was promoted to captain and went on to become an admiral.

43.

The flight to west field was colorful and enjoyable. I was going home! I'm not sure if calling it home was appropriate, but it was to be my home until the end of the war.

The C-54 taxied to the main ramp and cut the two engines on the port side as all the 58th Bomb Wing people disembarked. After we stepped out of the way the two engines were restarted and the plane left to make its stop at Okinawa.

We were met by the commanders of the 444th, and 9th Bomb Groups as well as other well wishers. I was most happy to see all the remaining members of our original crew. Jim and Rich gave me a bear hug and the others followed suit, they were as glad to see me as I was them.

The jeep pulled up in front of an ugly quonset hut which stood where our tent used to be. Every time I saw a quonset it reminded me of a turtle. Actually it was quite an improvement over the old tent. Jim had made a new bed and closet for me, I was impressed. We shared the hut with another crew, a new replacement crew, I knew none of them. The guys escorted me in to our new living quarters and I was truly happy. Jim had built a game table and chairs, it was a nice touch. He had also built a small front porch and a rear sun deck, he'd done a good job. In front of the hut staked firmly to prevent theft was the oxen wagon we'd recovered from the jungle a few months back.

"Now that we are together again let's drink a toast to our return and to the guys who made it possible," said Bart as he reached for the bottle of CC.

It was a bit early for drinking, but it was a special occasion and Bart, Jim, Rich and I lifted one.

"It really is odd, here we are the original four officers of the crew like it was before we got Roundy," said Rich.

"The cream always rises to the top," added Jim.

It was good to be back with my friends and I was anxious to

384

get back to work.

"One more short one to celebrate Johnny's release from the Navy," said Bart with a big smile. We all laughed.

That night at the club there was a party and I was the guest of honor. It was attended by such distinguished officers as the wing and group commanders. The big portion of the party was made up of the flying officers of the 444th Bomb Group, my friends. I was asked to make a speech to tell of my adventures, I made it short. When I finished many questions were asked and I was compelled to answer them. I proudly displayed the dolphins I'd been awarded, they made a big hit.

The talk I gave that night was to start a trend. For years to come I was asked to give the survival lecture to new people and those who had not heard the tale.

The party was a big success if one counted the headaches the following day. When I woke my head felt like it was going to explode and my eyes were bloodshot, I lived through it but for a while I wasn't sure I wanted to.

Bart and Jim requested to stay with the squadron until the rest of the original crew were finished with their missions, permission was granted. The new crew was built around the four remaining officers, the flight engineer, CFC, radio operator and the remaining scanner-gunner. It was not difficult, the personnel pool had many displaced souls. A radar operator who'd been wounded on the same mission we ditched was now available to finish his tour, his crew had been sent home. All they had to do was find a scanner and a tail gunner. My status had to be settled. I was told I didn't have to fly any more combat missions and could be rotated to the States on the first available transportation. I refused. I volunteered to stay with the crew as Bart had. We were back in business.

A training schedule was arranged to get us back in the groove. We flew two days in a row and were pronounced combat ready. On our second qualifying mission we bombed our neighboring island of Rota, still held by the Japanese. The island had been neutralized and bypassed before we arrived in the Marianas. I was sure the island would sink if one more bomb was dropped on the defunct runways.

I soon discovered we'd found some rare talent. The radar man was sharp and did not sleep at every opportunity. His name was Sam Jansen, he was from Seattle. His home was close to the

Boeing plant that had developed the B-29. All the new crew members had survived some catastrophe and all had over 25 missions.

We were getting a bit restless and wanted to fly. Our eagerness was noticeable, it was practically all we talked about. After a couple days we were informed we were scheduled to lead the group on a mission to the port city of Tsu east of Osaka and across the bay from Nagoya. It was a hot spot and had been hit four days earlier by both the 313th and 314th Bomb wings.

Two groups of our wing would attack Tsu and the other two groups would go after Aomori located on the northern part of Honshu. Both missions would be after port facilities as well as the urban area. Five other locations were targeted to be bombed by the other four wings of the 20th Air Force.

The night mission would have individual planes coming across the target. The plan called for a feint at Nagoya and then a turn to the left hitting Tsu then turning to the south and out to sea. By making a feint at Nagoya the enemy air defense would be confused and would wait some miles from the actual target. It was known by our intelligence people the Japanese had brought gun boats into the harbor for additional air defense. Imperial Navy flak was generally better than the Army. Knowing these facts didn't help our thoughts of survival.

As I sat in briefing listening to all the specialty briefings I thought of being shot down. I was more aware of the dangers now and I was sure the reason for the squadron releasing me from further combat was due to the psychological effects of being downed at sea and away from the flying business as long as I had. However, I had to do this for me and my peace of mind. I knew I had to fight it and conquer my fears. I tried not to think of it.

Our takeoff was planned for 1600 and all was in readiness as we sat in our plane awaiting the signal to start engines. The crew was eager to get going and I was no exception. I knew once I got to work all my anxieties would vanish.

We'd been airborne three hours as we passed over Iwo Jima on our way to the target three and a half hours to the north. The time had passed rapidly and the crew was wide awake and chattering on the intercom. This is a damn good crew, maybe better than our original one, I thought. It was a shame we'd only be together for a short time. Maybe they could melt together with parts of other crews and finish up their missions collectively. I felt more at ease back in my familiar surroundings as the mission progressed. I knew the mission was well planned and with good execution it would soon be history.

We arrived at the IP and started our feint toward Nagoya and then made our swing and came across the target at 9,000 feet. We made short work of the target. The mission was picture perfect with seventy-six planes dropping 730 tons of incendiaries on the primary. The 444th and the 40th lost no planes and had no real aerial opposition. We had another mission in the books.

The 462nd and the 468th returned from Aomori without a loss also. They'd hit their target with 64 planes and had dropped 547 tons. The wing had done a good nights work.

We were hopeful of flying the next mission scheduled for 1 August, but stood down due to an engine failure during run up. It was a wing mission with all four groups hitting Hachioji. 172 B-29's dropped 1573 tons on the primary. A single aircraft was lost from the 40th Bomb Group. Opposition had been stiff, but had cost the enemy 14 fighters with numerous damaged or probables.

We had time on our hands and we spent it at the beach relaxing. I had the feeling our squadron was not going to let us fly a mission which they considered extra dangerous. When asked, the operations people denied it and merely stated we would be scheduled as required.

We found ourselves being assigned training missions for new crews arriving. Each of the new crews brought a new aircraft with them, it was easy to see why the group reported being 100 percent manned.

The morning of 4 August we reported to operations ready to go out on another training mission and found we had been penciled in to fly the combat mission scheduled for the following day. We were delighted. I checked to see where the mission was schuduled to go and found it was a place called Saga. I went to the big map on the wall and found that Saga was located east of Sasebo and north of Nagasaki. This area was heavily defended and worse, it was defended by the Imperial Navy.

Information indicated the 20th Air Force would be hitting 6 scattered targets during the daylight hours. Over 600 B-29's were to be employed. Again our wing would hit two separate targets, another indication we were running out of the big targets. This mission would again be the 40th and the 444th and the other with the 462th and 468th. We seemed to work well with the 40th.

The planning went well and briefings indicated we would probably run into stiff opposition, "What the hell, that's why they pay us so good," said Bart.

We sat at the controls of our plane ready to go and finally got the word and headed for the runup spot. After checking three engines and finding no problems the fourth had a mag drop, but we considered it within limits and headed for the active runway.

Again, before we took off I felt the strain of what lay ahead, I was sure it was a little fatigue and nothing else. We seldom spoke of fear, we knew the other guy felt it too, but tried to not to show any signs. Anxiety generally disappeared once you were in the thick of it.

Our engines were at maximum RPM as the brakes were released and our plane sprang ahead down the almost two miles of concrete. We lifted off, pulled the gear and started our turn to our initial heading as the rest of our group followed.

The weather enroute was a bit suspect. Sam had his radar set tuned up and coming in as fine as I have ever seen a radar set paint. I was glad to have him along and would need him to help establish route and target.

Briefing indicated there would be a group of P-47's from Okinawa to help clear the air of enemy fighters and if after we departed they still had fuel they'd attack targets too small for us to waste bombs on. I felt good about fighter protection; we didn't get it very often. Now, if the weather would cooperate so they could get to the rendezvous all should go well. I thought, as we made the long climb to our cruising altitude, maybe John Houston will be one of the pilots of our fighter cover. If so I was sure the enemy was in trouble, especially if the other pilots in the 8th Fighter Wing were as sharp as he. From Iwo Jima there was to be a flight of P-51's doing their stuff over Japan, also. It was nice to know we finally had our fighters up there to help us subdue the enemy.

Dave was in the deputy lead right behind us. He had only been overseas for four months and only had ten missions to go. He'd been busy and lucky.

It was hard for me to understand why the Japanese government didn't throw in the sponge. The useless killing of their civilians was going on at an accelerated pace, war lords!

We passed Iwo Jima far below and were on the last leg to our target. The weather kept improving as we went north. It was a good sign, there was no excuse for our fighters not to make the rendezvous this time.

We arrived at the rendezous point on schedule and started our large circling flight allowing our formation to form up as we turned. The newly arriving aircraft could cut in across the imaginary circle and pull into formation without us slowing down. The circling continued for twenty minutes allowing all our flock to gather behind, now it was time to do our thing. The air was full of B-29's heading for different rendezvous locations and at times they were hard to locate or separate. I was sure we'd end up with planes of another organization, but no matter, all they had to do was get in the rear of the formation and bomb on our drop. We turned slowly for the last time and we were on the heading for the IP 30 miles away. The formation tightened for mutual protection as we neared the IP, still no P-47's. I was sure it was another plan which didn't get coordinated.

"Boggies at three o'clock level," called the CFC from his vantage point. "There's another off our right wing just out of range."

Where the hell were the damn P-47's? I was sure everyone aboard was asking the same question. The first pass by the three attacking enemy fighters did no appreciable harm and it was their last pass. The Jap plane who was off our right wing kept pace. We were sure he was flying at our speed and altitude to inform the ground defense of the necessary information to make their antiaircraft fire more accurate.

High above us came the "Jugs" screaming down at near mach one. Their fifties were blazing as they dove on the enemy planes. It was curtains for the three enemy fighters who never saw what hit them. The fourth plane peeled off and headed for the deck in an attempt to escape the deadly fire, but he didn't make it either.

We continued down track and were not bothered by another Jap plane, the P-47's had vacuumed them up and left nothing to molest us from the air. We still had to contend with the intense flak which came up in increasing regularity, but somehow after seeing the P-47's do their stuff our spirits were rejuvenated. We had to maintain our vigilance, it was easy to get faked out, it had happened before with deadly results, we weren't going to be easy meat for the butcher.

Our tailgunner was detailed to keep us informed on the rest of the formation. He happily reported all planes were close enough to count eyeballs. We had reached the IP. I had the formation on course and at the right speed and altitude. Now it was up to Rich. He took over the control of the big plane by use of the bomb sight. He picked up our target rapidly and was killing the drift and ground speed. He guided the plane with small corrections to keep the cross hairs on the target and now we were set up for the drop. The words all the crew waited to hear rang out, "bombs away." At that moment the control of the plane went back to the aircraft commander. "Door's coming closed, your airplane," was heard as Rich sat up from his hunched position over the bomb sight.

I navigated the formation right over the rendezvous point we had used earlier and headed out to sea between the main islands of Honshu and Shikoku. The flak continued until we were well out to sea. We had taken no hits and hope ran high that the others had escaped as easily.

We had just completed our turn and then we felt a strong buffeting not unlike clear air turbulence. "That's the damndest thing I've ever seen," said Rich from his vantage point in the nose.

"What the hell are you talking about?" asked Bart.

"It's a huge mushroom type cloud which is rising up through the cloud deck to a very high altitude. Take a look, it's on a bearing of 60 degrees," answered Rich.

"Christ almighty, I see it! Jim, what do you make of it?"

"I've never seen a weather cloud take that shape," he answered.

I unfastened my seat belt and took off my flak suit and went forward to see if I could determine what it was. "That has to be man-made," I said as I kneeled between the two pilots and viewed the rapidly rising mushroom cloud.

"Gunners don't take your eyes off the sky surrounding us, we can still get attacks," called Bart as a reminder. It was unnecessary, they hadn't relaxed their vigilance.

"Do you think the rough air had anything to do with the cloud?" asked Rich.

"Who the hell knows! I wouldn't rule it out. Maybe we can find out after we get back," said Bart.

Soon the mushroom cloud was forgotten as we took our sixty aircraft through the flak alley and out to sea. After we'd left land for thirty minutes we gave the order to loosen up the formation and headed for Iwo Jima.

Bart called for a damage report and was informed we had none. Reports from the formation indicated we'd come through the mission with only one plane unaccounted for and presumed lost.

We came directly over Iwo Jima and the aircraft who were either low on fuel or sustained serious damage were released to land, the rest continued south to Tinian.

It was usually our practice to turn on the HF radio and listen to news reports, some from as far away as the USA. The reports generally gave us an idea of how well we'd done on the mission. The radio stations usually got the news soon after a strike report was rendered and with some restrictions usually gave reports of targets hit and other information necessary to stimulate the interests of people back home. On this particular day the news carried something we did not expect to hear.

"On this date the 6th of August 1945, Tokyo time a lone B-29 dropped the world's first atomic bomb on the city of Hiroshima. Estimates of casualties and damage have not been released," cried the radio announcer as the static increased.

"Jesus, Christ, did you hear that?" asked Bart.

"I sure did. I've heard rumors about an atomic bomb, but I thought it was pure bullshit," I said.

"So, they dropped an atomic bomb. It must have come from that hush-hush outfit on north field at Tinian," said Bart.

"What pissed me off is the damn announcer said nothing of the other 600 B-29's up there busting their asses," added Jim.

After the debriefing and a couple shots of booze I felt strangely calm. We had just heard about the most devastating weapon known to man and had just returned from a mission which with the other five missions accounted for 4,811 tons of bombs being dropped on Japan. It was hard after all this time to realize the end of the war must be near. As we drank our booze we recalled the early days when all didn't go so well. Only two B-29's had been lost of 602 on this day. The average was great except for the crews who were not back on friendly territory.

I knew I could quit right now and go home, but something pulled at me. I felt the desire to stay until we had defeated the Imperial Japanese nation. I had to think about it alone.

Dave and his crew soon joined us in the large tent and we all lifted a fresh glass. "Dave you're really coming along fast with only ten missions to go. I'd make a bet you never get them all in."

"What the hell do you mean, Johnny?"

"This war is just about over, especially if they drop a couple more super bombs," I answered.

"It's all right with me. Then we can all go home," said Dave.

"What are your plans? Are you going to head back to Mississippi?"

"Why, hell no, I'm going to become a Californian, I hear it only takes a few weeks to be a native," he said with a drawl and a smile.

"Seems to me you were saying something about Australia," chimed in Bart.

"I think not. I've cooled off about going down under and getting tied up. I'm going home first and see what the future holds," I said seriously.

"Hell, maybe we can all get together and form a flying company," said Dave.

"Why do that when we can stay on active duty and get all the flying we want without paying for it," said Bart.

We discussed the subject until we were forced out of the tent by new arriving crews. Half drunk and too tired to care we walked down the coral street toward our quonset hut and not another word was spoken.

44.

The morning following completion of the magic number which meant I'd finished my combat missions was a clear hot day, you could see forever. In a rugged way Tinian was a beautiful place, undeveloped except for military roads and facilities. I lay in bed thinking of the future and wondered what was in store. I would probably be on my way home within days and my wartime flying would be ended. As I thought back on my military career it was hard for me to visualize myself as a civilian. I would have to wait and see what was in store for me after the war ended and then make my decision as to whether I was going to continue in the military or not.

I was ready to go out to the shower house to get cleaned up when I heard a vehicle pull up in front of our hut. A young sailor entered the door and quietly filled the ice box with beer and ice. I'd forgotten about the deal made with the SeeBee chief. I was glad to see it was still in operation.

My buddies heard the noise and one by one were all awake. "What are you up to, Johnny?" asked Bart as he hung his feet over the side of the bed and rubbed his thinning hair.

"I don't know! I slept like a log and I don't even have a hangover, must be because I feel so relaxed," I answered.

Bart, Jim, Rich and I took a refreshing cold salt water shower. "Ya know, we didn't even have salt water showers aboard the submarine, they made fresh water all the time and here we are on an island reported to have the sweetest water this side of hell and we can't even get a fresh water shower," I said with irritation.

"What the hell's the difference, we are practically on our way home," said Jim from the far end of the large open shower.

"You know, guys, this damn war is winding down. I have no idea how long the Japs can go without throwing in the towel, but my guess is it won't be long," said Bart.

"Those fanatic damn Japs have vowed to fight to the last man, so what makes you think they'll quit now?" asked Rich.

"It's one thing to fight for these damn islands but another thing when your country is being destroyed inch by inch," I added.

"What bothers me is the words, Unconditional Surrender," said Rich.

"Time will tell," said Jim.

"I see the ice box deal is still going on," I said.

"Yup, at least twice a day we get ice and beer, you made a good deal and we continued with it. When the old chief heard you were missing he was quite upset. I never figured out if he was unhappy because he thought your deal had fallen through or if he was sorry because he liked you," said Bart.

"We'll probably never know or give a damn," I said.

"Let's go get some chow and then wander over to ops and see what the hell is going on and what they have planned for us," said Bart. We dressed in our cut off pants and short sleeve shirts and felt comfortable, at least for the present.

After a breakfast of cold greasy bacon, powdered eggs and black coffee we headed to the operations building.

Colonel Bob Mitchell greeted us with a smile and said, "Well guys, it's all over for you unless you volunteer to stay on and get some more flying in."

"What's that supposed to mean, colonel?" asked Bart.

"You have already flown two or three over what you have to, I thought you might be back here to volunteer again."

"Do you need us?" asked Bart.

"Not exactly, but we are going to run short of lead crews in the next week. I'll figure something out, you don't have to worry," said Bob.

We glanced at each other for a moment and wondered what the hell was going on. "Do you know something we don't, colonel?" asked Bart.

"The word I got from group was that they were going to pour it on and see if the Nips break, especially after they dropped the atomic bomb. I heard a rumor to the effect the Japs put out some peace feelers, but I can't swear to it. We're going to have a couple balls out missions this week and we'll put everything we have up to try and help them with their decision."

Bob had to answer a phone and left us standing in front of the mission board. "Anyone want to fly one more?" asked Bart.

"I never thought I would see the day I got thirty-five in, and now I'm not sure I want to quit," I said.

"The last couple went so easily I was amazed. I don't care, I'd go one more if you guys want to," said Jim.

"Yeah, but look what's on the board," said Rich.

"Christ, the next mission is Yawata. Do you remember the first one? It was a piss cutter!" I said.

"They've had that mission up there on the board waiting for good weather to send it off and I think they have it," said Bart.

Colonel Mitchell hung up the phone and said, "It's on!"

"You mean we're finally going to hit Yawata again, Bob?" asked Bart.

"Briefing is set for 0600 in the morning. I've got to get my shit together and schedule the crews, see you later."

We four turned and headed back for our hut.

Briefing had ended and crew were hurrying for transportation to the flight line. The big mission was on and all we could do was watch. At times like this I felt left out of the war and useless. I wondered if this made me a "dog of war".

We sat waiting like all the crews in their planes the signal was given and the island seemed to shake as the engines of the B-29's belched to life. The noise brought out the Marines encamped near the end of the runways. It was their signal to take cover. More than one of the big planes had found it's final resting place on the hill near their tents. Soon motion was apparent as the lead ships made for the runup area followed by all the aircraft of each squadron of the four groups. Yawata would not be an easy target. It was hell before and figured to be as bad this time. There was one thing in our favor however, we knew the area better and were better prepared to protect each other as our formations crossed the target. On the first mission we had lost 14 B-29's and had 88 bomb the primary. On this mission we would have three wings with a total of 221 B-29's.

The same day the 58th, 73rd and the 313th Bomb Wings hit Yawata the 314th hit Tokyo with 60 B-29's. They lost 3 planes dropping 320 tons on their target. The fifth and newest B-29 wing, the 315th bombed Amagasaki the night of 9/10 August completing the devastation.

The strike reports came in as the Yawata mission was completed. 1,302 tons of high explosive bombs rained down on the primary and the losses were 4 planes, quite a difference from the first raid. Yawata was out of business.

Early the morning of 8 August saw the return of our planes from Yawata and the ground crews eagerly waited. It was up to them to get 100 B-29's ready for a late afternoon takeoff for yet another target. The target for tonight was a place called Fuku-yama. We would be after both the urban and industrial areas. It was tough on the 58th Bomb Wing we were the only wing called on to jump right back into the fray. All other wings would not be in action until the 10th or 11th. It proves the theory we knew from the start, the 58th was the first and the best, the cream always rises to the top.

Bart had gone to operations and found they desperately needed an experienced lead crew. He, without hesitation, volunteered our services, we had already agreed to fly if needed. Our group was to be the first over the target followed rapidly by the other three groups. I was happy that the mission was at night. The lead was much easier without having to fly in circles over a point waiting for stragglers. On the night missions you hit your IP and then crossed the target and got out as fast as possible. My primary concern was to stay right on course and send out signals for the others to follow.

I made my first visit to the personal equipment section and found it operating at high efficiency. I was greeted as a returning hero by all the fine men assigned there. I was sure it had operated without my help very well.

After all the briefings and other necessary things were accomplished it was time again to take to the air in our quest to defeat Japan before it was necessary to invade. The mission was another of those picture perfect ones. Everything seemed to go right from the beginning. We arrived over the target with 92 planes and 91 hit the primary. The flak as usual was heavy, but not as accurate. The fighter attacks lacked their normal tenacity.

After reurning to Tinian we discovered we had not lost a single B-29 and we had shot down 7 enemy fighters, not a bad nights work. The target received the full brunt with 556 tons of fire and high explosive bombs destroying the objective.

It was apparent that we had one of the finest combat crews in the 20th Air Force. Every member of our crew was a pro and their actions in a combat situation were flawless, it's no wonder the Japanese government was close to collapse. It would be a shame to disband such a fighting force as the XXI Bomber Command.

Things slowed down after the fast shuffle to put the Fukuyama raid together. In fact there were no mission assignments on the boards.

We learned that on this day, 9 August, the second A-Bomb was dropped on Nagasaki with devastating results. Still there was no word of surrender. It should be pointed out that Nagasaki was of little strategic importance and had been earlier bypassed as a target. Parts of the city had been hit only as targets of opportunity. Japan had sunk to its knees before either A-Bomb blasted the two cities, but we were sure the world would only remember the two single aircraft missions as defeating the once dreaded Empire of Japan.

News of the latest A-Bomb circulated around the area like a wild wind. Speculation ran high, but it was too early to celebrate, we were still at war and men were dying.

We relaxed that evening and decided to take in the outdoor movie. There was little chance we'd see a new film, but we liked to see the news. The other feature we enjoyed was the Marines displaying their skills with the 90mm antiaircraft batteries. As we sat on the hard seats we were treated to one of the best exhibitions of marksmanship I had ever experienced. Lucky for us these guys were on our side. They cut the cable of the towed target on the second burst and it floated to earth as we watched from our vantage point. The lights had picked up the target and the guns went into action. Within seconds the target was hit. What made you feel uneasy was the shaking as the batteries around us opened up, I felt like Tinian was about to fall off its pedestal and sink 8 miles down into the Marianas trench.

Soon after the guns fell silent the clouds came in and it started to rain, we were drenched to the bone. Getting soaked was nothing new, it was a way of life on the Pacific islands, a minor annoyance which we all took for granted.

The movie ended with a Donald Duck cartoon and the news reel, both were better than the feature. I looked forward to seeing the news with the Lowell Thomas narrative. He was, in my opinion, the best in the business and I always felt he told it like it was. He reported the news of how the B-29 command was systematically destroying the Japanese will to fight and the role of the 20th Air Force. He also reported how all the other services were involved and how as a team we were near victory. I enjoyed the propaganda, but felt the Japanese were not quite through. They were a tough lot and not easily talked into surrender.

As we returned to our hut we talked of the current events and what we felt.

"I think many things go into winning a war fought over the whole world. Some of the small things make the difference. The dropping of propaganda leaflets and the broadcasts on Saipan radio had helped, but spilled blood and guts is what wins and having a fighting machine like ours," I said.

"You have to give the Nips credit. They know it's a losing cause, but they go on as ordered. They have not faltered, they just keep coming at you like they think they can still win," said Jim.

"Remember, one thing was mighty apparent to all of us and the defenses last night proved it. They have lost the cream of the crop, they're fighting with kids in airplanes designed to sink ships instead of fighting in the air. Their industry is almost shut down and the submarines have denied them raw materials from their conquered empire. There is no way they can last much longer," said Bart seriously.

"Still, with the words 'unconditional surrender' we're making them lose face and that's something they don't take well," added Jim.

"I believe they knew they were beat at least a year ago, but they needed something to save face and now they have it, two A-Bombs," I said.

"There's another item that should not be over looked. Our intel people say the Japanese are not killing our POW's any more. It seems to indicate they now feel the end may near," said Bart.

"I sure hope so because if we have to invade it'll be a while before we can end it and the report of a 1,000,000 casualties has got to be avoided," I said.

"I think we have to go after them with our planes and destroy what will they have left to fight. We must convince the people in the 'Land of the Rising Sun' they've had it," said Jim as we arrived at our hut.

We had beer to drink and it was time to relax. Dave came over and couldn't believe we'd flown another combat mission. He thought we were crazy, but thanked us for bailing his crew out.

"You guys can leave anytime you want, what the hell are you doing flying combat? You must all be crazy," said Dave as he opened a beer.

"You know Johnny, the CeeBee chief felt so bad about you being missing he said we could skip a bottle on the payment, but we

398

told him not to worry we'd uphold your agreement," he added.

"Don't kid yourself, he'd sell his mother for a bottle of booze, but I must admit he was shaken when we told him you were lost out there on the briney," said Rich.

Sam came in a few minutes later and said, "I sure wish I could have been on this crew from the beginning, things would be different and I'd be going home with you."

"Don't worry Sam, when we go you will too if I have to smuggle you aboard," said Bart to the radar man.

"Let's hit the hay, we need to track down some of those nurses tomorrow and we'll need all our strength," said Bart as he pulled off his uniform and fell back on the bed. It had been a very eventful day.

45.

The days dragged on with little fresh news coming from the high command. Tension was mounting, the 20th Air Force had been sitting on the ground for five days. The Japanese government was vacillating and they needed a push to get them off high center. We were unaware of the power struggle going on in Nippon, but we were sure something was going to happen.

Then it happened! The entire XXI Bomber Command was ordered by 20th Air Force to deliver the coup de grace. A maximum effort involving all flyable B-29's was ordered to hit seven different targets on the same day. Over 775 B-29's would take part in what was to be the last bomb missions of World War II. Our wing would send over 160 aircraft after the Hikari Arsenal.

When the word was out that every resource available was to take part we knew we had to be in on it. After talking to the squadron operations officer we were selected as the lead crew for our squadron with Dave's crew as deputy lead. This mission would be the largest single day effort made by the B-29 command and it also marked the largest single mission the 58th Bomb Wing participated in.

The latest news indicated the Russians had declared war on Japan which made little difference to those of us who flew the combat missions. They could have done it much earlier and it may have made a difference, but the Russians were not thinking of a unified effort to defeat Japan, rather they wanted a piece of the action without spending the man power and money, nothing had changed.

The afternoon of 13 August was scheduled for a general briefing for the mission to be flown the next day. Maintenance personnel were working around the clock to squeeze out every resource available, this mission was going to be a show to remember. A great deal of extra effort was being expended by the flight crews as well. I had every navigator and radar man at a special briefing for the 678th squadron which proved to be very beneficial.

We were told every fighter available would be flying over Japan as well as other bombers. The Navy had moved into Japanese waters and would be launching all their aircraft against the smaller targets, as well. I hoped we wouldn't have a conflict over airspace. I had the feeling the Allies knew the war was near its end and they were going to push the Japanese into surrender with one more devastating blow.

After the navigation briefing Dave and I walked back to the quonset hut. As we strolled we talked of personal feelings.

"Dave, having you here with me has been one of the best things that's happened, but it's been a worry to me as well. I think of you as my brother and don't want anything to happen to you. Be careful tomorrow and stick close, okay?"

"Sure, Johnny, I know the feeling, I have it too," answered Dave.

Nothing more had to be said, we understood each other, a bond had been established upon our first meeting which would last as long as we both lived.

"When I lead a mission and see all the enemy fighters and flak I worry more about the formation behind me than I do for myself, it's a heavy responsibility," I said.

"I know what you mean. On my first lead I felt the same way. I guess it comes with the territory," said Dave.

"The best feeling after hitting a target is when your tail gunner reports they all made it. The bad feeling comes when you know you lost someone," I added.

"Let's forget about it for now, we have a little time to relax. Tomorrow will be a big day."

When we arrived at the hut we found the other eight officers waiting for us as they readied themselves for bed. 0300 would come all too soon.

It seemed as though I had just shut my eyes when the CQ woke us for final briefing. We all staggered to the latrine and tried to wake up as we walked, we looked like zombies. We headed for the mess hall to have an early meal. Activity was apparent everywhere, no one slept. The cool ocean breeze helped to get our heads clear as the scent of bacon filtered through the air. I was hungry.

We finished the briefing and headed for our transport. One thing stuck in my mind. "Monitor emergency frequency in case there is a recall." This meant our people expect the capitulaton of Japan at any moment. If this was the case thousands of tons of destruction would not be dropped on Japan, but in the open sea.

I walked toward Dave's truck and we shook hands. "I'll see you upstairs," I said as I turned to climb on the rear of the 6X6.

"Good enough, ya'all take care, ya hear!" he drawled as our trucks pulled away from their parking places.

We arrived at the plane and the pre-flight was accomplished. We were ready to pull the props through. Two lines were formed and we grabbed the long blades and pulled each prop through 20 blades. The trick was keeping it going, it was a struggle.

"Let's saddle up and get this show on the road," called Bart as he headed for the forward ladder to the flight deck. We headed for our entry doors and soon we were aboard and waiting for the signal to start engines. It was now 0600 hours and the sky was showing its beautiful colorful rays in the east.

The signal was received and 160 engines started simultaneously with black puffs of smoke trailing toward the tail. Within minutes we took the coral taxi strip and headed for the active runway followed by all the squadron. The 444th was the first to taxi and takeoff. There were B-29's with engines running everywhere, it was a sight to behold, I was thrilled to be a part of it.

Within minutes we were on the end of the runway, I could see Dave's plane on Baker runway also poised for takeoff. We got the order and our silver monster slowly picked up speed as we traveled down the concrete toward the end two miles away. We were at gross weight and had a full load of bombs weighing 20,000 lbs.

Bart held the plane on the runway as long as he could, the plane had reached flying speed and wanted to fly, but he fought it until the last minute and then pulled back the yoke and we were airborne. After leaving the runway we were over the ocean within seconds and turning toward the initial heading. If I thought the airfield we just left was busy it was nothing compared to the swarms of planes coming from all directions. In actual fact each was on a very definite heading and only turned as the stop watches reached the prearranged time and place. It was a tribute to the skill of our planners as well as the aircrews to be able to have this many planes airborne so close without collision.

We climbed steadily until we reached our cruising altitude of 10,000 feet. As soon as we reached our level off the radar was turned and it was as sharp as I had ever seen, Sam was a wizard.

After I was sure all our aircraft had become airborne I sent out the first radio signal for direction finding. Each plane behind knew exactly where I was and could keep close behind. Sam crawled down the tunnel and asked if he could assist. This was a real treat. It was quite a departure from how Roundy lazily volunteered nothing.

"Thanks Sam, come on down and we can talk. Everything is up to snuff, at least for thirty minutes or so, then I'll take a fix to be sure all is okay."

As long as the radar was operating there was no need for him to return to the rear. I was happy to have some company and if he felt like shooting the sun for me he could. Sam proved to be quite proficient as a navigator and he enjoyed getting involved. I took loran fixes as he shot the sun and his shot proved to be perfect.

"Navigator to pilot, over."

"Go, nav."

"Roger, we are right on time. Come right three degrees to 354."

"Right, 354 set."

Silence fell within the plane as the hum of the engines brought us closer to Japan. "When you give Bart a heading you can bet your bottom dollar he'll stay there until you tell him different. He's the best pilot in the group, possibly the wing," I explained.

"I've never heard anyone say that about their pilot," said Sam in amazement.

Time was passing rapidly without any indications of trouble. We soon found ourselves passing over Iwo Jima on the second leg of our mission. The target lay ahead about three and a half hours.

"That island doesn't look like much but it sure has saved many B29's and their crews," I said knowing he knew the statistics as well as I.

"Yeah, we sure paid for it in blood, though," he said.

"True, but still, without it we would not be as close to the end of this war as we are."

I gave Bart the new heading to bring us to our target and soon silence fell over the plane once more. Then pandemonium struck, as a group of P-51's closed around our plane. The plan worked, they were actually going with us to the target area. Their mission was to clear the skies of enemy aircraft and then hit small targets in the general area then join up with us to be navigated back to Iwo Jima. It should give all those on the ground a good look at hundreds of planes ready to deliver death and destruction.

"Navigator to pilot, over."

"Go ahead nav."

"Roger, we have thirty minutes to rendezvous pilot. Correct your heading to 350, over."

"Roger, 350 set. Jim, make sure everyone is up and ready, would you?"

"Sure thing. Let's have a check in starting with the radio operator."

Each crew position checked in and all was in readiness as the tail gunner re-entered the tail section.

The P-51's crowded in so close we could actually see the color of the pilot's eyes. I for one was delighted to have them with us. They were itching for combat and I was glad they were on our side.

We reached the predetermined point and started our circling to the left. Soon planes were joining in. We should have approximately forty planes in our group formation, it was difficult to count all of them. We spent twenty minutes to be sure all the late comers were with us and then we headed for the target closely followed by each of the other three groups of the 58th. I had forgot about the recall order, it was too late now, we were at the IP and turning for the target. Enemy fighters were otherwise engaged with our fighters and we saw few attacks. The flak was coming up but seemed to be less accurate than usual as we employed countermeasures.

Rich was in control of our plane as we neared the release point. The tail gunner reported at least thirty-six planes in formation. I could see them squeezed in a tight formation as we released our bombs. In the distance as we turned the formation we could see P-51's working over some Japanese fighters and the contest was one-sided. The black puffs of smoke continued to fill the immediate airspace around the group. I was sure someone was getting hit back there, but without the radar countermeasures it could have been much worse. During the crossing of the target Sam had gone back to the camera hatch to dispense the "window" through the opening. Strings of foil which played havoc with the enemy's radar controlled guns floated down. In addition some planes carried an extra crew member whose sole job was to jam frequencies of the enemy radars.

The mission was a complete success for our group. No reports of planes going down was a good sign. We prayed the other three groups fared as well. This was no time to become a statistic. We could see the other groups hitting the target as we headed toward the sea to the south. The earth below ceased to look like regular Japanese landscape. All you could see were explosions and fire with dense smoke rising. The poor son-of-a-bitch's down there were defenseless against this onslaught.

One by one the four groups of the 58th Bomb Wing left the target area and headed for Iwo Jima. Soon the P-51's rejoined us and the sky was full of silver planes gleaming in the mid-day sun.

"Those poor bastards in the '51's are probably stiff as boards cooped up in those cramped cockpits," said Bart as I sat next to him in Jim's vacated seat.

"It must be a ball to fly one," I said.

"Yeah, I'd give my left ball to fly one," answered Bart with his usual grin.

"I know you better, when this thing's over maybe you'll get a crack at fighters. Remember one thing, I won't be there to pull your chestnuts out of the fire," I said and we both had a hearty laugh.

"Johnny, we have a damn good crew now and being AC of it makes not being in fighters easier," confessed Bart.

"We've come a long way since we first met at Great Bend. It still seems like yesterday," I reminisced.

"Yeah, we fought the battle of Kansas, then India and China only to end up here waiting for the word to be passed out that they no longer need us. You have to admit, war is hell, but we had fun fighting it, didn't we?" said Bart as he looked out the window at some distant unknown spot.

"It's true. War brings people together. It makes the little discomforts diminish. These days will last in my memory for the rest of my life," I said with a sigh.

"What's our ETA for Iwo?" he asked.

"About forty-five minutes. We have plenty of fuel so there is no reason to stop, is there?"

"No, let's get back and see what the hell is happening in the war."

We finally reached Iwo and of our forty-two planes four had to make landings for maintenance and or fuel; the rest of us motored on toward home.

The P-51's pulled ahead of us wagged their wings and peeled

off toward the island far below. We really had a one-two punch over the target, air power had come alive in full bloom.

After landing at Tinian's west field we taxied back with the thought we'd done a good job up there today. Now, it was up to the politicians to determine if we were through fighting or whether we'd continue.

As we climbed to the ground Jim said something I had forgotten about. "This plane sure did do well, almost as well as *Lucky Lady* and *Here's Hopin'*. It's a damn shame *Here's Hopin'* is on the bottom of the sea."

I wondered why I felt so sad. An airplane in war becomes part of you and when it's injured it hurts, but when it is lost it's much worse. Her final resting place was deep in Davy Jones' locker guarded by one of its warriors.

We'd flown the newest plane in the squadron that day and we brought it back without a scratch. It would seem odd to see only one bomb painted on its side indicating the only combat mission it would fly.

We were transported to the debriefing area and sipped beer as we rode. The new crew chief had it chilled before we'd landed, nice touch. The truck stopped and we walked in single file to make our report. Uppermost in our minds was whether word had been received on the surrender. We were informed none had been received, as yet. An ultimatum had been delivered to the Japanese high command promising total destruction if they did not come to terms immediately. We had the power and they knew it was no bluff.

There was excitement in the air as we entered the tent to get our mission booze. As usual our hosts were well oiled and ready for more. We toasted everything and anything and were just about to leave the tent when Dave and his crew entered. Now I knew I'd need help to get back to our quarters, but who the hell cared! We needed to get back and put our heads on our pillows. All the adrenalin had drained from our glands and I felt like a limp doll. Only rest would make life return to our abused bodies.

We all dropped on our sacks half clothed. I had got my boots off before I fell back in a stupor. We had only been asleep for an hour when the world exploded.

The Japanese had surrendered unconditionally and the shooting war was over. We had survived the Air Offensive of Japan. We'd brought Japan to her knees and it had not been easy. The

Nips had been an adversary equal to the task of savage fighting, but the American way had prevailed, production and know how had done the trick. We had learned to fight against a enemy well versed in the use of arms and we beat him on his own terms. God must have been on our side.

The radio as expected broadcasted the news to the world, which included Tinian. Too much was being said about the two A-Bombs and how they ended the war. Let it never be forgotten, the A-Bombs merely gave the enemy an easy way out; we beat them and beat them good with blood, guts and determination.

The seven missions flown on 14 August had been a smashing success and the numbers proved the point. 754 B-29's had bombed Japan dropping over 4,687 tons of explosives and the best news was we hadn't lost an airplane. In fact, the last B-29 lost to combat during World War II was lost on 8 August by the 314th Bomb Wing. This meant no B-29's had been lost on the last eleven missions.

46.

The day broke like any other day on the island of Tinian with one major exception; the great war had ended. Peace had been declared on this date, 15 August 1945. It was hard to believe it was over. We'd been molded into a super fighting machine and now there was no one to fight. What lay ahead?

The celebration had started and it was bedlam. People were shooting weapons in the air, horns were blowing, everyone was partying. My personal feelings were hard to describe. I wanted to go home, but I didn't want to leave my friends, we'd formed a close bond. Combat brings men close to each other, living the same terror as well as enjoying the comradery. Families couldn't be closer.

We'd done a number on the Japanese Empire and now it was time to try and forget, it wouldn't be easy.

In a five month period, referred to as the "Air Offensive of Japan" the B-29's had practically eliminated all major cities as well as the smaller cities of strategic value. The war industry was smashed beyond expectations. Hundreds of missions had been flown and a quarter of a million tons of bombs had rained down on the enemy.

The 20th Air Force was fast to move to another more peaceful pursuit. POW relief missions were planned and scheduled. Some of the B-29's were painted on the underside of the wing in large block letters, PRISONER OF WAR SUPPLIES. Twenty such missions were flown to alleviate the suffering of the Allied prisoners of war held in Japan.

We immediately volunteered to fly the first mission from our squadron. We were the oldest crew and deserved to see Japan without getting shot at. Permission was granted. Planning commenced immediately. The POW camps were so well camouflaged they'd be difficult to locate. Intelligence reports indicated the prisoners had taken over most of the camps as the guards deserted their posts. The disturbing news was the POW's were dying every day due to a lack of medical supplies, food, and warm clothing.

The first mission was scheduled to depart the following morning. Tons of food, clothing, blankets, medical supplies as well as other necessities were being loaded. We were scheduled to reach a POW camp in the northern Japanese island of Hakiado. The whole crew looked forward to the mission of mercy. We'd be able to do a little sightseeing as well!

The following morning we took the active runway fully loaded with the precious supplies. Our plane lifted from the runway with ease. We knew we might have to spend considerable time locating the POW camp so we wasted no time. We had to arrive during daylight.

We climbed to altitude, the day was clear and bright. The attitude of the crew expressed the relaxed feeling. The pressure was off and this type mission seemed in keeping with our attitude about war. We had spent our entire adult lives as warriors, we knew little else.

We zipped past Iwo Jima and took a direct heading for our destination, there was no need for subterfuge, we weren't trying to fool the enemy as to our destination.

After three hours we could see the mountains of Honshu lying ahead. The mountains were green and the ugly, gutted, smoldering cities couldn't be seen from this distance. Japan was a beautiful country, it was a shame we were forced to destroy so much of it. We flew east of Tokyo as we headed to the northeast. Tokyo was a gigantic city at the foot of Mt. Fugiyama. The peak sparkled in the morning sunlight with its crown of snow. It was the first time we'd seen cultivation on the sides of the hills; every inch of land was used in some way.

We finally arrived in the vicinity of the POW camp; it was well camouflaged. We dropped down to a low altitude to search. After an hour of milling around we finally spotted three men on the crest of a small hill, one was waving a white flag or sheet. We'd found the camp. We turned slowly a click above the stall as flaps were lowered and a practice run was made. We had found a small field ideal for our purpose and came low over the field and dropped our precious cargo. After the drop we loitered over the area and could see the live skeletons rushing to the packages. I was sick inside knowing these emaciated men were once well-fed and healthy. I made a silent prayer for their safety and future well

409

being. They'd soon be rescued after we reported the location of their camp. The three men on the mound continued to wave their banner as we circled. Hundreds of prisoners below all looked up and waved their feeble arms. God bless them.

After circling to be sure no civilian activity interfered with the bonanza below we departed the area. We hated to leave them, but there was no way for us to land and help.

We flew directly over some of the large metropolitan areas. They looked worse than I'd remembered. Huge sections of Tokyo and Yokohama were laid to waste, it was not a pretty sight.

After leaving Japan the return trip to Tinian was uneventful and anticlimatic. We had expended our emotions over the POW camp.

On Tinian things were hectic as rumors ran rampant. The rumors had us going back to the states as a unit and touring the United States. These were followed by other and even more ridiculous rumors. There was one real fact, V-J Day had been established as 2 September 1945 and we'd fly a huge formation over the USS Missouri where the surrender was to be signed. The 20th Air Force was making preparations to fly all the B-29's under its command as a show of strength.

We immediately started flying practice missions in huge formations flying over ten established points as we would over Japan. The formations would fly at a low altitude to show the Japanese people what brought them defeat. We were selected to lead the 444th Bomb Group which was to lead the 58th Bomb Wing and the 58th was selected to be the first of five wings to fly over the *Missouri*. Timing was important, we had to be over the Battleship just as they signed the document. It was going to be a day to remember. We felt honored to be selected for such an event. Sadness crept into our preparation on the last day of practice. One of the planes from a sister group crashed on landing and all aboard perished, but as they say the show must go on.

This would be the last time we'd fly over Japan before heading home, I looked forward to the flight. The day finally arrived, 2 September 1945, V-J Day. The takeoff from all three islands in the Marianas was accomplished in an orderly manner and we headed north for mainland Japan.

Excitement ran high as we passed each planned point over Japan and turned for the next. Three hundred feet below runways were lined with hundreds of Japanese planes painted green and sporting their big red meat balls. The striking thing was each plane was without propellers, a condition of the surrender. I was sure they were in short supply in any case. We made our last turn for the *Missouri* and I could plainly see the decks lined with uniformed officials as well as white clad sailors hanging from every conceivable platform witnessing this historic event.

After flying over the *Missouri* we climbed and headed for home. We passed over Iwo Jima for the last time and knew what a blessing the island had been for the B-29's. The Marianas came into view as we strung out for landing. Once on the ground we all felt the letdown of the mission.

After our show of strength mission our crew was offered immediate transportation home. The transportation provided was to be ships. We'd be taken to Saipan and then board a troopship. After deliberating for all of thirty seconds we turned down the offer. Some didn't like the idea of a long ocean voyage, but for most it was the slowness of ocean travel that turned us off. A number of other high point men did leave for Saipan and last word was they were still waiting for a ship after a week or more. We were glad we waited to see what the final verdict would be. The airplanes had to go back and we were willing to sweat it out.

Delays were a way of life at our squadron, it seemed so different! When the war was raging there wasn't time for knitpicking inspections and parades. Most of us expressed disdain at this overseas peacetime Army. Our crew spoke only of getting off this rock and heading home.

The brass came up with one grandiose plan after another until they went back to square one. It made one wonder how we'd won the war! They finally decided on a plan which didn't fall through the cracks. It was a simple plan of transporting high point crews and passengers. The criterion for points was derived from a formula of months overseas, missions flown, and decorations. We topped the list and Dave and his bunch were close behind. I was ready, willing, and able, the sooner the better.

We waited impatiently for the final word. In the interim we didn't do much of anything and certainly no parades or inspections did we participate in!

"I'll be damed if I'm going to be a soldier boy, I'm going to sit on my ass until those dumb shits make up their feeble minds and tell us to take off," said Bart as he lay on his bunk.

I was flaked out in the bunk next to him with the other three officers in the line of beds beyond. "I hear it's all settled and we'll leave in a couple days," I said, sleepily.

"Why the hell don't we forget all about this bullshit, get up eat and then go down to the beach to get away from this funny farm!" said Rich.

He was right. We were all tight as a drum; we needed to get out and enjoy our final days on Tinian. After cleaning up we headed for chow and then returned and cranked up all our jeeps and sped toward the beach as if we didn't have a care in the world.

At the beach we lay in the sun after a refreshing dip and shot rats.

"Maybe we should go down on the flight line after we leave here and check out the bird, you never know, those ding-a-lings could pull the pin in hours and we sure don't want to break down on the way home," said Bart.

"As a matter of fact that's a good idea. I'd like to go by personal equipment and see the guys before we leave. I hear the dumb bastard who took over for me tried to change things the ole sarge almost ate him alive. I sure would've liked to have seen that!" I said.

The following day word came down, we would be pulling the plug the next day. There was pandemonium in the squadron area when word was received, we were actually going home, it seemed incredible after dreaming of it for so long.

The schedules and manifests were posted and the staggered departures would delay some of the crews for a day or two, but we were on the list to leave with the first of our bomb group.

The route of flight established was Kwajalien, Hawaii, and finally Castle AAF, Merced, California. We could land but we wouldn't be able to take off until they lengthened the runways to accommodate B-29's.

Our load of passengers lined up in front of the plane as the crew made its last walk-around and systems checks. The plane was ready and so were we!

We took off on time and the flight was as routine as they come. The weather was beautiful that morning in late September, 1945. Our plane was so crowded people seemed to be hanging from the top of the cabin. In the rear we were informed that people were stacked like cordwood, I was sure that was a bit of an exaggeration, but that it was crowded no one could deny. We allowed the passengers to come forward for short periods of time to see what it was like, it was too hard to get the work done stumbling over curious bodies.

We flew at 10,000 feet over the blue Pacific as we headed toward Kwajalien in the Marshall Island group to the southwest. The towering clouds climbed to great heights as we flew closer to the equator.

We had a total of twenty people aboard and you could feel the excitement as we traveled closer to our first stopover. Some slept others played cards and still others read books, but all were on pins and needles.

"Bart, this plane reminds me of a cattle car," I said trying to break the monotony.

"You ought to be back here," interjected Sam from the radar station.

"Say Sam, since you're awake, we're about two hours out and I'd like the radar to be tuned up about 100 miles out. I'll give you a call when I need it, okay?"

"Sure thing Johnny, I'm ready when you are!"

"I hear the celebration is going on all over the country. I wonder if they will still be celebrating by the time we get back or do you think they'll have forgotten we were at war?" said Jim.

"Who cares, we'll have our own celebration when we get our feet on mainland USA," answered Bart.

"Right now I'm looking forward to a swim at Kwajalien. I hear the water is great," said Rich.

"Yeah, I hear the sharks are thick as flies!" I said.

We were twenty minutes ahead of Dave's plane and approximately the same distance behind the ship in front of us, we flew a strict cruise-control to keep spacing. We spoke to them on a couple occasions since radio silence was no longer being observed. The crowded situation was the same on their plane.

At a hundred miles out without me calling Sam my radar scope came alive with small returns dotting the scope. The coral formed the atoll and the atolls spread approximately seventy-five miles from one end of the Marshalls to the other. Our radio helped to identify Kwajalien as well as the radar. The radar picture showed a large lagoon as part of Kwajalien, that was what Rich was referring to as the swimming beach.

We made our landing on the small island that had so much American blood soaked into it. It was an unattractive place with only one tree standing and it was only half there. Guards protected

413

it. Tinian by comparison was a place of beauty. The highest point on the island was seven feet above sea level. When you stood on the ground and looked toward the sea you had the feeling the sea was above you.

We unloaded our passengers and transportation whisked them off to different quarters than the aircrew. However, a major from wing headquarters who was on our plane decided he wanted to stay with the crew and raised hell with everyone about it. Why he wanted to stay in those tar paper shacks laughingly called officers quarters escaped me. He ordered people about until Bart stopped him in his tracks. The major promised retribution and Bart merely laughed as he informed the major that if he didn't understand the command structure while on a plane he should read up on it. The aircraft commander is the same as a captain of ship, his word is law. "Major, with all due respect, you are rocking the boat and I'd suggest you low key your demands and do as they request, otherwise I'll have to take other action."

The major's attitude changed drastically for the remainder of the trip, you could tell he thought all flyers were horses asses and ground pounders had to put up with them because they had to fly on their airplanes, our opinion differed greatly.

After chow we took a cold shower and after a few drinks hit the hay. The following day we were informed there would be at least an extra day's delay due to the heavy aircraft traffic transiting all the Pacific airlanes.

We decided to roll with the punch and headed for the lagoon for a swim. The heat was appalling, there was no breeze as yet, it seemed to take your breath away.

The water was warm and clear. The beach was crawling with humanity in and out of the water. About a half mile out in the lagoon was a half sunk Jap landing craft. Dave and I decided to swim out to it and look it over. We swam away from the throngs of people and in a short time made it to the landing craft. We climbed aboard and stayed for a few minutes before we started back to the beach. We both dove in and could see the coral formations below with the many colorful fish. When we were about half-way back when we heard people shouting and waving their arms, apparently at us! We couldn't understand them at first, then I heard someone yell, SHARKS! That got our attention and both of us could have qualified for the US Olympic team as we headed for shore. Cheers went up as we climbed out of the water to the safety of the sand. We both turned and for the first time saw the telltale dorsal fin circling not far from where we were standing, it was a close call! We'd had enough swimming on the atoll of Kwajalien, showers would have to do.

The following day we took off for Hawaii, our next stop. The long flight would be the next to last leg on our way home. The weather was smooth and clear, you could see forever as we flew to the northeast.

The flight was going in a routine manner. Ten hours wasn't a long flight, most we flew were much longer, but this one seemed to drag.

I looked forward with anticipation at seeing Hawaii, I had heard so much about the place. I had one important thing I had to do and that was to call Kim in Australia. I'd written her a couple times since I returned from my tour on the submarine, but I hadn't heard from her. I had to break off the relationship and let her get on with her life. I knew I wouldn't be getting back to Sydney in the forseeable future and it wasn't fair to string her along. I thought I should call my folks as well, but decided on surprising them.

We crossed the date line when we about half way to Johnston Island. We would land the day before we took off, crazy! We could have increased our speed, but if we got there too early our butts would be in a sling so we flew at the programed speed.

As we reached Johnston Island we only had a few hours to go. I hoped we would be there for a couple days. We wanted to see some of the sights and take in a hula dance.

Our radar finally picked up the Hawaiian Islands dead ahead. The crew as well as the passengers acted very anxious to get on the ground. I could taste the Mai-tai's from here!

When the island of Oahu came into view it reminded me of a diamond set in a sea of emeralds. It was beautiful and uncluttered.

We landed at Hickam and were parked in a long row of returning B-29's. As we parked and shut down the engines we could see Dave's plane just touching down. I knew we were going to have a good time here.

Our stay in Hawaii only lasted two days but we had wasted little time with such mundane things as sleeping. We had the opportunity to visit all the main visitor attractions including Pearl Harbor. It made me feel so insignificant as I gazed at the remains of the USS *Arizona* as it laid on the bottom of Pearl

Harbor with some of its mast showing. Oil seeped from its bowels and over 1100 men had found their final resting place down there. I felt a lot better about what we'd done to Japan after the visit.

"Seeing this place makes a guy mad all over," said Jim breaking the silence.

"It must have been like a turkey shoot. Pearl Harbor is a great harbor, but our ships were trapped allowing the enemy to have a field day."

The Royal Hawaiian was our setting for dinner on our last night in Hawaii. It was a beautiful balmy night and the food and music made you dream of better days. I loved the hula dancers, it made a lasting impression on us, it would remain our image of Hawaii.

The next day before reporting for briefing I finally got my call through to Kim. The vision of her lovely body came across the line like classical music, but I knew and so did she it was all over. We would have our memories of the days we spent together and that would be it. It was best for her and me.

We reported for briefing that evening and were informed our take off would be at 2200 hours. We were scheduled to fly at 17,500 feet and expected to arrive at Castle AAF just after daylight. We would be the first flight of the evening, others would follow at 500 foot intervals and 20 minute spacing.

We reported to our aircraft to load bags and make our final inspections before the passengers were delivered.

We taxied out on time and without difficulty were airborne. The long flight would be our last leg before reaching the states. We reached our cruising altitude and before long the only people awake up front were Walt and I, some things never change!

Three US Coast Guard cutters were spaced evenly at intervals from Hawaii to California they were a great help in navigating, receiving information on weather and lifesaving if necessary. We passed over the first of the ships and I contacted them and gave them our position report and they gave me weather and sea conditions. I found myself thirty minutes ahead of flight plan as we passed them, but we were flying the prescribed cruise control so I gave it little thought. I figured we would probably get a wind shift during the next few hours and it would average out. By the time I reached the mid-point and the second ship I was well over an hour ahead of flight plan. I knew if we continued without encountering a slowing trend we would arrive at Castle well before daylight. I rechecked all my work and was sure I was accurate and we had adhered to all the prerequisites of the flight plan. I wasn't about to slow the airplane down. I noticed Bart stirring and gave him a call. "Bart if you're coming back this way I'd like to show you something!"

"Be right there. I need a cup of coffee, anyway."

"Take a look at this!" I pointed to the chart spread out on my desk.

"It looks like we're making good time!"

"It sure as hell does! What do you want me to do?"

"Nothing. They gave us a constant speed to hold and we are doing just that, right?"

"We sure are." Then I showed him my log and flight plan.

"So we get there early. I know how to land at night!"

"Okay you're the boss, but we'll probably get our tit in a ringer."

"Screw them. They told us how to do it and that's what we're doing. Anyway we couldn't slow down or the rest of the stream would be running up our asses!"

"True. Let's let her all hang out!"

"Good enough; how about a cup of coffee?"

"Sure thing, if you're buying!"

He brought the two cups of coffee in the paper cups and he sat down next to my desk on the step to the flight deck. "Johnny, it's been a long pull and we have done and seen a lot of things; now we're just about home. Have you given any thought as to what you are planning to do?"

"Well, I thought I'd take the forty-five day overseas leave and make my decision during that time. If I sign over I'm going to put in for pilot training as soon as possible."

"That sounds great. As for me you've always known I was going to be a regular. I can't think of anything I'd rather do."

"How about flying for the airlines?"

"Naw, I think I would rather fly these things and maybe later on get into fighters. Jim hasn't decided either, but Rich is getting out and going back to Cal to finish his degree."

"Good idea, he's a smart guy."

"Let's plan for Jim, Walt, Rich and you and I to get together during our leave and talk over the future, okay?"

"Sounds great to me. I don't know how I'm going to take being away from you guys for a month and a half."

We talked of nothing important for a few more minutes and

417

then I had to get ready to shoot the stars. I wanted to confirm my position and ground speed. After completing my computations I found that we had gained more time and my findings were confirmed as we reached the third cutter. We would be arriving in a couple hours. I was sure when they got our ETA they would be surprised.

Time passed quickly and we were approaching the west coast. It was confirmed as the radar came on and the California coast was there to see in the darkness ahead. We were almost home.

We crossed the coast and called Castle tower. The tower operator was surprised as he received the call.

"164 you are cleared to left traffic landing runway one-two. The wind is 240 at ten knots, over."

"Roger tower, see ya on the ground."

"Be advised 164 there is construction equipment near the taxi ways," the tower operator added.

"Roger tower. We're turning final."

We made our landing in the darkness before dawn and were guided to the parking ramp by the "follow me" truck. We pulled in and shut down. Just as the props were winding down, a staff car raced up and came to a halt in front of the nose of our plane. Bart and Jim had descended the ladder and were waiting by the nose. I could see everything through the nose glass and hurried to gather my chart and log. I could see the two colonels red in the face and raising hell. I hurried down the ladder to the concrete below and stepped out of the nose wheel well. Bart and Jim were standing at attention and the wing commander was chewing them out. I approached just as Bart tried to explain. "Sir, we flew prescribed cruise control and just had a jet stream at our altitude. We couldn't slow down for fear of someone running up our tail. Lieutenant Lea has his chart and log for you to check."

As we stood there in front of the wing and group commanders I couldn't help but show a small smile, they were fast backing off and when the reporters arrived with the news that we had set a trans-pacific flight record they acted as if it had been their idea.

The reporters interviewed us and took a few pictures and then the wheels took over and made all the introductions. We were happy how it turned out.

Our transportation arrived and we were whisked off to the BOQ. I was bushed and needed a few hours shut-eye. We all hit the sack between real sheets, nice.

Just before noon we were up and feeling hungry. We were taken to the dining hall and told to order whatever we liked. Steaks seemed to be getting the biggest play. After we finished we headed for headquarters to find out about our leave and a way home. After arriving we were informed we would be shipped to Pittsburg, California to get transportation to the military base nearest our home. The next morning we were bussed to Camp Stoneman to get the train to Fort MacArthur.

A group of officers were walking past a fenced in area which we found to be the POW compound. Only German prisoners were kept there. Some of the POW's made some disparaging remarks and most of us felt like kicking their asses, but decided to ignore the arrogant bastards, discretion being the better part of valor. We also noticed the Italian POW's had the run of the camp and some were allowed off base. What a difference!

The following day we boarded our train for the south and bid good bye to all our friends heading in other directions wondering if we would ever see them again; it was sad after all we had been through together.

The train was packed with people but the ride was comfortable and scenic. We pulled into Fort MacArthur about eight hours later and were told we could leave whenever we liked. As for me right now was just fine. I found a phone and called a cab to pick me up at the base.

"Are you Lieutenant Lea?

"That's me!"

"Where to lieutenant?"

"Highland Park."

"Christ, that's a long way from here."

"So is India. Let's get going I'm anxious to get home."

"I understand, lieutenant, but it's a good fifty miles."

"Who gives a damn, let's hit it."

After a long ride the meter looked like the French war debt, but who cared! We pulled up in front of the place of my birth, it was just as I'd left it. I paid the cab driver and gave him a nice tip for his haste. He set my bags in front of me at the foot of the steps. There was something wrong, no lights! "Christ, wouldn't you know it! I sneak half way around the world to surprise my family and they aren't home!" I said aloud feeling sorry for myself. I climbed the steps, put my bags on the front porch, turned and sat on the top step, feeling neglected.

I felt like crying as I sat there looking down the street. After all this time, I come home to an empty house. After all I was a returning hero, somebody should've been here, I thought to myself. All at once the door flew open and the lights came on. The whole family led by my wonderful mother mobbed me. I was shocked and surprised.

"How did you know I was coming home?" I asked with a puzzled look on my face.

"Easy," explained my dad, "the radio station kept us informed as well as the *Los Angeles Times*. Your pictures have been all over it for a couple days."

"You're kidding!"

"They were all broadcasting your names and telling of your world record flight. It's big news locally because you had so many on your crew from Southern California."

I was utterly amazed at the way my family had me figured out. In addition to the family some of my old buddies who got home before me were there to greet me, too. I never could fool my mother, she could read me like a book. It was the 5th October 1945 and I was home.

* * *

"That's it guys from beginning to end. I hope I haven't bored you," I said to the group seated around me at the officers club.

"Colonel Lea, you'll have to write a book about your adventures, it's a great story. I for one really enjoyed it," said one of the young pilots.

"Maybe, someday after I retire I'll try to write about it; but for now I've better things to do, right Dave!"

"Let's go home, John, you rang me out with the memory of the big war."

"Good luck, sir. I hope we'll see you in the near future," said my friend Manny.

"You will, just look for me on the golf course."

The two old soldiers headed for the club door. Those who watched them depart knew the two had something special and knew an era had just ended.

GLOSSARY

A-1	Advanced base in China for the 40th Bomb Group.
A-3	Advanced base in China for the 444th Bomb Group.
A-5	Advanced based in China for the 462nd Bomb Group.
A-7	Advanced base in China for the 468th Bomb Group.
AAF	Army Air Force.
APQ-13	Aerial search radar set.
ASAP	As soon as possible.
Astrodome	Plexi-glass dome use for celestial navigation.
ATC	Army Transport Service.
Basha	Native hut.
Bloodchit	Guarantee to natives for return of airmen.
Boondocks	Countryside.
BOQ	Bachelor officer quarters.
CAVU	Clear and visibility unlimited.
CBI	China-Burma-India theater.
CeeBee	U.S. Naval Construction battalions. (CB's)
CFC	Central fire control.
CHT	Cylinder head temperature.
CP	Command post.
Cripple	Aircraft damaged in aerial combat.
Cumulo-Granite	Slang for mountains.
CW	Constant wave radio signal.
DF	Direction finder.
Dumbo	Air-Sea rescue aircraft.
Fire-fight	Aerial combat between aircraft.
Flimsies	Plastic insert in information folder
Frag	Fragmentation bombs.
GI	Government issue.

Glitch	Mistake or problem.
Gooks	Natives.
Gooney Bird	USAAF cargo and troop carrying aircraft.
GP's	General purpose bombs.
Hardstand	Individual aircraft parking spot.
HE's	High explosive bombs.
Honcho	Referring to individual in charge.
IFF	Instrument, used to determine friend or foe.
IG	Inspector General.
Interphone	Internal communication system aboard aircraft.
IP	Initial Point before target.
Jettison	To salvo load.
JCS	Joint Chiefs of Staff.
KIA	Killed in action.
Landfall	Location where aircraft crosses from sea to land.
Limey	Slang for British.
Loran	Long range navigation set which reads pulses.
Mayday	International radio signal, a distress call.
MIA	Missing in action.
MP	Military police.
Musette bag	Officers knapsack with shoulder strap.
NCOIC	Non-commissioned officer in charge.
Pathfinder	Aircraft which proceeds main force over target.
PBY	U.S. Navy patrol aircraft.
Pilotage	Aerial navigation by map reading.
Pre-comp	Computations made prior to celestial observation
PSL club	Permanent second lieutenants club.
RON	Remain overnight.
R & R	Rest and recovery.
Ruskies	Slang for Soviets.
Salvo	To drop all bombs at once.
Sextant	Instrument use in celestial navigation.
Shafted	Slang for being treated unfairly.
Shavetail	Second Lieutenant when used disparagingly.
SNAFU	Situation normal all fucked up (fouled up)
Sortie	One mission by a single plane.
Superfortress	USAAF B-29 bomber.

TDY	Temporary duty.
TU-4	Russian copy of the B-29.
USS	United States Ship.
Weenies	Slang for bases.
WILCO	Will comply.
Zee's	Slang for sleeping.

AUTHOR'S NOTE

The 58th Bomb Wing (Very Heavy), entered combat with the first operational B-29's. Originally scheduled to depart on 10 March 1944, however they were delayed because when the departure date arrived not a single B-29 had been delivered. It was 15 April 1944 before the wing was on its way to India. General Hap Arnold interceded and the big bombers rolled off the assembly lines.

The four groups of the wing were assigned separate bases in the Calcutta area of India. All the bases were sub-standard and of British origin. A fifth base had to be secured for the 444th due to the unsuitability of Charra.

Advanced bases were built in southern China across the Himalayas. The 58th was the only combat unit of the XX Bomber Command, 20th Air Force. The wing was compelled to fly both combat and resupply missions to the forward bases, under the worst flying conditions in the world.

With an untried new bomber the men of the 58th went to war. Forty-nine combat missions and hundreds of "Hump" missions were flown.

The combat missions were the longest ever attempted under demanding conditions. Not enough can be said for those pioneers who gave their lives as the bugs were worked out of the B-29.

During the period 5 June 1944 through 30 March 1945 the XX Bomber Command had compiled an impressive record. They had dropped over 9,800 tons of bombs and mines, had lost eighty-two B-29's and had shot down 154 enemy planes as well as 105 probables and 276 damaged. 2,228 sorties were flown to such far away targets as Japan, Manchuria, and southeast Asia. The entire burden had fallen to these units to keep the Japanese war-making capability in tow, as far as strategic bombing was concerned.

In April of 1945 the XX Bomber Command was deactivated and the 58th Bomb Wing(VH) was transferred to the XXI Bomber Command and departed to the island of Tinian. The 58th joined the 73rd., 313th., and the 314th Bomb Wings making up the XXI Bomber Command. In late June a fifth wing was assigned, its designation was the 315th Bomb Wing.

During the last nine months of World War II the 20th Air Force flew 331 combat missions (24,665 bombing sorties). Dropping 155,041 tons of bombs and mines. There were 318 B-29's lost. The enemy suffered 377 lost, 245 probables, and 417 badly damaged aircraft to the crews of the B-29's.

In addition to the combat sorties the following sorties were flown to Japan:

405 Weather Strike Sorties.

180 Weather Strike and Recon Sorties.

106 Weather Strike and Leaflet Sorties.

110 Sea Search Sorties.

153 Radar and Photo Recon Sorties.

73 Radar Scope Sorties.

9 Photo Recon Sorties.

In the course of the Weather and Leaflet sorties seven additional B-29's were lost.

The 3rd Photo Recon Squadron flew 427 Photo Recon Sorties and lost 6 B-29's.

31 Recon Sorties were flown by B-24's.

B-29's of the XX and XXI Bomber Commands of the 20th Air Force between 5 June 1944 and 15 August 1945 flew a combined 380 bombing missions (27,611 bomb sorties), dropped 167,448 tons of bombs and mines and lost 402 B-29's while shooting down 871 enemy aircraft as well as 565 probables, and damaging 1,090.

The greatest accomplishments of the Twentieth Air Force occurred during the last five months of the war. This period was referred to as the Fire Blitz or the Air Offensive of Japan.

Five major industrial areas suffered 44.1 percent of all the 20th Air Force tonnage. The industrial centers of Tokyo, Osaka, Nagoya, Yokohama, and Kobe were these major industrial centers. The damage to these areas ranged from 25 percent in Osaka to 43 percent in Nagoya. The aircraft industry within those areas was 50 percent destroyed. The industrial area of Kobe was 41 percent destroyed. An area of 103.22 square miles was gutted by the B-29's. These five major industrial areas were considered essentially out of the war. Occasional "policing" attacks were subsequently necessary.

Sixty-four other cities were pounded and burned to the ground.

Approximately, seventy-two square miles of urban area of these cities were wiped out. One of those cities, Takamatsu was 89.3 percent destroyed.

The low level raids wiped out 175 square miles of urban area in sixty-nine cities leaving over 9,000,000 people homeless.

The Twentieth Air Force took a promising, but untried bomber and developed it into a totally efficient weapon of war. Their efforts cut off Japan from its empire and strangled production. The capacity to wage war and the terrible total exacted from the enemy left the Japanese no choice but to surrender "unconditionally." The two atomic bombs were "war enders" and face savers to a totally beaten and demoralized nation.

The Twentieth Air Force's accomplishments will stand in military avation history as the high point.